THE
WORKS OF ARISTOTLE

TRANSLATED INTO ENGLISH

UNDER THE EDITORSHIP

OF

W. D. ROSS, M.A., Hon. LL.D. (Edin.)

PROVOST OF ORIEL COLLEGE
HONORARY FELLOW OF MERTON COLLEGE
FELLOW OF THE BRITISH ACADEMY

VOLUME III

METEOROLOGICA
By E. W. WEBSTER

DE MUNDO
By E. S. FORSTER

DE ANIMA
By J. A. SMITH

PARVA NATURALIA
By J. I. BEARE AND G. R. T. ROSS

DE SPIRITU
By J. F. DOBSON

OXFORD
AT THE CLARENDON PRESS

Oxford University Press, Ely House, London W. 1

GLASGOW NEW YORK TORONTO MELBOURNE WELLINGTON
CAPE TOWN SALISBURY IBADAN NAIROBI LUSAKA ADDIS ABABA
BOMBAY CALCUTTA MADRAS KARACHI LAHORE DACCA
KUALA LUMPUR HONG KONG TOKYO

FIRST EDITION 1931
REPRINTED LITHOGRAPHICALLY IN GREAT BRITAIN
AT THE UNIVERSITY PRESS, OXFORD, 1950, 1955, 1963, 1968
FROM SHEETS OF THE FIRST EDITION

Special thanks are due to the Trustees of the Jowett Copyright Fund for their assistance towards the publication of this Volume

PREFACE TO VOLUME III

IN this volume the last part of the translation to be published takes its place immediately before the first part to be published, the *Parva Naturalia*, which appeared in 1908. I must ask the indulgence of readers for the long interval that has elapsed between the two. The Great War, the death of some of the contributors before their translations were completed, the necessity for a considerable interchange of views between translators and editor,—these have been among the causes of delay. I hope that by delay something has been gained as well as something lost; I am conscious of realizing much more fully now than I did in 1908 the nature of the problem of translating Aristotle, and I hope that the later contributors have learned something from the work of their predecessors.

In the series as a whole, indexes have been placed sometimes after single works, sometimes after groups of works. It may help readers in the use of these if they are told exactly where to look for them. Indexes will be found as follows :

In vols. IV, VI, VII, VIII at the end.

In vol. I after *Analytica Posteriora* ; after *De Sophisticis Elenchis*.

In vol. II after *Physica*; after *De Caelo*; after *De Generatione et Corruptione*.

In vol. III after *Meteorologica*; after *De Anima*; after *Parva Naturalia*; after *De Mundo*; after *De Spiritu*.

In vol. V after *De Partibus Animalium*; after *De Incessu Animalium*; after *De Generatione Animalium*.

In vol. IX after *Ethica Nicomachea*; after *Magna Moralia*; after *De Virtutibus et Vitiis*.

In vol. X after *Politica*; after *Oeconomica*; after *Atheniensium Respublica*.

In vol. XI after *Rhetorica*; after *Rhetorica ad Alexandrum*; after *Poetica*.

I have to thank Mr. George Brown, Lecturer in Logic in the University of Glasgow, for kindly reading the proofsheets of the *De Anima*, as he did those of the *Physics*. And

in taking leave of this work of many years I must thank
the Master and Fellows of Balliol, the Trustees of the Jowett
Copyright Fund, and the Delegates of the Press for their
financial support of the translation; my former co-editor,
Prof. J. A. Smith, for the large part he played in the early
stages of the work and for the advice which has always been
at my disposal since; and the officials and staff of the Press
for their interest and care in the production of the work.

21 *February*, 1931.

PREFACE TO THE *PARVA NATURALIA*[1]

IT was the desire of the late Master of Balliol, Dr. Benjamin Jowett, as formulated in his will, that the proceeds from the sale of his works, the copyright in which he bequeathed to Balliol College, should be used to promote the study of Greek Literature, especially by the publication of new translations and editions of Greek authors. In a codicil to his will he expressed the hope that the translation of Aristotle's works begun by his own translation of the *Politics* should be proceeded with as speedily as possible. The College resolved that the funds thus accruing to them should, in memory of his services to the College and to Greek letters, be applied to the subvention of a series of translations of the works of Aristotle. Through the co-operation, financial and other, of the Delegates of the University Press it has now become possible to begin the realization of this design. By agreement between the College and Delegates of the Press the present editors were appointed to superintend the carrying out of the scheme. The series, of which the first instalment is now brought before the public, is published at the joint expense and risk of the College and the Delegates of the Press.

The editors have secured the co-operation of various scholars in the task of translation. The translations make no claim to finality, but aim at being such as a scholar might construct in preparation for a critical edition and commentary. The translation will not presuppose any critical reconstitution of the text. Wherever new readings are proposed the fact will be indicated, but notes justificatory of conjectural emendations or defensive of novel interpretations will, where admitted, be reduced to the smallest compass. The editors, while retaining a general right of revision and annotation, will leave the responsibility for

[1] The *Parva Naturalia* (1908) was the first part of the series to be published.

each translation to its author, whose name will in all cases be given.

Translators have been found for the *Organon, Physics, De Caelo, De Anima, Historia Animalium, De Animalium Generatione, De Insecabilibus Lineis, Metaphysics, Eudemian Ethics, Rhetoric,* and *Poetics,* and it is hoped that the series may in course of time include translations of all the extant works of Aristotle. The editors would be glad to hear of scholars who are willing to undertake the translation of such treatises as have not already been provided for, and invite communications to this end.

The editors desire to acknowledge their obligation to Mr. Charles Cannan for valuable aid in the revision of the present volume, and to Mr. G. R. T. Ross for the preparation of the Index.

J. A. S.
W. D. R.

December, 1907.

METEOROLOGICA

BY

E. W. WEBSTER

OXFORD
AT THE CLARENDON PRESS

FIRST EDITION 1923
METEOROLOGICA: DE MUNDO: DE ANIMA: DE SPIRITU

REPRINTED LITHOGRAPHICALLY IN GREAT BRITAIN
AT THE UNIVERSITY PRESS, OXFORD, 1950, 1955, 1963, 1968
FROM SHEETS OF THE FIRST EDITION

PREFACE

THE translation of the *Meteorologica* which follows is
the work of a scholar whose death was one of the severest
losses which the University of Oxford suffered through
the Great War. Erwin Wentworth Webster came up to
Wadham as a Scholar in 1898. Besides taking First Classes
of unusual brilliance in Classical Moderations and in Literae
Humaniores, he won the Taylorian Scholarship for German
and the John Locke Scholarship for Mental Philosophy.
Shortly after taking his degree he was elected to a Fellow-
ship of his own College, and undertook tutorial work in
philosophy, to which he devoted himself with immense
energy and great success. He was (in addition to his
general philosophical interests) a keen student of Aristotle,
and one of the most faithful members of the Aristotelian
Society which met week after week under the presidency
first of Professor Bywater and then of Professor J. A. Smith,
and at which many of us younger men learned from these
masters of the art how to tackle the interpretation of the
Greek philosophers. He took up the *Meteorologica* fairly
early as a special study. His notes, apart from the translation, are unfortunately not in a suitable form for publication, but show how wide and how deep was his study of all
that bore on the subject, and how valuable a contribution
he would have made, if he had been spared, to our knowledge of it. But things were otherwise ordained. On the
outbreak of war he offered himself for service in the Royal
Flying Corps. An accident during his training compelled
him to give up this prospect ; and he thereupon applied for
and received a commission in the 13th King's Royal Rifle
Corps, in which he later became a Captain. He went to

France in July, 1915, and saw much hard service there. He was more than once practically ordered home to hospital, but insisted on remaining with his battalion. He was killed at Monchy-le-Preux, near Arras, on the ninth of April, 1917, while leading his company in an attack.

All who knew Webster will remember the modesty which was one of the leading features of a most attractive personality. Even if he had lived to give the finishing touches to his translation, he would have been the first to depreciate its merits, and I cannot hope that, lacking as it does his final correction, it will be found free from error. But I think that the errors will not be found to be very serious ones, and it is a satisfaction, though a melancholy one, to give to the world this slight memorial of one who if he had lived would undoubtedly have made a considerable mark both as a teacher and as a student.

The translation has been based on Bekker's quarto text, but in editing it I have made constant use of the valuable new edition of the *Meteorologica* by my former pupil Mr. F. H. Fobes, which gives with admirable completeness and precision the whole evidence for the text, and in very many respects improves on all previous editions.

CONTENTS

BOOK I

BOOK II

BOOK III

BOOK IV

METEOROLOGICA

BOOK I

1 WE have already discussed the first causes of nature, 20 and all natural[1] motion,[2] also the stars ordered in the motion of the heavens,[3] and the physical elements—enumerating and specifying them and showing how they change into one another—and becoming and perishing in general.[4] There remains for consideration a part of this inquiry which all our predecessors called meteorology. It is concerned with events that are natural, though their **338ᵇ** order is less perfect than that of the first of the elements 21 of bodies. They take place in the region nearest to the motion of the stars.[5] Such are the milky way, and comets, and the movements of meteors.[6] It studies also all the affections we may call common to air and water,[7] and the kinds and parts of the earth and the affections of its parts.[8] These throw light on the causes of winds and earthquakes and all **339ᵃ** the consequences the motions of these kinds and parts involve.[9] Of these things some puzzle us, while others admit of explanation in some degree. Further, the inquiry is concerned with the falling of thunderbolts and with whirlwinds and fire-winds, and further, the recurrent affections produced in these same 5 bodies by concretion[10]. When the inquiry into these matters is concluded let us consider[11] what account we can give, in accordance with the method we have followed, of animals and plants, both generally and in detail. When that has been done we may say that the whole of our original undertaking will have been carried out.

---

[1] i.e. neither purposive nor constrained.
[2] *Physics.*   [3] *De Caelo*, esp. i and ii.
[4] *De Gen. et Corr.*, and perhaps *De Caelo*, iii, iv.
[5] i.e. just below the sphere of the moon.
[6] Bk. i. 4-8.   [7] Bks. i. 9-12, iii. 2-6. 378ᵃ 14.
[8] Bks. i. 13-ii. 3.   [9] Bk. ii. 4-8.   [10] Bks. ii. 9, iii. 1.
[11] *De An., Parv. Nat., H.A., P.A., I.A., G.A.*

10   After this introduction let us begin by discussing our immediate subject.

We have already laid down that there is one physical **2** element which makes up[1] the system of the bodies that move in a circle, and besides this four bodies owing their existence to the four principles,[2] the motion of these latter bodies being 15 of two kinds: either from the centre or to the centre. These four bodies are fire, air, water, earth. Fire occupies the highest place among them all, earth the lowest, and two elements correspond to these in their relation to one another, air being nearest to fire, water to earth. The[3] 20 whole world surrounding the earth,[4] then, the affections of which are our subject, is made up of these bodies. This world necessarily has a certain continuity with the upper motions: consequently all its power and order is derived from them. (For the originating principle of all motion is 25 the first cause. Besides, that element is eternal and its motion has no limit in space, but is always complete; whereas all these other bodies have separate regions which limit one another.)[5] So we must treat fire and earth and the elements like them as the material causes of the events 30 in this world[4] (meaning by material what is subject and is affected), but must assign causality in the sense of the originating principle of motion to the influence of the eternally moving bodies.

Let us first recall[6] our original principles and the **3**

---

[1] Read ἐξ ἧς in l. 12 with Vicomercato.

[2] Hot, cold, dry, moist.

[3] Read commas for colons in ll. 15, 17, 18, and a colon for the full stop in l. 19, where the apodosis begins.

[4] The sublunary world.

[5] ὅθεν . . . ἀλλήλων (ll. 23-27) is parenthetical.

[6] The argument of this confused chapter seems to be as follows: 339^a 33–^b 2 introductory; 339^b 2-16 the main question is stated to be the nature of air and its relations to the other elements: 339^b 16–340^a 18 a preliminary question about the nature of the element in the celestial sphere is discussed. Two views are dismissed, (a) that the stars and the interval between them are of fire, while the space from the earth to the moon is air, 339^b 30-340^a 3, (b) that the whole world from the earth to the stars, including the intervals between them, is of air, 340^a 3-18. 340^a 19-24 the original question is restated; it now appears in two parts, (a) relation of fire and air to the celestial element,

distinctions already drawn and then explain the 'milky way' and comets and the other phenomena akin to these. 35

Fire,[1] air, water, earth, we assert, originate from one another, and each of them exists potentially in each, as all **339ᵇ** things do that can be resolved into a common and ultimate substrate.[2]

The first difficulty is raised by what is called the air. What are we to take its nature to be in the world surrounding the earth? And what is its position relatively to 5 the other physical elements. (For there is no question as to the relation of the bulk of the earth to the size of the bodies which exist around it, since astronomical demonstrations have by this time proved to us that it is actually far smaller than some individual stars. As for the water, it is not observed to exist collectively and separately, nor can 10 it do so apart from that volume of it which has its seat about the earth: the sea, that is, and rivers, which we can see, and any subterranean water that may be hidden from our observation.) The question is really about that which lies between the earth and the nearest stars. Are we to consider it to be one kind of body or more than one? 15 And if more than one, how many are there and what are the bounds of their regions?

We have already described and characterized the first element, and explained that the whole world of the upper motions is full of that body.[3]

This is an opinion we are not alone in holding: it 20 appears to be an old assumption and one which men have held in the past, for the word ether has long been used to denote that element. Anaxagoras,[4] it is true, seems to me to think that the word means the same as fire. For

---

(*b*) question about the origination of heat by the celestial bodies (now recognized as not themselves hot) on earth. This change in the formulation of the question is due to the answers given to the preliminary question. 340ᵃ 24–ᵇ 3 a preliminary discussion about the nature of air and difficulties raised about the formation of clouds in it: 340ᵇ 4–341ᵃ 12 question (*a*) is answered and the difficulty about clouds solved: 341ᵃ 12–end question (*b*) solved.

[1] Read δή with JFHN and Thurot in l. 36.
[2] Cp. *De Gen. et Corr.* ii. 4, *De Caelo*, iii. 6 and **7**.
[3] *De Caelo*, i. 3.
[4] Ibid. i. 270ᵇ 24.

he thought that the upper regions were full of fire, and that
men [1] referred to those regions when they spoke of
25 ether. In the latter point he was right, for men seem to
have assumed that a body that was eternally in motion [2]
was also divine [3] in nature ; and, as such a body was different
from any of the terrestrial elements, they determined to
call it ' ether '.

For the same opinions appear in cycles among men not
once nor twice, but infinitely often.

30   Now there are some who maintain that not only the
bodies in motion but that which contains them is pure fire,
and the interval between the earth and the stars air : but
if they had considered what is now satisfactorily established
by mathematics, they might have given up this puerile
opinion. For it is altogether childish to suppose that the
35 moving bodies are all of them of a small size, because they
seem so to us, looking at them from the earth.

This is a matter which we have already discussed in our
treatment of the upper region,[4] but we may return to the
point now.

340[a]   If the intervals were full of fire and the bodies consisted
of fire every one of the other elements would long ago have
vanished.

However, they cannot simply be said to be full of air
either ; for even if there were two elements to fill the space
between the earth and the heavens,[5] the air would far exceed
the quantity required to maintain its proper proportion to
5 the other elements. For the bulk of the earth (which
includes the whole volume of water) is infinitesimal in
comparison with the whole world that surrounds it. Now
we find that the excess in volume is not proportionately
10 great where water dissolves into air or air into fire.
Whereas the *proportion* between any given small quantity
of water and the air that is generated from it ought to hold
good between the total amount of air and the total amount of
water. Nor does it make any difference if any one [6] denies [7]

---

[1] Read κἀκείνους (Thurot) in l. 24.   [2] θέον.   [3] θεῖον.
[4] *De Caelo*, ii. 298[a] 15 (the smallness of the earth).
[5] The outermost heaven.   [6] Empedocles.
[7] Read φησὶ with E₁JF in l. 13.

that the elements *originate from one another*, but asserts
that they are equal in power. For on this view it is 15
certain amounts of each that are equal in power, just as
would be the case if they actually *originated from one
another*.[1]

So it is clear that neither air nor fire alone [2] fills the
intermediate space.[3]

It remains to explain, after a preliminary discussion of
difficulties, the relation of the two elements air and fire to
the position of the first element, and the reason why the 20
stars in the upper region impart heat [4] to the earth and its
neighbourhood. Let us first treat of the air, as we proposed,[5] and then go on to these questions.

Since [6] water is generated from air, and air from water,
why are clouds not formed in the upper air ? They ought 25
to form there the more, the further from the earth and the
colder that region is. For it is neither appreciably near to
the heat of the stars, nor to the rays reflected from the
earth. It is these that dissolve any formation by their 30
heat and so prevent clouds from forming near the earth.[7]
For clouds gather at the point where the reflected rays

---

[1] *De Gen. et Corr.* ii. 6. A. there argues that if the elements are
comparable a common substrate and transmutation are implied. But
Empedocles says the elements are 'equal' while denying their transmutation. If he means (*a*) 'equal in quantity', there is something
common to them in virtue of which they are measured, and transmutation follows. If he means (*b*) 'equal in power', e. g. 1 c.c. water has as
much refrigerating power as 10 c.c. air, the water and the air must
have something in common in virtue of which they refrigerate, and
transmutation follows again. A. might prove on the same principle
that since gold and lead can both be weighed they must be trans-
mutable.

[2] Nor both together.

[3] Between the earth and the outermost heaven. The conclusion,
which is not expressed, is : therefore there must be a fifth element in
the celestial region.

[4] As soon as the stars and the upper region are not considered to be
of fire, this requires explanation.

[5] This is misleading if it refers back to 339[b] 3, since it is not so much
the aporetic discussion about the clouds in the air 340[a] 24–[b] 3, as the
two discussions in 340[b] 4–341[a] 36, especially the first 340[b] 3–341[a] 12,
which answer the original question.

[6] This passage 340[a] 24–[b] 3 is purely aporetic. No account is taken
of results already arrived at.

[7] For A.'s conception of the stratification of the air, cp. Gilbert,
Meteor. Theorien d. gr. Altertums, 476 sqq. (doubtful on some details),
Meteor. 340[b] 29, 361[a] 22, 373[a] 23 and note.

disperse in the infinity of space and are lost. To explain this we must suppose either that it is not all air from which water is generated, or, if it is produced from all air alike, that what immediately surrounds the earth is not mere air, but a sort of vapour, and that its vaporous nature is the
35 reason why it condenses back to water again. But if the whole of that vast region is vapour, the amount of air and of water will be disproportionately great. For the spaces left by
340ᵇ the heavenly bodies must be filled by some element. This cannot be fire, for then all the rest would have been dried up. Consequently, what fills it must be air and the water that surrounds the whole earth—vapour being water dissolved.

After this exposition of the difficulties involved, let us
5 go on to lay down the truth, with a view at once to what follows and to what has already been said. The upper region as far as the moon[1] we affirm to consist of a body distinct both from fire and from air, but varying in degree
10 of purity and in kind, especially towards its limit on the side of the air, and of the world surrounding[2] the earth. Now the circular motion of the first element and of the bodies it contains dissolves, and inflames by its motion, whatever part of the lower world is nearest to it, and so generates heat. From another point of view we may look at the
15 motion as follows. The body that lies below the circular motion of the heavens is, in a sort, matter, and is potentially hot, cold, dry, moist, and possessed of whatever other qualities are derived from these.[3] But it actually acquires or retains one of these in virtue of motion or rest, the cause and principle of which has already been explained.[4] So at
20 the centre and round it we get earth and water, the heaviest and coldest elements, by themselves; round them and contiguous[5] with them, air and what we commonly call fire. It is not really fire, for fire is an excess of heat and a sort of ebullition;[6] but in reality, of what we call air,
25 the part surrounding the earth is moist and warm, because it contains both vapour and a dry exhalation from the

---

[1] i.e. the region between the air properly so called and the moon.
[2] i.e. immediately surrounding.
[3] *De Gen. et Corr.* ii. 2.
[4] Ibid. ii. 10.
[5] Omitting τά in l. 21, with JF Al.
[6] Cp. 341ᵇ21.

earth. But the next part, above that, is warm and dry. For vapour is naturally moist and cold,[1] but the exhalation warm and dry; and vapour is potentially like water, the exhalation potentially like fire. So we must take the reason why clouds are not formed in the upper region to 30 be this: that it is filled not with mere air but rather with a sort of fire.

However, it may well be that the formation of clouds in that upper region is also prevented by the circular motion. For the air round the earth is necessarily all of it in motion, except that which is cut off inside the circumference which 35 makes the earth a complete sphere.[2] In the case of winds it is actually observable that they originate in marshy districts of the earth; and they do not seem to blow above **341ᵃ** the level of the highest mountains. It is the revolution of the heaven which carries the air with it and causes its circular motion, fire being continuous with the upper element and air with fire. Thus its motion is a second reason why that air is not condensed into water.

But whenever a particle of air grows heavy,[3] the warmth 5 in it is squeezed out into the upper region and it sinks, and other particles in turn are carried up together with the fiery exhalation. Thus the one region is always full of air and the other of fire, and each of them is perpetually in a state of change.

So much to explain why clouds are not formed and why 10 the air is not condensed into water,[4] and what account must be given of the space between the stars and the earth, and what is the body that fills it.

As for the heat derived from the sun, the right place for a special and scientific account of it is in the treatise about sense,[5] since heat is an affection of sense, but we may now 15 explain how it can be produced by the heavenly bodies which are not themselves hot.

---

[1] Read ψυχρόν in l. 27 with E₁ and cod. Par. suppl. 314, cp. 360ᵃ 22 sq.

[2] i.e. up to the height of the highest mountains. But cp. with the whole passage 361ᵃ 22, 373ᵃ 23, 340ᵃ 25 above.

[3] i.e. becomes ἀτμίς.   [4] In the upper air.

[5] No such account is to be found in the *De Sensu*.

We see that motion is able to dissolve and inflame the air ; indeed, moving bodies are often actually found to melt. Now the sun's motion alone is sufficient to account for the 20 origin of terrestrial warmth and heat. For a motion that is to have this effect must be rapid and near, and that of the stars is rapid but distant, while that of the moon is near but slow, whereas the sun's motion combines both conditions in a sufficient degree. That most heat should be generated 25 where the sun is present [1] is easy to understand if we consider the analogy of terrestrial phenomena, for here, too, it is the air that is nearest to a thing in rapid motion which is heated most. This is just what we should expect, as it is the nearest air that is most dissolved by the motion of a solid body.

30 This then is one reason why heat reaches our world. Another is that the fire surrounding the air is often scattered by the motion of the heavens and driven downwards in spite of itself.

Shooting-stars further suffice to prove that the celestial sphere is not hot or fiery : for they do not occur in that upper region but below : yet the more and the faster [2] 35 a thing moves, the more apt it is to take fire.[3] Besides, the sun, which most of all the stars is considered to be hot, is really white and not fiery in colour.

341ᵇ Having determined these principles let us explain the 4 cause of the appearance in the sky of burning flames and of shooting-stars, and of 'torches', and 'goats', as some people call them. All these phenomena are one and the 5 same thing, and are due to the same cause, the difference between them being one of degree.

The explanation of these and many other phenomena is this. When the sun warms the earth the evaporation which takes place is necessarily of two kinds, not of one only as some think.[4] One kind is rather of the nature of vapour,

---

[1] i. e. by day.
[2] Read τὰ μᾶλλον κινούμενα καὶ θᾶττον ἐκπυροῦται θᾶττον in l. 34 with JF and the lemma in Philoponus.
[3] And the outer sphere moves fastest.
[4] Perhaps Plato, *Timaeus*, 56 D.

the other of the nature of a windy exhalation. That which
rises from the moisture contained in the earth and on its
surface is vapour, while that rising from the earth itself, 10
which is dry, is like smoke. Of these the windy exhalation,
being warm, rises above the moister vapour, which is heavy
and sinks below the other. Hence the world surrounding
the earth is ordered as follows. First below the circular
motion comes the warm and dry element, which we call fire,
for there is no word fully adequate to every state of the fumid 15
evaporation: but we must use this terminology since this
element is the most inflammable of all bodies. Below this
comes air. We must think of what we just called fire as
being spread round the terrestrial sphere on the outside like 20
a kind of fuel, so that a little motion often makes it burst
into flame just as smoke does: for flame is the ebullition of
a dry exhalation.[1] So whenever the circular motion stirs
this stuff up in any way, it catches fire at the point at which
it is most inflammable. The result differs according to the
disposition and quantity of the combustible material. If 25
this is broad and long, we often see a flame burning as
in a field of stubble: if it burns lengthwise only, we see
what are called 'torches' and 'goats' and shooting-stars.
Now when the inflammable material is longer than it is
broad sometimes it seems to throw off sparks as it burns. 30
(This happens because matter catches fire at the sides in
small portions but continuously with the main body.) Then
it is called a 'goat'. When this does not happen it is
a 'torch'. But if the whole length of the exhalation is
scattered in small parts and in many directions and in
breadth and depth alike, we get what are called shooting-
stars.
                                                               35
The cause of these shooting-stars is sometimes the motion
which ignites the exhalation. At other times the air is con- **342^a**
densed by cold and squeezes out and ejects [2] the hot element;
making their motion look more like that of a thing thrown
than like a running fire. For the question might be raised

---

[1] Cp. 340^b 23.
[2] Read ἐκθλίβεται καὶ ἐκκρίνεται with JFHN and the lemma in
Philoponus.

whether the 'shooting' of a 'star' is the same thing as when
5 you put an exhalation below a lamp and it lights the lower
lamp from the flame above.   For here too the flame passes
wonderfully quickly and looks like a thing thrown, and
not as if one thing after another caught fire.   Or is a 'star'
when it 'shoots' a single [1] body that is thrown? Apparently [2]
both cases occur : sometimes it is like the flame from the
lamp and sometimes bodies are projected by being squeezed
10 out (like fruit stones from one's fingers) and so are seen to
fall into the sea and on the dry land, both by night and by
day when the sky is clear.   They are thrown downwards
because the condensation which propels them inclines
downwards. Thunderbolts fall downwards for the same
15 reason : their origin is never combustion but ejection under
pressure, since naturally all heat tends upwards.

When the phenomenon is formed in the upper region [3] it
is due to the combustion of the exhalation.   When it takes
place at a lower level it is due to the ejection of the exhalation by the condensing and cooling of the moister evapo-
20 ration : for this latter as it condenses and inclines downward
contracts, and thrusts out the hot element and causes it to
be thrown downwards.   The motion is upwards or downwards or sideways according to the way in which the
evaporation lies, and its disposition in respect of breadth
and depth.   In most cases the direction is sideways because
25 two motions are involved, a compulsory motion downwards
and a natural motion upwards, and under these circumstances an object always moves obliquely.   Hence the
motion of 'shooting-stars' is generally oblique.

So the material cause of all these phenomena is the
exhalation, the efficient cause sometimes the upper motion,
30 sometimes the contraction and condensation of the air.
Further, all these things happen below the moon.   This is
shown by their apparent speed, which is equal to that of
things thrown by us ; for it is because they are close to us,

---

[1] Read τοῦ αὐτοῦ τινος in l. 7 with JF₂HN Ol. (lemma).
[2] Om. δέ in l. 8 with all the MSS.
[3] Omit μᾶλλον and read ἄνω in l. 17 with E and the lemma in
Olympiodorus. μᾶλλον and the superlative ἀνωτάτω are explanations
of ἄνω.

that these latter seem far to exceed in speed the stars, the sun, and the moon.

5   Sometimes on a fine night we see a variety of appearances that form in the sky : 'chasms' for instance and 'trenches' and blood-red colours. These, too, have the same cause.[1] For we have seen that the upper air condenses into an inflammable condition and that the combustion sometimes takes on the appearance of a burning flame, sometimes that of moving torches and stars. So it is not surprising that this same air when condensing should assume a variety of colours. For a weak light shining through a dense air, and the air when it acts as a mirror, will cause all kinds of colours to appear, but especially crimson and purple. For these colours generally appear when fire-colour and white are combined by superposition. Thus on a hot day, or through a smoky medium, the stars when they rise and set look crimson. The light will also create colours by reflection when the mirror is such as to reflect colour only and not shape.[2]

These appearances do not persist long, because the condensation of the air is transient.

'Chasms' get their appearance of depth from light breaking out of a dark blue or black mass of air. When the process of condensation goes further in such a case we often find 'torches' ejected. When the 'chasm' contracts it presents the appearance of a 'trench'.[3]

In general, white in contrast with black creates a variety of colours ; like flame, for instance, through a medium of smoke. But by day the sun obscures them, and, with the exception of crimson, the colours are not seen at night because they are dark.[4]

The marginal references are: 35 (line 1), 342^b, 5, 10, 15, 20.

---

[1] As the phenomena described in c. 4. The obscurity of this chapter is due to the attempt to assimilate these phenomena of cloud coloration to the meteorites, &c., of c. 4. Ar. seems entirely to neglect the most obvious causes of these φάσματα, e.g. the sun, and obscures the fact that the phenomena of c. 4 are καθ' ὑπόστασιν, in the language of later writers, while those of c. 5 are κατ' ἔμφασιν. Cf. Gilbert, *Meteor. Theorien d. gr. Altertums*, pp. 594 sqq.

[2] Cp. 372^a 29 sq.

[3] Read in l. 17 συνιὸν δὲ ⟨βόθυνος εἶναι τὸ⟩ χάσμα δοκεῖ after Thurot.

[4] Read ὁμόχροιαν in l. 20 with all the MSS.

These then must be taken to be the causes of 'shooting-stars' and the phenomena of combustion and also of the other transient appearances of this kind.

25 Let us go on to explain the nature of comets and the 'milky **6** way', after a preliminary discussion of the views of others.

Anaxagoras [1] and Democritus [2] declare that comets are a conjunction of the planets approaching one another and so appearing to touch one another.

30 Some of the Italians called Pythagoreans [3] say that the comet is one of the planets, but that it appears at great intervals of time and only rises a little above the horizon. This is the case with Mercury too; because it only rises a little above the horizon it often fails to be seen and con-35 sequently appears at great intervals of time.

A view like theirs was also expressed by Hippocrates of 343^a Chios and his pupil Aeschylus.[4] Only they say that the tail does not belong to the comet itself, but is occasionally assumed by it on its course in certain situations, when our sight is reflected to the sun from the moisture attracted by the comet. It appears at greater intervals than the 5 other stars because it is slowest to get clear of the sun and has been left behind by the sun to the extent of the whole of its circle before it reappears at the same point. It gets clear of the sun both towards the north and towards the south. In the space between the tropics it does not draw water to itself because that region 10 is dried up by the sun on its course. When it moves towards the south it has no lack of the necessary moisture, but because the segment of its circle which is above the horizon is small, and that below it many times as large, it is impossible for the sun to be reflected to our sight, either 15 when it approaches the southern [5] tropic, or at the summer solstice. Hence in these regions it does not develop a tail at all. But when it is visible in the north it assumes a tail because the arc above the horizon is large and that below it

---

[1] Diels, *Frag. d. Vorsokratiker*, 46 A 81.
[2] Ibid. 55 A 92.   [3] Diels, 30. 5.   [4] Ibid.
[5] Read νότῳ for τροπικῷ in l. 14 with E₁ and perhaps Al. (The lemma in Philoponus has νοτίῳ τόπῳ.)

small. For under these circumstances there is nothing to
prevent our vision from being reflected to the sun.   20

These views involve impossibilities, some of which are
common to all of them, while others are peculiar to some
only.

This is the case, first, with those who say that the comet
is one of the planets. For all the planets appear in the
circle of the zodiac, whereas many comets have been seen 25
outside that circle. Again more comets than one have
often appeared simultaneously. Besides, if their tail is due
to reflection, as Aeschylus and Hippocrates say, this planet
ought sometimes to be visible without a tail since, as they
say, it does not possess a tail in every place in which it 30
appears. But, as a matter of fact, no planet has been observed besides the five. And all of them are often visible
above the horizon together at the same time. Further,
comets are often found to appear, as well when all the
planets are visible as when some are not, but are obscured
by the neighbourhood of the sun. Moreover the statement 35
that a comet only appears in the north, with the sun at the
summer solstice,[1] is not true either. The great comet which 343ᵇ
appeared at the time of the earthquake in Achaea[2] and the
tidal wave rose due west; and many have been known
to appear in the south. Again in the archonship of
Euclees, son of Molon, at Athens[3] there appeared a comet 5
in the north in the month Gamelion,[4] the sun being about
the winter solstice. Yet they themselves admit that reflection over so great a space is an impossibility.

An objection that tells equally against those who hold
this theory and those who say that comets are a coalescence
of the planets is, first, the fact that some of the fixed stars
too get a tail. For this we must not only accept the 10
authority of the Egyptians who assert it, but we have ourselves observed the fact. For a star in the thigh of the Dog
had a tail, though a faint one. If you fixed your sight on

---

[1] Cp. ᵇ9. This condition was not stated in ª 10 sq. Thurot would introduce it there by emendation. Probably Aristotle is at fault and not
the text.
[2] Cp. ᵇ 18, 344ᵇ 34, 368ᵇ 6. The date is 373-2 B.C.
[3] 427-6 B.C.   [4] Jan.-Feb.

it its light was dim, but if you just glanced at it,[1] it appeared
15 brighter. Besides, all the comets that have been seen in
our day have vanished without setting, gradually fading
away above the horizon ; and they have not left behind
them either one or more stars. For instance the great
comet we mentioned before [2] appeared to the west in
winter in frosty weather when the sky was clear, in the
20 archonship of Asteius. On the first day it set before the
sun and was then not seen. On the next day it was seen,
being ever so little behind the sun and immediately setting.
But its light extended over a third part of the sky like
a leap, so that people called it a 'path'. This comet re-
25 ceded as far as Orion's belt and there dissolved. Democritus
however, insists upon the truth of his view and affirms that
certain stars have been seen when comets dissolve. But on
his theory this ought not to occur occasionally but always.
Besides, the Egyptians affirm that conjunctions of the
planets with one another, and with the fixed stars, take
30 place, and we have ourselves observed Jupiter coinciding [3]
with one of the stars in the Twins and hiding it, and yet no
comet was formed. Further, we can also give a rational
proof of our point. It is true that some stars seem to be bigger
than others, yet each one by itself looks indivisible. Con-
35 sequently, just as, if they really had been indivisible, their
conjunction could not have created any greater magnitude, so
344ᵃ now that they are not in fact indivisible but look as if
they were, their conjunction will not make them look any
bigger.

Enough has been said, without further argument, to show
that the causes brought forward to explain comets are false.

5   We consider a satisfactory explanation of phenomena in- **7**
accessible to observation to have been given when our
account of them is free from impossibilities. The observations before us [4] suggest the following account of the

---

[1] The peripheral parts of the retina are more sensitive to illumination
than the central. Wundt, *Phys.-Psych.*[5], ii. 181, 502.
[2] ᵇ I.   [3] Omitting δίς in l. 31 with E₁JFHN Al Ph Ol.
[4] ὑπόκειται (l. 8) . . . διαδρομάς (l. 15) is a parenthesis. The apodosis
of the main sentence is ἀστὴρ τοῦτο γίγνεται (l. 20).

phenomena we are now considering. We know that the
dry and warm exhalation is the outermost part of the 10
terrestrial world which falls below the circular motion. It,
and a great part of the air that is continuous with it below,
is carried round the earth by the motion of the circular
revolution. In the course of this motion it often ignites
wherever it may happen to be of the right consistency, and
this we maintain to be the cause of the 'shooting' of 15
scattered 'stars'. We may say, then, that a comet is
formed when the upper motion [1] introduces into a gathering
of this kind a fiery principle not of such excessive strength
as to burn up much of the material quickly, nor so weak as
soon to be extinguished, but stronger and capable of
burning up much material, and when exhalation of the 20
right consistency rises from below and meets it. The kind
of comet varies according to the shape which the exhalation
happens to take. If it is diffused equally on every side the
star is said to be fringed, if it stretches out in one direction
it is called bearded. We have seen that when a fiery
principle of this kind moves we seem to have a shooting- 25
star: similarly when it stands still we seem to have a star
standing still. We may compare these phenomena to
a heap or mass of chaff into which a torch is thrust, or
a spark thrown. That is what a shooting-star is like. The
fuel is so inflammable that the fire runs through it quickly
in a line. Now if this fire were to persist instead of running 30
through the fuel and perishing away, its course through the
fuel would stop at the point where the latter was densest,
and then the whole might begin to move. Such is a comet—
like a shooting-star that contains its beginning and end in
itself.

When the matter begins to gather in the lower region independently the comet appears by itself. But when the 35
exhalation is constituted [2] by one of the fixed stars or the
planets, owing to their motion, one of them becomes a comet.
The fringe is not close to the stars themselves. Just as 344^b

---

[1] Omitting τῶν in l. 16 with JHN, and Philoponus.
[2] 345^a 7, ^b 34.

haloes appear to follow the sun and the moon as they move,[1]
5 and encircle them, when the air is dense enough for them to
form along under the sun's course, so too the fringe. It
stands in the relation of a halo to the stars, except that the
colour of the halo is due to reflection, whereas in the case of
comets the colour is something that appears actually on
them.

Now when this matter gathers in relation to a star the
10 comet necessarily appears to follow the same course as the
star. But when the comet is formed independently it falls
behind the motion of the universe, like the rest of the
terrestrial world. It is this fact, that a comet often forms
independently,[2] indeed oftener than round one of the
regular stars, that makes it impossible to maintain that
15 a comet is a sort of reflection, not indeed, as Hippocrates
and his school say,[3] to the sun, but to the very star it is
alleged to accompany—in fact, a kind of halo in the pure
fuel of fire.[4]

As for the halo we shall explain its cause later.[5]

The fact that comets when frequent[6] foreshadow wind
20 and drought must be taken as an indication of their fiery
constitution. For their origin is plainly due to the plentiful
supply of that secretion. Hence the air is necessarily drier
and the moist evaporation is so dissolved and dissipated by
the quantity of the hot exhalation as not readily to con-
25 dense into water.—But this phenomenon too shall be
explained more clearly later when the time comes to
speak of the winds.—So when there are many comets
and they are dense, it is as we say, and the years
are clearly dry and windy. When they are fewer and
fainter this effect does not appear in the same degree,
30 though as a rule the wind is found to be excessive either in
duration or strength. For instance when the stone at
Aegospotami fell out of the air—it had been carried up by

---

[1] Omit τῶν ἄστρων in l. 4 with EJHN and the lemmata in Philoponus
and Olympiodorus.
[2] Comma after πολλάκις in l. 16, with Philoponus.
[3] 342[b] 36.   [4] Comma after καθαρῷ in l. 14.
[5] iii. 2.
[6] Omit οἱ in l. 20 with the MSS., Alexander, and Philoponus.

a wind and fell down in the daytime—then too a comet happened to have appeared in the west. And at the time of the great comet [1] the winter was dry and north winds pre- 35 vailed, and the wave was due to an opposition of winds. For in the gulf a north wind blew and outside it a violent **345^a** south wind. Again in the archonship of Nicomachus [2] a comet appeared for a few days about the equinoctial circle (this one had not risen in the west), and simultaneously with it there happened the storm at Corinth. 5

That there are few comets and that they appear rarely and outside the tropic circles [3] more than within them is due to the motion of the sun and the stars.[4] For this motion does not only cause the hot principle to be secreted but also dissolves it when it is gathering. But the chief reason is that most of this stuff collects in the region of the milky way. 10

8 Let us now explain the origin, cause, and nature of the milky way. And here too let us begin by discussing the statements of others on the subject.

(1) Of the so-called Pythagoreans [5] some say that this is the path of one of the stars that fell from heaven at the time of 15 Phaethon s downfall. Others say that the sun used once to move in this circle and that this region was scorched or met with some other affection of this kind, because of the sun and its motion.

But it is absurd not to see that if this were the reason the circle of the Zodiac ought to be affected in the same way, and indeed more so than that of the milky way, since not 20 the sun only but all the planets move in it. We can see the whole of this circle (half of it being visible at any time of the night), but it shows no signs of any such affection [6] except where a part of it touches the circle of the milky way.

(2) Anaxagoras, Democritus, and their schools say that 25

---

[1] Cp. 343^b 1.
[2] 341-40 B.C. Omit Ἀθήνησιν in l. 2 with E₁JFHN.
[3] 346^a 14.　　　　　　　　　[4] 344^a 35.
[5] Diels, 45 B. 37^c; 29. 10.
[6] Read πεπονθώς in l. 23 with EFH Al.

the milky way is the light of certain stars. For, they say, when the sun passes below the earth some of the stars are hidden from it. Now the light of those on which the sun shines is invisible, being obscured by the rays of the sun. 30 But the milky way is the peculiar light of those stars which are shaded by the earth from the sun's rays.

This, too, is obviously impossible. The milky way is always unchanged and among the same constellations (for it is clearly a .greatest circle),[1] whereas, since the sun does not remain in the same place, what is hidden from it differs 35 at different times. Consequently with the change of the sun's position the milky way ought to change its position **345ᵇ** too: but we find that this does not happen. Besides, if astronomical demonstrations are correct and the size of the sun is greater than that of the earth and the distance of the stars from the earth many times greater than that of the sun (just as the sun is further from the earth than the 5 moon), then the cone made by the rays of the sun would terminate at no great distance from the earth, and the shadow of the earth (what we call night) would not reach the stars. On the contrary, the sun shines on all the stars and the earth screens none of them.

10 (3) There is a third theory about the milky way. Some say that it is a reflection of our sight to the sun, just as they say that the comet is.[2]

But this too is impossible. For if the eye and the mirror and the whole of the object were severally at rest, then the same part of the image would appear at the same 15 point in the mirror. But if the mirror and the object move, keeping the same distance from the eye which is at rest, but at different rates of speed and so [3] not always at the same interval from one another, then it is impossible for the same image always to appear in the same part of the mirror. Now the constellations included in the circle of the milky way move; and so does the sun, the object to which 20 our sight is reflected; but we stand still. And the distance

---

[1] 346ª 17 and note.   [2] 342ᵇ 35 ; Diels, 30. 6.
[3] Reading μή . . . μηδέ in l. 17 with E, Alexander (citation), and Philoponus.

of those two from us is constant and uniform, but their distance from one another varies. For the Dolphin sometimes rises at midnight, sometimes in the morning. But in each case the same parts of the milky way are found near it. But if it were a reflection and not a genuine affection of these regions, this ought not to be the case.

Again, we can see the milky way reflected at night in 25 water and similar mirrors. But under these circumstances it is impossible for our sight to be reflected to the sun.

These considerations show that the milky way is not the path of one of the planets, nor the light of imperceptible stars, nor a reflection. And those are the chief theories 30 handed down by others hitherto.

Let us recall our fundamental principle and then explain our views. We have already laid down [1] that the outermost part of what is called the air is potentially fire and that therefore when the air is dissolved by motion, there is separated off a kind of matter—and of this matter we assert that comets consist. We must suppose that what happens 35 is the same as in the case of the comets when the matter does not form independently but is formed by one of the **346**^a fixed stars or the planets. Then these stars appear to be fringed, because matter of this kind follows their course. In the same way, a certain kind of matter follows the sun, and we explain the halo as a reflection from it when the 5 air is of the right constitution. Now we must assume that what happens in the case of the stars severally happens in the case of the whole of the heavens and all the upper motion. For it is natural to suppose that, if the motion of a single star excites a flame, that of all the stars should have a similar result,[2] and especially in that region in which 10 the stars are biggest and most numerous and nearest to one another. Now the circle of the zodiac dissolves this kind of matter because of the motion of the sun and the planets,

---

[1] 340^b 4–32.

[2] Fobes inserts after ἐκριπίζειν (l. 9) the following words from FHN— ἀέρα τε καὶ διακρίνειν διὰ τὸ τοῦ κύκλου μέγεθος, and the following lemmata from Ol.—ἀνάγκη τοίνυν τῶν αὐτῶν μεγίστων κύκλων μάλιστα τὴν μέλλουσαν τοῦτο ποιήσειν φοράν . . . χρὴ γὰρ τοῦτο, ἵνα πολλὴ κίνησις ᾖ διὰ τὸ μέγεθος γιγνομένη καὶ πλείονα τὴν ἔξαψιν ποιήσῃ. Al. Phil. seem to have had our text without these additions.

and for this reason most comets are found outside the
tropic circles.[1] Again, no fringe appears round the sun or
15 moon : for they dissolve such matter too quickly to admit
of its formation. But this circle in which the milky way
appears to our sight is the greatest circle,[2] and its position
is such that it extends far outside the tropic circles. Besides
the region is full of the biggest and brightest constellations
20 and also of what are called ' scattered ' stars (you have only
to look to see this clearly). So for these reasons all this
matter is continually and ceaselessly collecting there.
A proof of the theory is this : In the circle itself the light
is stronger in that half where the milky way is divided, and
in it the constellations are more numerous and closer to one
25 another than in the other half ; which shows that the cause
of the light is the motion of the constellations and nothing
else. For if it is found in the circle in which there are
most constellations and at that point in the circle at which
they are densest and contain the biggest and the most
30 stars, it is natural to suppose that they are the true cause
of the affection in question. The circle and the constellations in it may be seen in the diagram.[3] The so-called
' scattered ' stars it is not possible to set down in the same
way on the sphere because none of them have an evident

---

[1] 345ᵃ 6.

[2] It is difficult to understand what is meant by 'the greatest circle'.
Cf. 345ᵃ 33 and 346ᵇ 6. The meaning cannot be ' a great circle of the
celestial sphere ' in the ordinary sense ; for, (1) this would not justify
the article here and in 346ᵇ 6, (2) the fact that a circle is a 'great
circle' in the ordinary sense does not involve any part of it, except
the points at which it cuts the equator, moving fastest ; unless it
happens to be the equator, and Ar. does not suppose that the milky
way is. Vicomercatus suggests that μέγιστος refers to the *breadth* of the
band, but this is unsatisfactory. We are forced to assume that Ar. was
thinking in a confused way of the outermost *sphere*, that of the fixed
stars. Every point of this does, of course, move faster than every
corresponding point on an interior sphere. This will also justify the
article. It also explains 345ᵃ 33 : 'the milky way is in the sphere of
the fixed stars and cannot therefore move about, as the hypothesis would
require '. It is true that the theory still does not work, even on its own
presuppositions. But it could only work if we supposed the milky way
to rotate on an axis at right angles to its own plane ; and Ar. certainly
did not think it did that.

[3] Aristotle must be supposed to have illustrated his theory here by
a diagram of the milky way, but the Greek commentators have not
preserved any tradition of the particular diagram used.

permanent position ; but if you look up to the sky the point is clear. For in this circle alone are the intervals full 35 of these stars :.in the other circles there are obvious gaps. Hence if we accept the cause assigned for the appearance 346ᵇ of comets as plausible we must assume that the same kind of thing holds good of the milky way. For the fringe which in the former case is an affection of a single star here forms in the same way in relation to a whole circle. So if 5 we are to define the milky way we may call it ' a fringe attaching to the greatest circle, and due to the matter secreted '. This, as we said before,[1] explains why there are few comets and why they appear rarely ; it is because at each revolution of the heavens this matter has always been and is always being separated off and gathered into this region.

We have now explained the phenomena that occur in that 10 part of the terrestrial world which is continuous with the motions of the heavens, namely, shooting-stars and the burning flame, comets and the milky way, these being the chief affections that appear in that region.   15

9 Let us go on to treat of the region which follows next in order after this and which immediately surrounds the earth.   It is the region common to water and air, and the processes attending the formation of water above [2] take place in it. We must consider the principles and causes of all these phenomena too as before.   ·

The efficient and chief and first cause is the circle in 20 which the sun moves.[3] For the sun as it approaches or recedes, obviously causes dissipation and condensation and so gives rise to generation and destruction.   Now the earth remains but the moisture surrounding it is made to evaporate by the sun's rays and the other heat from above, and rises. 25 But when the heat which was raising it leaves it, in part dispersing to the higher region, in part quenched through rising so far into the upper air, then the vapour cools

[1] 345ᵃ 7.
[2] As distinguished from its formation on and under the earth, cc. 13–ii. 3.
[3] Cp. *De Gen. et Corr.* ii. 10 ; esp. 336ᵇ 15 sqq.

because its heat is gone and because the place is cold, and
30 condenses again and turns from air into water. And after
the water has formed it falls down again to the earth.[1]

The exhalation of water is vapour : air condensing into
water is cloud. Mist is what is left over when a cloud
condenses into water, and is therefore rather a sign of fine
weather than of rain ; for mist might be called a barren
cloud.

35 So we get a circular process that follows the course of
347ᵃ the sun. For according as the sun moves to this side or
that,[2] the moisture in this process rises or falls. We must
think of it as a river flowing up and down in a circle and
made up partly of air, partly of water. When the sun is
near, the stream of vapour flows upwards ; when it recedes,
5 the stream of water flows down : and the order of sequence,
at all events, in this process always remains the same. So
if ' Oceanus ' had some secret meaning in early writers,
perhaps they may have meant this river that flows in
a circle about the earth.[3]

So the moisture is always raised by the heat and descends
10 to the earth again when it gets cold. These processes and, in
some cases, their varieties are distinguished by special
names. When the water falls in small drops it is called
a drizzle ; when the drops are larger it is rain.

Some of the vapour that is formed by day does not rise 10
high because the ratio of the fire that is raising it to the
15 water that is being raised is small. When this cools and
descends at night it is called dew and hoar-frost. When
the vapour is frozen before it has condensed to water again
it is hoar-frost ; and this appears in winter and is commoner
in cold places. It is dew when the vapour has condensed
into water and the heat is not so great as to dry up the
20 moisture that has been raised, nor the cold sufficient (owing
to the warmth of the climate or season) for the vapour itself
to freeze. For dew is more commonly found when the
season or the place is warm, whereas the opposite, as has

---

[1] Cp. 359ᵇ 34 sq.
[2] i. e. north and south on the ecliptic ; cp. 361ᵃ 4 sq.
[3] Cp. 359ᵇ 34.

been said, is the case with hoar-frost. For obviously
vapour is warmer than water, having still the fire that
raised it : consequently more cold is needed to freeze it.   25

Both dew and hoar-frost are found when the sky is clear
and there is no wind. For the vapour could not be raised
unless the sky were clear, and if a wind were blowing
it could not condense.

The fact that hoar-frost is not found on mountains
contributes to prove that these phenomena occur because
the vapour does not rise high. One reason for this is that 30
it rises from hollow and watery places, so that the heat
that is raising it, bearing as it were too heavy a burden
cannot lift it to a great height but soon lets it fall again.
A second reason is that the motion of the air is more
pronounced at a height, and this dissolves a gathering of
this kind.

Everywhere, except in Pontus, dew is found with south 35
winds and not with north winds. There the opposite is the
case and it is found with north winds and not with south.
The reason is the same as that which explains why dew 347^b
is found in warm weather and not in cold. For the south
wind brings warm, and the north, wintry weather. For the
north wind is cold and so quenches the heat of the evaporation. But in Pontus the south wind does not bring warmth
enough to cause evaporation, whereas the coldness of the 5
north wind concentrates the heat by a sort of recoil, so
that there is more evaporation and not less.[1] This is a thing
which we can often observe in other places too. Wells, for
instance, give off more vapour [2] in a north than in a south
wind. Only [3] the north winds quench the heat before any
considerable quantity of vapour has gathered, while in 10
a south wind the evaporation is allowed to accumulate.

Water,[4] once formed, does not freeze on the surface of
the earth, in the way that it does in the region of the
clouds.

---

[1] As you might expect from the coldness of the wind.
[2] Read ἀτμίζει in l. 8 with the MSS.
[3] i. e. in places other than Pontus.
[4] As contrasted with vapour. Ar. is thinking merely of the lack of
an analogue to hail.

From the latter there fall three bodies condensed by cold, 11
namely rain, snow, hail. Two of these correspond to the
phenomena on the lower level and are due to the same
15 causes, differing from them only in degree and quantity.

Snow and hoar-frost are one and the same thing, and so
are rain and dew : only there is a great deal of the former
and little of the latter. For rain is due to the cooling
of a great amount of vapour, for the region from which
and the time during which the vapour is collected are
20 considerable. But of dew there is little : for the vapour
collects for it in a single day and from a small area, as its
quick formation and scanty quantity show.

The relation of hoar-frost and snow is the same : when
cloud freezes there is snow, when vapour freezes there
is hoar-frost. Hence snow is a sign of a cold season or
25 country. For a great deal of heat is still present and
unless the cold were overpowering it the cloud would not
freeze. For there still survives in it a great deal of the heat
which[1] caused the moisture to rise as vapour from the
earth.

Hail on the other hand is found in the upper region, but
the corresponding phenomenon in the vaporous region near
30 the earth is lacking. For, as we said, to snow in the upper
region corresponds hoar-frost in the lower, and to rain in
the upper region, dew in the lower. But there is nothing
here to correspond to hail in the upper region. Why this
is so will be clear when we have explained the nature
of hail.

But we must go on to collect the facts bearing on the 12
35 origin of it, both those which raise no difficulties and those
which seem paradoxical.

348^a   Hail is ice, and water freezes in winter ; yet hailstorms
occur chiefly in spring and autumn and less often in the
late summer, but rarely in winter and then only when the
cold is less intense. And in general hailstorms occur in
warmer, and snow in colder places. Again, there is
5 a difficulty about water freezing in the upper region. It

---

[1] Omit πυρὸς in l. 28 with E₁ and (apparently) Alexander.

cannot have frozen before becoming water: and water cannot remain suspended in the air for any space of time. Nor can we say that the case is like that of particles of moisture which are carried up owing to their small size and rest on the air (the water swimming on the air just as 10 small particles of earth and gold often swim on water). In that case large drops are formed by the union of many small, and so fall down. This cannot take place in the case of hail, since solid bodies cannot coalesce like liquid ones. Clearly then drops of that size were suspended in the air or else they could not have been so large when frozen.

Some [1] think that the cause and origin of hail is this. The cloud is thrust up into the upper atmosphere, which is 15 colder because the reflection of the sun's rays from the earth ceases there,[2] and upon its arrival there the water freezes. They think that this explains why hailstorms are commoner in summer and in warm countries; the heat is greater and it thrusts the clouds further up from the earth. But the fact is that hail does not occur at all at a great 20 height: yet it ought to do so, on their theory, just as we see that snow falls most on high mountains. Again clouds have often been observed moving with a great noise close to the earth, terrifying those who heard and saw 25 them as portents of some catastrophe. Sometimes, too, when such clouds have been seen, without any noise, there follows a violent hailstorm, and the stones are of incredible size, and angular in shape. This shows that they have not been falling for long and that they were frozen near to the earth, and not as that theory would have it. Moreover, 30 where the hailstones are large, the cause of their freezing must be present in the highest degree: for hail is ice as every one can see. Now those hailstones are large which are angular in shape. And this shows that they froze close to the earth, for those that fall far are worn away by the 35 length of their fall and become round and smaller in size.

It clearly follows that the congelation does not take 348[b]

[1] i.e. Anaxagoras, cp. [b] 12, Diels, 46 A 85.
[2] Cp. 340[a] 27 sqq.

place because the cloud is thrust up into the cold upper
region.

Now we see that warm and cold react upon one another
by recoil. Hence in warm weather the lower parts of
5 the earth are cold and in a frost they are warm. The
same thing, we must suppose, happens in the air, so that in
the warmer seasons the cold is concentrated by the surrounding heat and causes the cloud to go over into water
suddenly.[1] (For this reason rain-drops are much larger on
warm days than in winter, and showers more violent.
10 A shower is said to be more violent in proportion as the
water comes down in a body, and this happens when the
condensation takes place quickly,—though this is just the
opposite of what Anaxagoras says. He says that this happens
when the cloud has risen into the cold air ; whereas we say
that it happens when the cloud has descended into the warm
air, and that the more the further the cloud has descended).
15 But when the cold has been concentrated within still more
by the outer heat, it freezes the water it has formed and
there is hail. We get hail when the process of freezing is
quicker than the descent of the water. For if the water
falls in a certain time and the cold is sufficient to freeze it
20 in less, there is no difficulty about its having frozen in the
air, provided that the freezing takes place in a shorter time
than its fall. The nearer to the earth, and the more
suddenly, this process takes place, the more violent is the
rain that results and the larger the raindrops and the
25 hailstones because of the shortness of their fall. For
the same reason large raindrops do not fall thickly. Hail
is rarer in summer than in spring and autumn, though
commoner than in winter, because the air is drier in
summer, whereas in spring it is still moist, and in autumn
it is beginning to grow moist. It is for the same reason
that hailstorms sometimes occur in the late summer as we
have said.[2]

30   The fact that the water has previously been warmed

---

[1] Omit ὁτὲ δὲ χάλαζαν in l. 8, with all the MSS. except N corr. ὁτὲ
μέν is answered by ὁταν δ' [b] 15 below and the intervening lines διὸ
καὶ ... ὁταν μάλιστα are parenthetical and should be printed accordingly.
[2] a I.

contributes to its freezing quickly : for so it cools sooner.
Hence many people, when they want to cool hot water [1]
quickly, begin by putting it in the sun.   So the inhabitants
of Pontus when they encamp on the ice to fish (they cut 35
a hole in the ice and then fish) pour warm water round
their reeds that it may freeze the quicker, for they use the 349[a]
ice like lead to fix the reeds.   Now it is in hot countries
and seasons that the water which forms soon grows warm.

It is for the same reason that rain falls in summer and
not in winter in Arabia and Ethiopia too, and that in 5
torrents and repeatedly on the same day.   For the concentration or recoil due to the extreme heat of the country
cools the clouds quickly.

So much for an account of the nature and causes of rain, 10
dew, snow, hoar-frost, and hail.

13   Let us explain the nature of winds, and all windy
vapours, also of rivers and of the sea.   But here, too, we
must first discuss the difficulties involved : for, as in other
matters, so in this no theory has been handed down to us 15
that the most ordinary man could not have thought of.

Some [2] say that what is called air, when it is in motion
and flows, is wind, and that this same air when it condenses
again becomes cloud and water, implying that the nature
of wind and water is the same.   So they define wind as
a motion of the air.   Hence some, wishing to say a clever 20
thing, assert that all the winds are one wind, because
the air that moves is in fact all of it one and the
same ; they maintain that the winds appear to differ owing
to the region from which the air may happen to flow [3] on
each occasion, but really do not differ at all.   This is just 25
like thinking that all rivers are one and the same river, and
the ordinary unscientific view is better than a scientific
theory like this.   If all rivers flow from one source, and
the same is true in the case of the winds, there might be
some truth in this theory ; but if it is no more true in the 30
one case than in the other, this ingenious idea is plainly

[1] Read τὸ θερμόν in l. 33 with all the MSS. except F corr.
[2] Hippocrates περὶ φυσῶν (Opp., vol. i, 571. 12, ed. Kühn).
[3] Read ῥέων in l. 24 with the MSS.

false. What requires investigation is this: the nature of wind and how it originates, its efficient cause and whence they derive their source; whether one ought to think of the wind as issuing from a sort of vessel and flowing until
35 the vessel is empty, as if let out of a wineskin, or, as
349ᵇ painters represent the winds, as drawing their source from themselves.

We find analogous views about the origin of rivers.[1] It is thought that the water is raised by the sun and descends in rain and gathers below the earth and so flows from a great reservoir, all the rivers from one, or each
5 from a different one. No water at all is generated, but the volume of the rivers[2] consists of the water that is gathered into such reservoirs in winter. Hence rivers are always fuller in winter than in summer, and some are perennial, others not. Rivers are perennial where the reservoir is large
10 and so enough water has collected in it to last out and not be used up before the winter rain returns. Where the reservoirs are smaller there is less water in the rivers, and they are dried up and their vessel empty before the fresh rain comes on.

15 But if any one will picture to himself a reservoir adequate to the water that is continuously flowing day by day, and consider the amount of the water, it is obvious that a receptacle that is to contain all the water that flows in the year would be larger than the earth, or, at any rate, not much smaller.

20 Though it is evident that many reservoirs of this kind do exist in many parts of the earth, yet it is unreasonable for any one to refuse to admit that air becomes water in the earth for the same reason as it does above it. If the cold causes the vaporous air to condense into water above the earth we must suppose the cold in the earth to produce
25 this same effect, and recognize that there not only exists in it and flows out of it actually formed water, but that water is continually forming in it too.

---

[1] Cp. Anaxagoras, Burnet, *Early Greek Philosophy*, § 135 = Diels, 46 A. 42 § 5.
[2] Read τὸ τῶν in l. 7 with J (τούτων E).

Again, even in the case of the water that is not being
formed from day to day but exists as such, we must not
suppose as some do that rivers have their source in definite 30
subterranean lakes. On the contrary, just as above the
earth small drops form and these join others, till finally the
water descends in a body as rain, so too we must suppose
that in the earth the water at first trickles together little
by little, and that the sources of the rivers drip, as it were,
out of the earth and then unite. This is proved by facts. 35
When men construct an aqueduct they collect the water in **350ª**
pipes and trenches, as if the earth in the higher ground
were sweating the water out. Hence, too, the head-waters
of rivers are found to flow from mountains, and from the
greatest mountains there flow the most numerous and
greatest rivers. Again, most springs are in the neighbour- 5
hood of mountains and of high ground, whereas if we
except rivers, water rarely appears in the plains. For
mountains and high ground, suspended [1] over the country
like a saturated sponge, make the water ooze out and trickle
together in minute quantities but in many places. They
receive a great deal of water falling as rain (for it makes no 10
difference whether a spongy receptacle is concave and turned
up or convex and turned down : in either case it will contain
the same volume of matter) and they also cool the vapour
that rises and condense it back into water.

Hence, as we said, we find that the greatest rivers flow
from the greatest mountains. This can be seen by looking 15
at itineraries : what is recorded in them consists either of
things which the writer has seen himself or of such as he
has compiled after inquiry from those who have seen
them.

In Asia we find that the most numerous and greatest
rivers flow from the mountain called Parnassus,[2] admittedly 20
the greatest of all mountains towards the south-east. When
you have crossed it you see the outer ocean,[3] the further
limit of which is unknown to the dwellers in our world.

---

[1] Read ἐπικρεμαμένοι in l. 8 with EJF₂HN.
[2] Paropamisus or Hindu Kush.
[3] Indian Ocean.

Besides other rivers there flow from it the Bactrus,[1] the
Choaspes,[2] the Araxes:[3] from the last a branch separates
25 off and flows into lake Maeotis[4] as the Tanais.[5] From it,
too, flows the Indus, the volume of whose stream is greatest
of all rivers. From the Caucasus flows the Phasis,[6] and
very many other great rivers besides. Now the Caucasus
is the greatest of the mountains that lie to the north-east,
30 both as regards its extent and its height. A proof of its
height is the fact that it can be seen from the so-called
' deeps '[7] and from the entrance to the lake.[8] Again, the
sun shines on its peaks for a third part of the night before
sunrise and again after sunset. Its extent is proved by the
fact that though it contains many inhabitable regions which
are occupied by many nations and in which there are said
35 to be great lakes, yet they say that all these regions are
350ᵇ visible up to the last peak.[9] From Pyrene[10] (this is
a mountain towards the west in Celtice) there flow the
Istrus[11] and the Tartessus.[12] The latter flows outside the
pillars,[13] while the Istrus flows through all Europe into the
Euxine. Most of the remaining rivers flow northwards
5 from the Hercynian mountains[14], which are the greatest in
height and extent about that region. In the extreme north,
beyond furthest Scythia, are the mountains called Rhipae.[15]
The stories about their size are altogether too fabulous:
however, they say that the most and (after the Istrus) the
10 greatest rivers flow from them. So, too, in Libya there flow
from the Aethiopian mountains the Aegon and the Nyses;[16]
and from the so-called Silver Mountain the two greatest
of named rivers, the river called Chremetes[17] that flows into

---

[1] Balch-âb.   [2] Kunar.
[3] A. probably means the Oxus or Amu-Darya.
[4] Sea of Azov.   [5] Don.   [6] Rion.
[7] Cp. 351ᵃ 11.   [8] Maeotis.
[9] This is unintelligible: our text, though it goes back to Alexander,
must be corrupt.
[10] Pyrenees.   [11] Danube.   [12] Baetis or Guadalquivir.
[13] Of Heracles.
[14] The mountains of Bohemia, Silesia, Moravia, and northern
Austria.
[15] A mythical northern range to which no definite locality can be
assigned.
[16] Read Νύσης in l. 12 with the MSS.
[17] Sagiet el Hamra.

the outer ocean, and the main source of the Nile. Of the 15
rivers in the Greek world, the Achelous flows from Pindus,
the Inachus from the same mountain; the Strymon, the
Nestus, and the Hebrus all three from Scombrus; many
rivers, too, flow from Rhodope.

All other rivers would be found to flow in the same way,
but we have mentioned these as examples. Even where 20
rivers flow from marshes, the marshes in almost every case
are found to lie below mountains or gradually rising ground.

It is clear then that we must not suppose rivers to originate
from definite reservoirs: for the whole earth, we might
almost say, would not be sufficient (any more than the 25
region of the clouds would be) [1] if we were to suppose that
they were fed by actually existing water only and it were
not the case that as some water passed out of existence
some more came into existence, but rivers always drew their
stream from an existing store. Secondly, the fact that
rivers rise at the foot of mountains proves that a place
transmits the water it contains by gradual percolation of
many drops, little by little, and that this is how the sources
of rivers originate. However, there is nothing impossible 30
about the existence of such places containing a quantity of
water like lakes: only they cannot be big enough to produce the supposed effect. To think that they are is just as
absurd as if one were to suppose that rivers drew all their
water from the sources we see (for most rivers do flow from
springs). So it is no more reasonable to suppose those 35
lakes to contain the whole volume of water than these
springs.

That there exist such chasms and cavities in the earth we **351**[a]
are taught by the rivers that are swallowed up. They are
found in many parts of the earth: in the Peloponnesus, for
instance, there are many such rivers in Arcadia. The
reason is that Arcadia is mountainous and there are no
channels from its valleys to the sea. So these places get 5
full of water, and this, having no outlet, under the pressure
of the water that is added above, finds a way out for itself

---

[1] i.e. any more than the region of clouds could be supposed to
contain ready-made all the water that falls as rain.

underground. In Greece this kind of thing happens on
quite a small scale, but the lake at the foot of the Caucasus,[1]
which the inhabitants of these parts call a sea, is consider-
10 able.[2]   Many great rivers fall into it and it has no visible
outlet but issues below the earth off the land of the
Coraxi[3] about the so-called 'deeps of Pontus'. This is
a place of unfathomable depth in the sea : at any rate no
one has yet been able to find bottom there by sounding.
At this spot, about three hundred stadia from land, there
15 comes up sweet water over a large area, not all of it together
but in three places.   And in Liguria a river[4] equal in size
to the Rhodanus[5] is swallowed up and appears again elsewhere : the Rhodanus being a navigable river.

The same parts of the earth are not always moist or dry, 14
20 but they change according as rivers come into existence and
dry up.   And so the relation of land to sea changes too and
a place does not always remain land or sea throughout all
time, but where there was dry land there comes to be sea, and
where there is now sea, there one day comes to be dry land.
25 But we must suppose these changes to follow some order
and cycle.   The principle and cause of these changes is
that the interior of the earth grows and decays, like the
bodies of plants and animals.   Only in the case of these
latter the process does not go on by parts, but each of them
30 necessarily grows or decays as a whole, whereas it does go
on by parts in the case of the earth.   Here the causes are
cold and heat, which increase and diminish on account of
the sun and its course.   It is owing to them that the parts
of the earth come to have a different character, that some
parts remain moist for a certain time, and then dry up and
35 grow old, while other parts in their turn are filled with life

---

[1] Caspian Sea.

[2] φανερά (l. 9) is certainly wrong—it makes indifferent sense and is
omitted by all the MSS. except S rec.   Thurot thinks that a word
(such as μεγάλη) or words expressing the contrast to μικρά above are
wanted, but this is not certain.

[3] On the east coast of the Black Sea, about the modern Abkasia.

[4] Perhaps the Eridanus (Po).   Pliny alleges (falsely) that it flows
underground (Pliny iii. 16).

[5] Rhône.

and moisture. Now when places become drier the springs
necessarily give out, and when this happens the rivers first **351^b**
decrease in size and then finally become dry ; and when
rivers change and disappear in one part and come into
existence correspondingly in another, the sea must needs be
affected.

If the sea was once pushed out by rivers and encroached 5
upon the land anywhere, it necessarily leaves that place dry
when it recedes ; again, if the dry land has encroached on
the sea at all by a process of silting set up by the rivers
when at their full, the time must come when this place will
be flooded again.[1]

But the whole vital process of the earth takes place so
gradually and in periods of time which are so immense
compared with the length of our life, that these changes are 10
not observed, and before their course can be recorded from
beginning to end whole nations perish and are destroyed.
Of such destructions the most utter and sudden are due to
wars ; but pestilence or famine cause them too. Famines,
again, are either sudden and severe or else gradual. In the 15
latter case the disappearance of a nation is not noticed
because some leave the country while others remain; and
this goes on until the land is unable to maintain any
inhabitants at all. So a long period of time is likely to
elapse from the first departure to the last, and no one 20
remembers and the lapse of time destroys all record even
before the last inhabitants have disappeared. In the same

---

[1] Read a comma after ἐπλεόναζεν in l. 6, ἀπιοῖσαν with E₂J₂FHN,
and πληθύουσι. The version given implies this line of thought : rivers
fall into the sea at *A* and push it out (by silting) so that it floods the
land at *B*; when those rivers dry up the sea will recede from *B*.
Again, a river fills up its estuary with silt and so land encroaches on
the sea; when the river dries up the sea will return.

The two ὅπου clauses are concerned with one and the same process,
but the first considers the effect on the place *B*, the second the effect
on the place *A*.

The general principle seems to be that when wet predominates in
a place rivers rise there : this makes the sea recede from the mouth of
the rivers (by silting) and *ipso facto* encroach elsewhere ; when dry
predominates in the place the rivers shrink, then the sea returns there
and *ipso facto* leaves the other place which it had invaded, dry.

Aristotle is hampered by the fact that from the nature of the case
he is really familiar, as his examples show, with one side of the process
only, the encroaching of land on sea.

way a nation must be supposed to lose account of the time
when it first settled in a land that was changing from
25 a marshy and watery state and becoming dry.   Here, too,
the change is gradual and lasts a long time and men do not
remember who came first, or when, or what the land was
like when they came.   This has been the case with Egypt.
Here it is obvious that the land is continually getting drier
and that the whole country is a deposit of the river Nile.
30 But because the neighbouring peoples settled in the land
gradually as the marshes dried, the lapse of time has hidden
the beginning of the process.   However,[1] all the mouths of
the Nile, with the single exception of that at Canopus, are
obviously artificial and not natural.   And Egypt was
35 nothing more than what is called Thebes, as Homer, too,
shows, modern though he is in relation to such changes.
352^a For Thebes is the place that he mentions ; which implies
that Memphis did not yet exist, or at any rate was not as
important as it is now.   That this should be so is natural,
since the lower land came to be inhabited later than that
which lay higher.   For the parts that lie nearer to the
place where the river is depositing the silt are necessarily
marshy for a longer time since the water always lies most
5 in the newly formed land.   But in time this land changes
its character, and in its turn enjoys a period of prosperity.
For these places dry up and come to be in good condition
while the places that were formerly well-tempered some
day [2] grow excessively dry and deteriorate.   This happened
to the land of Argos and Mycenae in Greece.   In the time
10 of the Trojan wars the Argive land was marshy and could
only support a small population, whereas the land of
Mycenae was in good condition (and for this reason Mycenae
was the superior).   But now the opposite is the case, for
the reason we have mentioned : the land of Mycenae has
become completely dry and barren, while the Argive land
that was formerly barren owing to the water has now
become fruitful.   Now the same process that has taken

---

[1] i. e. though there is no record of the beginning of this process the
facts alleged prove the thesis.

[2] Read ποτε in l. 8 with EJF₁HN.

place in this small district must be supposed to be going on 15 over whole countries and on a large scale.

Men whose outlook is narrow suppose the cause of such events to be change in the universe, in the sense of a coming to be of the world as a whole.[1] Hence they say that the sea is being dried up and is growing less, because 20 this is observed to have happened in more places now than formerly. But this is only partially true. It is true that many places are now dry, that formerly were covered with water. But the opposite is true too : for if they look they will find that there are many places where the sea has invaded the land. But we must not suppose that the cause 25 of this is that the world is in process of becoming. For it is absurd to make the universe to be in process because of small and trifling changes, when the bulk and size of the earth are surely as nothing in comparison with the whole world. Rather we must take the cause of all these changes to be that, just as winter occurs in the seasons of the year, so in determined periods there comes a great winter of 30 a great year and with it excess of rain. But this excess does not always occur in the same place. The deluge in the time of Deucalion, for instance, took place chiefly in the Greek world and in it especially about ancient Hellas, the 35 country about Dodona and the Achelous, a river which has often changed its course. Here the Selli dwelt and those **352ᵇ** who were formerly called Graeci and now Hellenes. When, therefore, such an excess of rain occurs we must suppose that it suffices for a long time. We have seen that some[2] say that the size of the subterranean cavities is what makes 5 some rivers perennial and others not, whereas we maintain that the size of the mountains is the cause, and their density and coldness; for great, dense, and cold mountains catch and keep and create most water : whereas if the mountains that overhang the sources of rivers are small or porous and 10 stony and clayey, these rivers run dry earlier. We must recognize the same kind of thing in this case too. Where such abundance of rain falls in the great winter

---

[1] Cp. *De Caelo*, 279ᵇ 12 ; cp. 352ᵇ 16, 353ᵇ 10, 356ᵇ 10.
[2] 349ᵇ 3.

it tends to make the moisture of those places almost ever-
lasting.[1] But as time goes on places of the latter type
dry up[2] more, while those of the former, moist type,
15 do so less: until at last the beginning of the same cycle
returns.

Since there is necessarily some change in the whole world,
but not in the way of coming into existence or perishing (for
the universe is permanent), it must be, as we say, that the
same places are not for ever moist through the presence of
sea and rivers, nor for ever dry. And the facts prove this.
20 The whole land of the Egyptians, whom we take to be the
most ancient of men, has evidently gradually come into
existence and been produced by the river. This is clear
from an observation of the country, and the facts about the
Red Sea suffice to prove it too. One of their kings tried
25 to make a canal to it (for it would have been of no little
advantage to them for the whole region to have become
navigable; Sesostris is said to have been the first of the
ancient kings to try), but he found that the sea was higher
than the land. So he first, and Darius afterwards, stopped
making the canal, lest the sea should mix with the river
30 water and spoil it. So it is clear that all this part was once
unbroken sea. For the same reason Libya—the country of
Ammon—is, strangely enough, lower and hollower than the
land to the seaward of it. For it is clear that a barrier of silt
35 was formed and after it lakes and dry land, but in course of
time the water that was left behind in the lakes dried up and
353^a is now all gone. Again the silting up of the lake Maeotis by
the rivers has advanced so much that the limit to the size of
the ships which can now sail into it to trade is much lower
than it was sixty years ago. Hence it is easy to infer that

---

[1] Read οἴεσθαι δεῖ (l. 11) with cod. Par. suppl. 314 and Bag., and
punctuate with οὗτοι . . . ποιοῦσιν in a parenthesis and commas after
ποιοῦσιν and προαπολείπειν. Also in l. 13 omit μᾶλλον, probably
introduced from the next sentence (Par. 2032 and Ol. (lemma) have τῶν
ποταμῶν without μᾶλλον).

[2] Omit γιγνόμενα in l. 14 with Ideler (Alexander seems not to have
read it) and read ἔλαττον (so probably Al.). The version given follows
Vicomercato in making ταῦτα and θάτερα refer to ὅσοις δέ and οὗτοι γάρ,
respectively. But text and interpretation of the whole passage are
doubtful.

it, too, like most lakes, was originally produced by the rivers 5
and that it must end by drying up entirely.

Again, this process of silting up causes a continuous
current through the Bosporus [1]; and in this case we can
directly observe the nature of the process.   Whenever
the current from the Asiatic shore threw up a sandbank,
there first formed a small lake behind it.   Later it dried up 10
and a second sandbank formed in front of the first and
a second lake.   This process went on uniformly and without
interruption.   Now when this has been repeated often
enough, in the course of time the strait must become like
a river, and in the end the river itself must dry up.

So it is clear, since there will be no end [2] to time and the 15
world is eternal, that neither the Tanais nor the Nile has
always been flowing, but that the region whence they flow
was once dry: for their effect may be fulfilled, but time
cannot.   And this will be equally true of all other rivers.
But if rivers come into existence and perish and the same 20
parts of the earth were not always moist, the sea must
needs change correspondingly.   And if the sea is always
advancing in one place and receding in another it is clear
that the same parts of the whole earth are not always either
sea or land, but that all this changes in course of time.

So we have explained that the same parts of the earth are 25
not always land or sea and why that is so: and also why
some rivers are perennial and others not.

BOOK II

1 LET us explain the nature of the sea and the reason why
such a large mass of water is salt and the way in which it
originally came to be.

The old writers who invented theogonies say that the
sea has springs,[3] for they want earth and sea to have 35
foundations and roots of their own.   Presumably they **353[b]**

---

[1] The Cimmerian and not the Thracian Bosporus is meant: cp.
Reclus *Nouv. Géog. Universelle,* v, p. 788 sqq.
[2] Read ὑπολείψει in l. 15 with JFHN Al. Ol. (lemma).
[3] e.g. Hesiod., *Theog.* 282.

thought that this view was grander and more impressive as
implying that our earth was an important part of the
universe. For they believed that the whole world had
been built up round our earth and for its sake, and that
the earth was the most important and primary part of it.
5 Others,[1] wiser in human knowledge, give an account of its
origin. At first, they say, the earth was surrounded by
moisture. Then the sun began to dry it up, part of it
evaporated and is the cause of winds and the turnings back
of the sun and the moon,[2] while the remainder forms the
10 sea. So the sea is being dried up and is growing less, and
will end by being some day entirely dried up.[3] Others [4]
say that the sea is a kind of sweat exuded by the earth
when the sun heats it, and that this explains its saltness:
for all sweat is salt. Others [5] say that the saltness is due
to the earth. Just as water strained through ashes becomes
15 salt, so the sea owes its saltness to the admixture of earth
with similar properties.

We must now consider the facts which prove that the
sea cannot possibly have springs. The waters we find on
the earth either flow or are stationary. All flowing water
20 has springs. (By a spring, as we have explained above,[6]
we must not understand a source from which waters are
ladled as it were from a vessel, but a first point at which
the water which is continually forming and percolating
gathers.[7]) Stationary water is either that which has

---

[1] Alexander refers this to Anaximander (Diels, 2. 27) and Diogenes
of Apollonia (Diels, 51 A. 9, 17); but it would fit almost any of the
' Milesians ', e.g. Thales (cp. Burnet, § 9); Anaximenes (Diels, 3 A. 7, § 5).
[2] Cp. 354^b 33 sqq. The 'turnings back' were explained as due to
the resistance of compressed air by Anaximenes (Diels, 3 A. 15) and
Anaxagoras (Diels, 46 A. 42, § 9); as due to a lack of the moisture
that nourished them, according to Alexander (on the authority of
Theophr.) on 354^b 33 sq. below, by Anaximander and Diogenes. Zeller
I⁵. p. 223, n. 3, and Heath, *Aristarchus*, p. 33, refuse to attribute the
view to Anaximander and interpret τροπαί as ' revolutions '.
[3] Cp. 352^a 19.
[4] Empedocles, cp. 357^a 24. Diels, 21 B. 55, A. 25 and 66, cp.
55 A. 99^a (Democritus) and 80 B. 32 (Antiphon).
[5] Cp. Diels, 11 A. 33 (Xenophanes); 57 A. 19 (Metrodorus of Chios);
46 A. 90 (Anaxagoras).   [6] 349^b 27.
[7] Read ταμιευομένων in l. 21 with E₂ and Cod. Par. Suppl. 314, εἰς
ἥν in l. 22 with E₁H and Alexander, and ἀπαντᾷ with E₁HN and
Alexander.

collected and has been left standing, marshy pools, for
instance, and lakes, which differ merely in size, or else it
comes from springs. In this case it is always artificial, 25
I mean as in the case of wells, otherwise the spring would
have to be above the outlet. Hence the water from
fountains and rivers flows of itself, whereas wells need to
be worked artificially. All the waters that exist belong to
one or other of these classes.

On the basis of this division we can see that the sea 30
cannot have springs. For it falls under neither of the two
classes ; it does not flow and it is not artificial; whereas
all water from springs must belong to one or other of them.
Natural standing water from springs is never found on such
a large scale.

[1] Again, there are several seas that have no communication 35
with one another at all. The Red Sea,[2] for instance, com- 354^a
municates but slightly with the ocean outside the straits[3],
and the Hyrcanian[4] and Caspian seas are distinct from this
ocean and people dwell all round them. Hence, if these
seas had had any springs anywhere they must have been
discovered.

It is true that in straits, where the land on either side 5
contracts an open sea into a small space, the sea appears
to flow. But this is because it is swinging to and fro. In
the open sea this motion is not observed, but where the
land narrows and contracts the sea the motion that was 10
imperceptible in the open necessarily strikes the attention.

The whole of the Mediterranean does actually flow.
The direction of this flow is determined by the depth of
the basins and by the number of rivers. Maeotis flows

---

[1] Omit ἐπεί in l. 35 with Bon. *Ar. St.* iii.

[2] i.e. the Indian Ocean, cp. Partsch, ' Ar. über d. Steigen des Nil,'
Abh. d. kön. Sächs. Ges. d. Wiss., 1909, p. 569.

[3] i.e. the Atlantic.

[4] If this is not the Aral, which A. can hardly have known, we must
explain the plural thus : ' Hyrcanian ' is used to denote the Caspian,
e. g. in Hecataeus ; A. does not seem to have noticed that one and the
same lake was meant and imagines the Hyrcanian distinct from the
Caspian by a mere blunder. Or he may have thought of the two as
different parts of the same sea in the way in which the Aegean and
Adriatic might be called distinct seas by a writer who knew they were
one in a sense. Cp. Bolchert, *Aristoteles' Erdkunde v. Asien u.
Libyen*, p. 10.

into Pontus[1] and Pontus into the Aegean. After that the
15 flow of the remaining seas is not so easy to observe. The
current of Maeotis and Pontus is due to the number of
rivers (more rivers flow into the Euxine and Maeotis than
into the whole Mediterranean with its much larger basin),
and to their own shallowness. For we find the sea getting
20 deeper and deeper. Pontus is deeper than Maeotis, the
Aegean than Pontus, the Sicilian sea than the Aegean;
the Sardinian and Tyrrhenic being the deepest of all.
(Outside the pillars of Herakles the sea is shallow owing to
the mud, but calm, for it lies in a hollow.)[2] We see, then,
that just as single rivers flow from mountains, so it is
25 with the earth as a whole: the greatest volume of water
flows from the higher regions in the north. Their alluvium
makes the northern seas shallow, while the outer seas are
deeper. Some further evidence of the height of the
northern regions of the earth is afforded by the view of
many of the ancient meteorologists.[3] They believed that
30 the sun did not pass below the earth, but round its northern
part, and that it was the height of this which obscured the
sun and caused night.

So much to prove that there cannot be sources of the
sea and to explain its observed flow.

354[b] We must now discuss the origin of the sea, if it has an
origin, and the cause of its salt and bitter taste. **2**

What made earlier writers consider the sea to be the
original and main body of water is this. It seems reasonable
5 to suppose that to be the case on the analogy of the other
elements. Each of them has a main bulk which by
reason of its mass is the origin of that element,
and any parts which change and mix with the other
elements come from it. Thus the main body of fire is in

---

[1] Black Sea.

[2] i. e. it is shallow, yet the water does not flow back (as you might
expect on the analogy of Maeotis, &c.), because the sea lies in a hollow
as is proved by the calm (Alexander). This seems the best that can
be made of this suspicious sentence. The 'mud' is an echo of the
Sargasso Sea.

[3] e. g. Anaximenes, Diels, 3 A. 7 (§ 6), 14. Aristotle is not endorsing
the view about the sun, and there is no need to condemn this passage
in consequence as Berger does.

the upper region; that of air occupies the place next inside
the region of fire; while the mass of the earth is that
round which the rest of the elements are seen to lie. So 10
we must clearly look for something analogous in the case
of water. But here we can find no such single mass, as in
the case of the other elements, except the sea. River water
is not a unity, nor is it stable, but is seen to be in a continuous process of becoming from day to day. It was this 15
difficulty which made people regard the sea as the origin
and source of moisture and of all water. And so we find
it maintained that rivers not only flow into the sea but
originate from it,[1] the salt water becoming sweet by
filtration.

But this view involves another difficulty. If this body
of water is the origin and source of all water, why is it 20
salt and not sweet? The reason for this, besides answering
this question, will ensure our having a right first conception
of the nature of the sea.

The earth is surrounded by water, just as that is by the
sphere of air, and that again by the sphere called that of
fire (which is the outermost[2] both on the common view 25
and on ours). Now the sun, moving as it does, sets up
processes of change and becoming and decay, and by its
agency the finest and sweetest water is every day carried
up and is dissolved into vapour and rises to the upper
region, where it is condensed again by the cold and so 30
returns to the earth. This, as we have said before,[3] is the
regular course of nature.

Hence all my predecessors[4] who supposed that the sun
was nourished by moisture are absurdly mistaken. Some[5]
go on to say that the solstices are due to this, the reason **355^a**
being that the same places cannot always supply the sun
with nourishment and that without it he must perish. For
the fire we are familiar with lives as long as it is fed, and 5

---

[1] e. g. Xenophanes, Diels, 11 B. 30.
[2] Read τούτων in l. 25 with JFHN and Alexander, for πάντων.
[3] I. 9.
[4] Cp. 353^b 5. Cp. Burnet, § 9 (Thales); Diels, 3 A. 7, § 5 (Anaximenes).
[5] Perhaps Anaximander and Diogenes; cp. 353^b 6 and 355^a 22.

the only food for fire is moisture.[1] As if the moisture
that is raised could reach the sun! or this ascent were
really like that performed by flame as it comes into
being, and to which they supposed the case of the sun
to be analogous! Really there is no similarity. A flame
is a process of becoming, involving a constant interchange
10 of moist and dry. It cannot be said to be nourished since
it scarcely persists as one and the same for a moment.
This cannot be true of the sun; for if it were nourished
like that, as they say it is, we should obviously not only
have a new sun every day, as Heraclitus[2] says, but a new
15 sun every moment. Again, when the sun causes the
moisture to rise, this is like fire heating water. So, as the
fire is not fed by the water above it, it is absurd to suppose
that the sun feeds on that moisture, even if its heat made
all the water in the world evaporate. Again, it is absurd,
considering the number and size of the stars, that these
20 thinkers should consider the sun only and overlook the question how the rest of the heavenly bodies subsist. Again,
they are met by the same difficulty as those[3] who say that
at first the earth itself was moist and the world round the
earth was warmed by the sun, and so air was generated
and the whole firmament grew, and the air caused winds
25 and solstices. The objection is that we always plainly see
the water that has been carried up coming down again.
Even if the same amount does not come back in a year or
in a given country, yet in a certain period all that has been
carried up is returned. This implies that the celestial
bodies do not feed on it, and that we cannot distinguish
between some air which preserves its character once it is
30 generated and some other which is generated but becomes

---

[1] καὶ διὰ τοῦτ' . . . μόνον (354ᵇ 34–355ª 5) is a parenthesis (Thurot).
[2] Diels, 12 B. 6.
[3] Diels, 51 A. 9 refers this specially to Diogenes. Alexander identifies
the doctrine with that of 353ᵇ 6 and refers it to Anaximander and
Diogenes (on the authority of Theophrastus). It seems impossible
to distinguish the ἔνιοι of 354ᵇ 34 and the οἱ φάσκοντες here, 355ª 22. It
looks as if the real distinction was that between those who explained
the 'turnings' by compressed air and those who explained them by
lack of nourishment. But in that case Aristotle, Theophrastus, and
Alexander are all confused and have failed to maintain the distinction.

water again and so perishes; on the contrary, all the
moisture alike is dissolved and all of it condensed back
into water.

The drinkable, sweet water, then, is light and is all of it
drawn up: the salt water is heavy and remains behind, but not
in its natural place. For this is a question which has been
sufficiently discussed (I mean about the natural place 35
that water, like the other elements, must in reason have),
and the answer is this. The place which we see the sea **355**^b
filling is not its natural place but that of water. It seems
to belong to the sea because the weight of the salt water 5
makes it remain there, while the sweet, drinkable water
which is light is carried up. The same thing happens in
animal bodies. Here, too, the food when it enters the body
is sweet, yet the residuum and dregs of liquid food are
found to be bitter and salt. This is because the sweet and
drinkable part of it has been drawn away by the natural animal 10
heat and has passed into the flesh and the other parts of
the body according to their several natures. Now just as
here it would be wrong for any one to refuse to call the
belly the place of liquid food because that disappears from
it soon, and to call it the place of the residuum because
this is seen to remain, so in the case of our present subject.
This place, we say, is the place of water. Hence all rivers 15
and all the water that is generated flow into it: for water
flows into the deepest place, and the deepest part of the
earth is filled by the sea. Only all the light and sweet
part of it is quickly carried off by the sun, while the rest
remains for the reason we have explained. It is quite 20
natural that some people should have been puzzled by the
old question why such a mass of water leaves no trace
anywhere (for the sea does not increase though innumerable
and vast rivers are flowing into it every day). But if one
considers the matter the solution is easy. The same 25
amount of water does not take as long to dry up when it
is spread out as when it is gathered in a body, and indeed
the difference is so great that in the one case it might
persist the whole day long while in the other it might all
disappear in a moment—as for instance if one were to

30 spread out a cup of water over a large table. This is the
case with the rivers: all the time they are flowing their
water forms a compact mass, but when it arrives at a vast
wide place it quickly and imperceptibly evaporates.

But the theory of the Phaedo[1] about rivers and the sea
is impossible. There it is said that the earth is pierced
35 by intercommunicating channels and that the original head
356[a] and source of all waters is what is called Tartarus—a mass
of water about the centre, from which all waters, flowing
and standing, are derived. This primary and original water
is always surging to and fro, and so it causes the rivers to
flow on this side of the earth's centre and on that; for it
has no fixed seat but is always oscillating about the centre.
5 Its motion up and down is what fills rivers. Many of these
form lakes in various places (our sea is an instance of one
of these), but all of them come round again in a circle to
the original source of their flow, many at the same point,
but some at a point opposite to that from which they
10 issued ; for instance, if they started from the other side of
the earth's centre, they might return from this side of it.
They descend only as far as the centre, for after that all
motion is upwards. Water gets its tastes and colours from
the kind of earth the rivers happened to flow through.

But on this theory rivers do not always flow in the same
15 sense. For since they flow to the centre from which they issue
forth they will not be flowing down any more than up, but
in whatever direction the surging of Tartarus inclines to.
But at this rate we shall get the proverbial rivers flowing
upwards,[2] which is impossible. Again, where is the water
that is generated and what goes up again as vapour to come
20 from? For this must all of it simply be ignored,[3] since
the quantity of water is always the same and all the water
that flows out from the original source flows back to it
again. This itself is not true, since all rivers are seen to
end in the sea except where one flows into another. Not
one of them ends in the earth, but even when one is
25 swallowed up it comes to the surface again. And those

---

[1] *Phaedo*, 111 c sq.   [2] Eur. *Med.* 410.
[3] Read ἐξαιρεῖν in l. 20.

rivers are large which flow for a long distance through
a low-lying country, for by their situation and length they
cut off the course of many others and swallow them up.[1]
This is why the Istrus and the Nile are the greatest of
the rivers which flow into our sea. Indeed, so many rivers
fall into them that there is disagreement as to the sources 30
of them both.[2] All of which is plainly impossible on
the theory, and the more so as it derives the sea from
Tartarus.

Enough has been said to prove that this is the natural
place of water and not of the sea, and to explain why sweet
water is only found in rivers, while salt water is stationary, 35
and to show that the sea is the end rather than the source 356^b
of water, analogous to the residual matter of all food, and
especially liquid food, in animal bodies.

3   We must now explain why the sea is salt, and ask whether
it eternally exists as identically the same body, or whether
it did not exist at all once and some day will exist no
longer, but will dry up as some people think.   5

Every one admits this, that if the whole world originated
the sea did too; for they make them come into being at
the same time. It follows that if the universe is eternal
the same must be true of the sea. Any one who thinks
like Democritus[3] that the sea is diminishing and will 10
disappear in the end reminds us of Aesop's tales.   His
story was that Charybdis had twice sucked in the sea :
the first time she made the mountains visible ; the second
time the islands ; and when she sucks it in for the last time
she will dry it up entirely.   Such a tale is appropriate 15
enough to Aesop in a rage with the ferryman, but not to
serious inquirers.   Whatever made the sea remain at first,
whether it was its weight, as some even of those who hold
these views say (for it is easy to see the cause here), or
some other reason—clearly the same thing must make it 20
persist for ever.   They must either deny that the water
raised by the sun will return at all, or, if it does, they

---

[1] Whereas on the theory these conditions would be unnecessary.
[2] Omit αἰτίας in l. 30 with Alexander and Thurot.
[3] Diels, 55 A. 99^a and 100. Cp. 352^a 19.

must admit that the sea persists for ever or as long as this process goes on, and again, that for the same period of time that sweet water must have been carried up before-
25 hand. So the sea will never dry up: for before that can happen the water that has gone up beforehand will return to it :[1] for if you say that this happens once you must admit its recurrence. If you stop the sun's course there is no drying agency. If you let it go on it will draw up the sweet water as we have said whenever it approaches, and let
30 it descend again when it recedes. This notion about the sea is derived from the fact that many places are found to be drier now than they once were. Why this is so we have explained.[2] The phenomenon is due to temporary excess of rain and not to any process of becoming in which
35 the universe or its parts are involved. Some day the
357^a opposite will take place and after that the earth will grow dry once again. We must recognize that this process always goes on thus in a cycle, for that is more satisfactory than to suppose a change in the whole world in order to explain these facts. But we have dwelt longer on this point than it deserves.

5   To return to the saltness of the sea : those who create the sea once for all, or indeed generate it at all, cannot account for its saltness. It makes no difference whether the sea is the residue of all the moisture that is about the earth and has been drawn up by the sun, or whether all the flavour existing in the whole mass of sweet water is due to the admixture of a certain kind of earth. Since the
10 total volume of the sea is the same once the water that evaporated has returned, it follows that it must either have been salt at first too, or, if not at first, then not now either. If it was salt from the very beginning, then we want to know why that was so ; and why, if salt water was drawn up then, that is not the case now.

Again, if it is maintained that an admixture of earth
15 makes the sea salt (for they say that earth has many flavours and is washed down by the rivers and so makes the sea salt by its admixture), it is strange that rivers

---

[1] Omitting τήν in l. 26.   [2] I. 14.

should not be salt too. How can the admixture of this earth have such a striking effect in a great quantity of 20 water and not in each river singly? For the sea, differing in nothing from rivers but in being salt, is evidently simply the totality of river water, and the rivers are the vehicle in which that earth is carried to their common destination.[1]

It is equally absurd to suppose that anything has been explained by calling the sea 'the sweat of the earth', like 25 Empedocles.[2] Metaphors are poetical and so that expression of his may satisfy the requirements of a poem, but as a scientific theory it is unsatisfactory. Even in the case of the body it is a question how the sweet liquid drunk becomes salt sweat—whether it is merely by the departure of some element in it which is sweetest, or by the admixture 30 of something, as when water is strained through ashes. Actually the saltness seems to be due to the same cause as in the case of the residual liquid that gathers in the bladder. That, too, becomes bitter and salt though the liquid we drink and that contained in our food is sweet. If then the 357^b bitterness is due in these cases (as with the water strained through lye) to the presence of a certain sort of stuff that is carried along by the urine (as indeed we actually find a salt deposit settling in chamber-pots) and is secreted from the flesh in sweat (as if the departing moisture were washing 5 the stuff out of the body), then no doubt the admixture of something earthy with the water is what makes the sea[3] salt.

Now in the body stuff of this kind, viz. the sediment of food, is due to failure to digest: but how there came to be any such thing in the earth requires explanation. Besides, how 10 can the drying and warming of the earth cause the secretion of such a great quantity of water; especially as that must be a mere fragment of what is left in the earth? Again, waiving the question of quantity,[4] why does not the earth

---

[1] And it is therefore absurd that they should not be salt.
[2] Diels, 21 A. 66; B. 55. Cp. 353^b 11.
[3] Read κἄν in l. 6.
[4] Read πλεῖον (with J₁F₁) and ἔλαττον in ll. 13, 14; 'waiving the point of quantity raised in the preceding argument'.

sweat now when it happens to be in process of drying?[1] If
15 it did so then, it ought to do so now. But it does not: on
the contrary, when it is dry it grows moist, but when it is
moist it does not secrete anything at all. How then[2] was
it possible for the earth at the beginning when it was moist
to sweat as it grew dry? Indeed, the theory[3] that maintains that most of the moisture departed and was drawn up
20 by the sun and that what was left over is the sea is more
reasonable ; but for the earth to sweat when it is moist is
impossible.

Since all the attempts to account for the saltness of the
sea seem unsuccessful let us explain it by the help of the
principle we have used already.[4]
25   Since we recognize two kinds of evaporation, one moist,
the other dry, it is clear that the latter must be recognized
as the source of phenomena like those we are concerned
with.

But there is a question which we must discuss first.
Does the sea always remain numerically one and consisting
of the same parts, or is it, too, one in form and volume
while its parts are in continual change, like air and sweet
30 water and fire? All of these[5] are in a constant state of
change, but the form and the quantity[6] of each of them are
fixed, just as they are in the case of a flowing river or
a burning flame. The answer is clear, and there is no doubt
that the same account holds good of all these things alike.
358[a] They differ in that some of them change more rapidly or
more slowly than others ; and[7] they all are involved
in a process of perishing and becoming which yet affects
them all in a regular course.

---

[1] Omit ἡ γὰρ . . . πικρός in l. 14 with (apparently) some MSS. of
Alexander. The point is not that the earth secretes moisture but not
salt moisture ; but, as the following lines show, that it does not
secrete anything at all under the conditions supposed. The addition
may be due to the idea that A. had admitted in the account of rivers
(1. 13) that the earth did secrete moisture.
[2] Read οὖν in l. 17 with JFHN Al. for δ' οὖν.
[3] Cp. 353[b] 6, 356[b] 9.   [4] 341[b] 6 ff.
[5] ἀεὶ . . . ῥεῦμα (ll. 30-32) is a parenthesis (Bonitz). The apodosis
begins with φανερόν l. 32.
[6] Read τὸ δ' εἶδος καὶ τὸ πλῆθος in l. 31 with Bonitz.
[7] Read τε for τε καί in l. 1 with JFHN.

This being so we must go on to try to explain why the
sea is salt.   There are many facts which make it clear that
this taste is due to the admixture of something.   First, in 5
animal bodies what is least digested, the residue of liquid
food, is salt and bitter, as we said before.   All animal
excreta are undigested, but especially that which gathers in
the bladder (its extreme lightness proves this ; for everything that is digested is condensed), and also sweat ; in 10
these then is excreted (along with other matter) an
identical substance to which this flavour is due.   The
case of things burnt is analogous.   What heat fails to
assimilate becomes the excrementary residue in animal
bodies, and, in things burnt, ashes.   That is why some
people say that it was burnt earth that made the sea salt.
To say that it was burnt earth is absurd; but to say that it 15
was something like burnt earth is true.   We must suppose
that just as in the cases we have described, so in the world
as a whole, everything that grows and is naturally generated
always leaves an undigested residue, like that of things
burnt, consisting of this sort of earth.   All the earthy stuff in
the dry exhalation [1] is of this nature, and it is the dry ex- 20
halation which accounts for its great quantity.   Now since,
as we have said, the moist and the dry evaporations are
mixed, some quantity of this stuff must always be included
in the clouds and the water that are formed by condensation, and must redescend to the earth in rain.   This process 25
must always go on with such regularity as the sublunary
world admits of, and it is the answer to the question how
the sea comes to be salt.

It also explains why rain that comes from the south, and
the first rains of autumn, are brackish.   The south is
the warmest of winds [2] and it blows from dry and hot 30
regions.   Hence it carries little moist vapour and that is
why it is hot.   (It makes no difference even if this is not

[1] Read ἀναθυμιάσει in l. 20 with Thurot. ἀναθυμίασιν is read by all
the MSS. and by Alexander.   The mistake may be due to the failure
to recognize that the ἀναθυμίασις may be charged with earthy particles.
[2] Omit καὶ τῷ μεγέθει καὶ τῷ πνεύματι (l. 29), which make no sense
in connexion with ἀλεεινότατος. Al. does not seem to have read the
words. Ol. does, but the γρ. " ἀληθινώτατος " which he records suggests
that the received text was seen to be nonsense.

its true character and it is originally a cold wind, for it becomes warm on its way by incorporating with itself a great quantity of dry evaporation from the places it passes over.)
35 The north wind, on the other hand, coming from moist
358ᵇ regions, is full of vapour and therefore cold. It is dry in our part of the world because it drives the clouds away before it, but in the south it is rainy ; just as the south is a dry wind in Libya. So the south wind charges the rain that falls with a great quantity of this stuff. Autumn[1] rain
5 is brackish because the heaviest water must fall first ; so that that which contains the greatest quantity of this kind of earth descends quickest.

This, too, is why the sea is warm. Everything that has been exposed to fire contains heat potentially, as we see in the case of lye and ashes and the dry and liquid excreta of
10 animals. Indeed those animals which are hottest in the belly have the hottest excreta.

The action of this cause is continually making the sea more salt, but some part of its saltness is always being drawn up with the sweet water. This is less than the sweet water in the same ratio in which the salt and brackish
15 element in rain is less than the sweet, and so the saltness of the sea remains constant on the whole. Salt water when it turns into vapour becomes sweet, and the vapour does not form salt water when it condenses again. This I know by experiment. The same thing is true in every case of the kind : wine[2] and all fluids that evaporate and condense
20 back into a liquid state become water. They all are water modified by a certain admixture, the nature of which determines their flavour. But this subject must be considered on another more suitable occasion.

For the present let us say this. The sea is there and
25 some of it is continually being drawn up and becoming sweet ; this returns from above with the rain. But it is now different from what it was when it was drawn up, and its weight makes it sink below the sweet water.[3] This process

---

[1] καί (ᵇ 4) corresponds to τε (ᵃ 29) (Thurot).
[2] It is not true of wine.
[3] Cp. ᵇ 5.

prevents the sea, as it does rivers,[1] from drying up except
from local causes (this must happen to sea and rivers alike).
On the other hand the parts neither of the earth nor of the sea 30
remain constant but only their whole bulk. For the same
thing is true of the earth as of the sea : some of it is carried
up and some comes down with the rain, and both that which
remains on the surface and that which comes down again
change [2] their situations.

There is more evidence to prove that saltness is due to the
admixture of some substance, besides that which we have 35
adduced. Make a vessel of wax and put it in the sea, 359[a]
fastening its mouth in such a way as to prevent any water
getting in. Then the water that percolates through the wax
sides of the vessel is sweet, the earthy stuff, the admixture
of which makes the water salt, being separated off as it were
by a filter.[3] It is this stuff which makes salt water heavy 5
(it weighs more than fresh water) and thick. The difference
in consistency is such that ships with the same cargo very
nearly sink in a river when they are quite fit to navigate in
the sea. This circumstance has before now caused loss to 10
shippers freighting their ships in a river. That the thicker
consistency is due to an admixture of something is proved
by the fact that if you make strong brine by the admixture
of salt, eggs, even when they are full, float in it. It almost
becomes like mud ; such a quantity of earthy matter is there 15
in the sea. The same thing is done in salting fish.

Again if, as is fabled, there is a lake in Palestine, such
that if you bind a man or beast and throw it in it floats and
does not sink, this would bear out what we have said. They 20
say that this lake is so bitter and salt that no fish live in it
and that if you soak clothes in it and shake them it cleans
them. The following facts all of them support our theory
that it is some earthy stuff in the water which makes it salt.
In Chaonia there is a spring of brackish water that flows into 25
a neighbouring river which is sweet but contains no fish. The
local story is that when Heracles came from Erytheia driving

---

[1] Cp. 359[b] 22.
[2] Read μεταβάλλει in l. 33 with EJFHN₂.
[3] Cp. *Hist. An.* viii. 590[a] 24. Diels, 21 A. 66. Facts do not bear
out this statement; cp. Diels, *Hermes*, xl, p. 310.

the oxen and gave the inhabitants the choice, they chose salt
30 in preference to fish. They get the salt from the spring.
They boil off some of the water and let the rest stand ; when
it has cooled and the heat and moisture have evaporated
together it gives them salt, not in lumps but loose and light
like snow. It is weaker than ordinary salt and added freely
35 gives a sweet taste, and it is not as white as salt generally
359ᵇ is. Another instance of this is found in Umbria. There is
a place there where reeds and rushes grow. They burn
some of these, put the ashes into water and boil it off.
When a little water is left and has cooled it gives a quantity
of salt.[1]

5 Most salt rivers and springs must once have been hot.
Then the original fire in them was extinguished but the earth
through which they percolate preserves the character of lye
or ashes. Springs and rivers with all kinds of flavours are
found in many places. These flavours must in every case
10 be due to the fire that is or was[2] in them, for if you expose
earth to different degrees of heat it assumes various kinds
and shades of flavour. It becomes full of alum and lye and
other things of the kind, and the fresh water percolates
through these and changes its character. Sometimes it be-
15 comes acid as in Sicania, a part of Sicily. There they get
a salt and acid water which they use as vinegar to season
some of their dishes. In the neighbourhood of Lyncus, too,
there is a spring of acid water, and in Scythia a bitter
spring. The water from this makes the whole of the river
into which it flows bitter.[3] These differences are explained
20 by a knowledge of the particular mixtures that determine
different savours.[4] But these have been explained in
another treatise.[5]

We have now given an account of waters and the sea,

---

[1] Cp. *John Boyes, King of the Wa-Kikuyu*, p. 108. ' They (the
Kikuyu) used to burn large quantities of green papyrus reed, mixing
the ashes with their food instead of salt.'
[2] Read ἐγγενομένην in l. 10 with J Al.
[3] Cp. Herod. iv. 52, 81.
[4] Read δῆλαι, ποῖοι in l. 20 ; omitting δέ after ποῖοι with E₁JFHN₁Al.
and keeping δέ after εἴρηται with E (original reading) JFHN.
[5] Perhaps *De Sensu* c. 4 ; though Ol. (and more doubtfully Al.) refers
to a treatise π. χυμῶν.

why they persist, how they change, what their nature is, and have explained most of their natural operations and 25 affections.

4   Let us proceed to the theory of winds.   Its basis is a distinction we have already made.¹ We recognize two kinds of evaporation, one moist, the other dry.   The former is called vapour : for the other there is no general name but 30 we must call it a sort of smoke, applying to the whole of it a word that is proper to one of its forms.   The moist cannot exist without the dry nor the dry without the moist : whenever we speak of either we mean that it predominates. Now² when the sun in its circular course approaches, it draws up by its heat the moist evaporation : when it 35 recedes the cold makes the vapour that had been raised con- 360^a dense back into water which falls and is distributed through the earth.³ (This explains why there is more rain in winter and more by night than by day : though the fact is not recognized because rain by night is more apt to escape ob- servation than by day.)   But there is a great quantity of fire 5 and heat in the earth, and the sun not only draws up the moisture that lies on the surface of it, but warms and dries the earth itself.   Consequently, since there are two kinds of evaporation, as we have said, one like vapour, the other like smoke, both of them are necessarily generated. That in which 10 moisture predominates is the source of rain, as we explained before,⁴ while the dry evaporation is the source and sub- stance of all winds.   That things must necessarily take this course is clear from the resulting phenomena themselves,⁵ for the evaporation that is to produce them must necessarily 15 differ ; and the sun and the warmth in the earth not only can but must produce these evaporations.

Since the two evaporations are specifically distinct, wind and rain obviously differ and their substance is not the same, as those say who maintain that one and the same air when 20 in motion is wind, but when it condenses again is water.

---

¹ 341ᵇ 6 ff.
² Punctuate with Bonitz—διὸ . . . μᾶλλον (ll. 2-4) in a parenthesis, commas after μᾶλλον and after γῆν (l. 5), and colon after θερμαίνων (l. 8).
³ Cp. 346ᵇ 21, 35.   ⁴ 1. 9.   ⁵ i. e. rain and wind.

[1] Air, as we have explained in an earlier book,[2] is made up of
these as constituents. Vapour is moist and cold (for its
fluidity is due to its moistness, and because it derives from
water it is naturally cold, like water that has not been
25 warmed): whereas the smoky evaporation is hot and dry.
Hence each contributes a part, and air is moist and hot.[1]
It is absurd that this air that surrounds us should become
wind when in motion, whatever be the source of its motion—
on the contrary the case of winds is like that of rivers. We
30 do not call water that flows anyhow a river, even if there is
a great quantity of it, but only if the flow comes from
a spring. So too with the winds; a great quantity of air
might be moved by the fall of some large object without
flowing from any source or spring.[3]

    The facts bear out our theory. It is because the evapora-
35 tion takes place uninterruptedly but differs in degree and

360ᵇ quantity that clouds and winds appear in their natural
proportion according to the season ; and it is because there
is now a great excess of the vaporous, now of the dry and
smoky exhalation, that some years are rainy and wet, others
5 windy and dry. Sometimes there is much drought or rain,
and it prevails over a great[4] and continuous stretch of
country. At other times it is local ; the surrounding
country often getting seasonable or even excessive rains
10 while there is drought in a certain part ; or, contrariwise, all
the surrounding country gets little or even no rain while
a certain part gets rain in abundance. The reason for
all this is that while the same affection is generally apt to
prevail over a considerable district because adjacent places
(unless there is something special to differentiate them)
15 stand in the same relation to the sun, yet on occasion the
dry evaporation will prevail in one part and the moist in
another, or conversely. Again the reason for this latter is

    [1-1] The connexion of thought would be easier if this passage were
transposed (as by Thurot), to follow πηγήν ª 33. If the traditional order
is kept this passage must be treated as a sort of parenthesis.
    [2] *De Gen. et Corr.* ii. 4.
    [3] And we should not call it a wind.
    [4] Read κατὰ πολλὴν συνεχῆ in l. 6 with E. If either πολλήν or συνεχῆ
must go it should be συνεχῆ as a gloss on πολλήν. Al. certainly read
πολλήν.

that each evaporation goes over to that of the neighbouring
district: for instance, the dry evaporation circulates in its
own place while the moist migrates to the next district or 20
is even driven by winds to some distant place: or else the
moist evaporation remains and the dry moves away. Just
as in the case of the body when the stomach is dry the
lower belly is often in the contrary state, and when it is dry
the stomach is moist and cold, so it often happens that 25
the evaporations reciprocally take one another's place and
interchange.

Further, after rain wind generally rises in those places
where the rain fell,[1] and when rain has come on the wind
ceases. These are necessary effects of the principles we
have explained. After rain the earth is being dried by its 30
own heat and that from above and gives off the evaporation
which we saw to be the material cause of wind. Again,
suppose this secretion is present and wind prevails; the
heat is continually being thrown off, rising to the upper
region, and so the wind ceases; then the fall in temperature 35
makes vapour form and condense into water.[2] Water also **361ᵃ**
forms and cools the dry evaporation when the clouds are
driven together and the cold concentrated in them. These
are the causes that make wind cease on the advent of rain,
and rain fall on the cessation of wind.

[3] The cause of the predominance of winds[4] from the 5
north and from the south is the same. (Most winds, as
a matter of fact, are north winds or south winds.[5]) These
are the only regions which the sun does not visit: it
approaches them and recedes from them, but its course is
always over the west and the east. Hence clouds collect on
either side, and when the sun approaches it provokes the 10

---

[1] Read γενέσθαι in l. 28 with JFHN.

[2] Cp. 346ᵇ 26. Thurot would read νέφος for ὕδωρ in l. 35. Then
the next sentence would not give an alternative mode of the formation
of water but complete the account given in this. Against this is the
fact that in the account given in 346ᵇ 20 there is no mention of the
driving together of clouds or of ἀντιπερίστασις.

[3] The doctrine of the south wind here is irreconcilable with that in
c. 5, 362ᵃ 31. Berger, *Gesch. der wissensch. Erdk. d. Griechen*, 280, n. 2.

[4] Read ἀπό τε τῆς in l. 5 with JFHN Al.

[5] Cp. 363ᵃ 3, 364ᵃ 5.

moist evaporation, and when it recedes to the opposite side
there are storms and rain. So summer and winter are due
to the sun's motion to and from the solstices, and water
ascends and falls again for the same reason.[1] Now since
15 most rain falls in those regions towards which and from
which the sun turns and these are the north and the south,
and since most evaporation must take place where there is
the greatest rainfall, just as green wood gives most smoke,
20 and since this evaporation is wind, it is natural that the
most and most important winds should come from these
quarters. (The winds from the north are called Boreae,
those from the south Noti.[2])

The course of winds is oblique : for though the evaporation rises straight up from the earth, they blow round it
because all the surrounding air follows the motion of the
25 heavens.[3] Hence the question might be asked whether
winds originate from above or from below. The motion
comes from above : before[4] we feel the wind blowing the
air betrays its presence if there are clouds or a mist, for
their motion shows that the wind has begun to blow before
it has actually reached us ; and this implies that the source
30 of winds is above. But since wind is defined as 'a quantity
of dry evaporation from the earth moving round the earth ',
it is clear that while the origin of the motion is from
above, the matter and the generation of wind come from
below. The oblique movement of the rising evaporation is
caused from above : for the motion of the heavens determines the processes that are at a distance from the earth,
35 and the motion from below[5] is vertical and every cause is
more active where it is nearest to the effect[6] ; but in its
generation and origin wind plainly derives from the earth.

---

[1] Cp. 346ᵇ 35.

[2] This sentence informs us of what was assumed to be known in ᵃ6
above, and is singularly pointless even for a gloss.

[3] But cp. 340ᵇ 33.

[4] Read comma after ἄνωθεν (l. 27), no stop after πνεῖν, omit δ᾿ (J corr.
Al. Bag.), no stop after ἐπίδηλος, ἄν for κἄν, κινουμένη for κινουμένην
(J corr. and perhaps Al.).

[5] There is nothing to answer μέν in l. 35. There should be a colon
at least after ἐγγύς.

[6] Therefore the circular motion of winds cannot be attributed to the
earth or it would begin at its surface and not at a height.

The facts bear out the view that winds are formed by the **361ᵇ** gradual union of many evaporations just as rivers derive their sources from the water that oozes from the earth. Every wind is weakest in the spot from which it blows [1] ; as they proceed and leave their source at a distance they gather strength. Thus the winter in the north is windless 5 and calm : that is, in the north itself ; but the breeze that blows from there so gently as to escape observation becomes a great wind as it passes on.

We have explained the nature and origin of wind, the occurrence of drought and rains, the reason why rain stops 10 wind and wind rises after rain, the prevalence of north and south winds and also why wind moves in the way it does.[2]

5   The sun both checks the formation of winds and stimulates it. When the evaporation is small in amount and 15 faint the sun wastes it and [3] dissipates by its greater heat the lesser heat contained in the evaporation. It also dries up the earth, the source of the evaporation, before the latter has appeared in bulk : just as, when you throw a little fuel into a great fire, it is often burnt up before giving off any smoke. In these ways the sun checks winds and prevents them 20 from rising at all : it checks them by wasting the evaporation, and prevents their rising by drying up the earth quickly. Hence calm is very apt to prevail about the rising of Orion [4] and lasts until the coming of the Etesiae and their ' forerunners '.

Calm is due to two causes. Either cold quenches the 25 evaporation, for instance a sharp frost : or excessive heat wastes it. In the intermediate periods, too,[5] the causes are generally either that the evaporation has not had time to develop or that it has passed away and there is none as yet to replace it.

---

[1] But cp. 364ᵇ 5.
[2] i. e. obliquely, round the earth.
[3] Transpose καί to follow μαραίνει (ll. 16, 17).   So perhaps Ol.
[4] The morning rising, about July 13.
[5] Delete comma after ὥραις (l. 28).

30   Both the setting [1] and the rising [2] of Orion are considered
to be treacherous and stormy, because they take place at
a change of season (namely of summer or winter; and
because the size of the constellation makes its rise last over
many days [3]) and a state of change is always indefinite and
therefore liable to disturbance.

35   The Etesiae blow after the summer solstice and the rising
362^a of the dog-star [4]: not at the time when the sun is closest nor
when it is distant; and they blow by day and cease at
night.   The reason is that when the sun is near it dries up
the earth before evaporation has taken place, but when it
has receded a little its heat and the evaporation are present
5 in the right proportion; so the ice melts and the earth, dried
by its own heat and that of the sun, smokes and vapours.
They abate at night because the cold of the nights checks
the melting of the ice.   What is frozen gives off no evapora-
10 tion, nor does that which contains no dryness at all: it is
only where something dry contains moisture that it gives
off evaporation under the influence of heat.

The question is sometimes asked: why do the north
winds which we call the Etesiae blow continuously after the
summer solstice, when there are no corresponding south
winds after the winter solstice?   The facts are reasonable
enough: for the so-called 'white south winds' do blow at
the corresponding season, though they are not equally con-
15 tinuous and so escape observation and give rise to this
inquiry.   The reason for this is that the north wind blows
from the arctic regions which are full of water and snow.

---

[1] The morning setting, about mid-November.
[2] The morning rising.   There is no contradiction between this and
l. 23 above.   Both statements are vague and each may be referred to
a different time, especially as in a constellation like Orion the date may
vary according to the star chosen for observation.   The time referred
to in l. 23 must be earlier than that indicated here.   For the latter cp.
Polyb. i. 37.
[3] This is suspicious.   The times meant are the change from early
summer to late summer (ὀπώρα) and from late summer to winter (cp.
Theoph. *De Lap.* ix. 55); Eudoxus supposed ὀπώρα to begin with
the rise of Sirius (about the end of July).   But this is expressed very
unsymmetrically in θέρους ἢ χειμῶνος.   γίνεται too suggests a gloss; if
the clause is kept we must read γίνεσθαι or insert διότι before διὰ τό
(Ideler's conjecture).
[4] About 28 July.

The sun thaws them and so the Etesiae blow: after rather
than at the summer solstice. (For the greatest heat is 20
developed not when the sun is nearest to the north, but
when its heat has been felt for a considerable period and it
has not yet receded far. The 'bird winds' blow in the
same way after the winter solstice. They, too, are weak
Etesiae, but they blow less and later than the Etesiae.
They begin to blow only on the seventieth day because the 25
sun is distant and therefore weaker. They do not blow so
continuously because only things on the surface of the earth
and offering little resistance evaporate then, the thoroughly
frozen parts requiring greater heat to melt them. So they
blow intermittently till the true Etesiae come on again at
the summer solstice: for from that time onwards the wind 30
tends to blow continuously.) But the south wind blows
from the tropic of Cancer and not from the antarctic region.[1]

There are two inhabitable sections of the earth: one near
our upper, or northern [2] pole, the other near the other or
southern pole; and their shape is like that of a tambourine. 35
If you draw lines from the centre of the earth they cut out **362ᵇ**
a drum-shaped figure. The lines form two cones; the base
of the one is the tropic, of the other the ever visible circle,[3]
their vertex is at the centre of the earth. Two other cones
towards the south pole give corresponding segments of the
earth. These sections alone are habitable. Beyond the 5
tropics no one can live: for there the shade would not fall [4]

---

[1] And therefore we cannot expect any south winds to correspond to the
trade winds.

[2] Contrast *De Caelo* 285ᵇ 14.

[3] i. e. that of the circumpolar stars. This is relative to latitude and
so does not serve the purpose of delimiting zones at all well; though
no doubt Aristotle meant the ever visible circles of a given place, e. g.
Athens. Poseidonius criticizes Aristotle accordingly, cp. Strabo ii. 95,
Berger *Geschichte*, p. 306, n. 1. It would be more consonant with the
principles on which Aristotle determined the torrid zone if he meant
here the arctic circle = that determined by a longest day of 24 hours,
and Ideler supposes that this is the meaning, and the facts about
the southern hemisphere support this. For Aristotle cannot have
thought that the base of the corresponding cone there was the ἀεὶ
ἀφανὴς κύκλος of any place in his own hemisphere. If this view is
correct the phrase διὰ παντὸς φανερός is singularly unfortunate. Cp.
363ᵇ 32, and Berger, *Eratosthenes*, 74, n. 4.

[4] The sense required is 'always fall'; and Ideler would insert ἀεί
after οὐκ in l. 6. But Aristotle may have written carelessly.

to the north, whereas the earth is known to be uninhabitable before the sun is in the zenith or the shade is thrown to the south : and the regions below the Bear[1] are uninhabitable because of the cold.

10 [The Crown, too, moves over this region : for it is in the zenith when it is on our meridian].[2]

So we see that the way in which they now describe the geography of the earth is ridiculous. They depict the inhabited earth as round, but both ascertained facts and general considerations show this to be impossible. If we reflect we see that the inhabited region is limited in 15 breadth, while the climate admits of its extending all round the earth. For we meet with no excessive heat or cold in the direction of its length but only in that of its breadth ; so that there is nothing to prevent our travelling round the earth unless the extent of the sea presents an obstacle anywhere. The records of journeys by sea and land bear this 20 out. They make the length far greater than the breadth. If we compute these voyages and journeys the distance from the Pillars of Heracles to India exceeds that from Aethiopia to Maeotis and the northernmost Scythians by a ratio of more than 5 to 3, as far as such matters admit of 25 accurate statement. Yet[3] we know the whole breadth[4] of the region we dwell in up to the uninhabited parts : in one

---

[1] i. e. where the Bear is in the zenith when it is on the meridian.

[2] The Crown is in the zenith on the meridian at Athens, and the Bear marks the limit of the circumpolar stars at Athens. Therefore at a place where the Bear is in the zenith the Crown will be circumpolar. ' This region ' then is the place where the Bear is in the zenith.

This is taken to be Aristotle's meaning here by Müllenhoff, *Deutsche Altertumskunde*, i, p. 235 n.: cp. Berger, *Geschichte*, p. 305.

Al. and Ol. take the statement to be a proof that we live in the northern temperate zone. ' The Crown is obviously between the circle of the Bear and the summer tropic ; it is in the zenith on our meridian, therefore we are in the zone between the Bear and the summer tropic.' Then ' this region ' = Greece.

Both explanations fail to give any point to the remark, which must be a learned interpolation.

[3] The connexion of thought is : ' our inhabitable zone is not round : the ascertained width is to the ascertained length as 3 : 5 ; and the excess of length over breadth is really greater than that since the 3 represents the whole breadth, the 5 not all the length '.

[4] Read πλάτος' in l. 25 with the MSS.

direction no one lives because of the cold, in the other because of the heat.

But it is the sea[1] which divides as it seems the parts beyond India from those beyond the Pillars of Heracles[2] and prevents the earth from being inhabited all round.

Now since there must be a region bearing the same rela- 30 tion to the southern pole as the place we live in bears to our pole, it will clearly correspond in the ordering of its winds as well as in other things. So just as we have a north wind here, they must have a corresponding wind from the antarctic.[3] This wind cannot reach us since our own 35 north wind is like a land breeze[4] and does not even reach[5] **363^a** the limits of the region we live in.[6] The prevalence of north winds[7] here is due to our lying near the north. Yet even here they give out and fail to penetrate far: in the 5 southern sea beyond Libya east and west winds are always blowing alternately, like north and south winds with us.[8] So it is clear that the south wind is not the wind that blows from the south pole. It is neither that nor the wind from the winter tropic. For symmetry would require another 10 wind blowing[9] from the summer tropic, which there is not, since we know that only one wind blows from that quarter. So the south wind clearly blows from the torrid region. Now the sun is so near to that region that it has no water, or snow[10] which might melt and cause Etesiae. But because 15 that place is far more extensive and open the south wind is greater and stronger and warmer than the north and penetrates farther to the north than the north wind does to the south.[11]

---

[1] And not the climate.
[2] Delete the comma before τῷ (l. 29).
[3] Omit ὤν in line 34 with E₁N₁ Al.
[4] i.e. it has a short range.
[5] Omit ἐστιν in l. 1 with E₁ and supply διήκει from δυνατὸν διήκειν.
[6] Omit ἔως ... πνεῖ (l. 2) with E₁H₁ N₁ Al. Whoever put it in missed the point of ἀπόγειον.
[7] Cp. 364ª 5, 361ª 4.
[8] Punctuate: δέοι ... τόπων (ll. 10–12) a parenthesis: colon after ἀποδώσει: colon after τόπων (Bonitz). Read ὁ νότος (JFHN) in l. 8.
[9] i.e. southwards.
[10] Read χιόνας (comp. Partsch, p. 586ⁿ) in l. 14 and τῆξιν (EJ₂F corr. HN), cp. 362ª 18, 364ª 8–10.
[11] But cp. 364ª 5.

The origin of these winds[1] and their relation to one
20 another has now been explained.

Let us now explain the position of the winds,[2] their oppo- **6**
sitions, which can blow simultaneously with which, and
which cannot, their names and number, and any other of
their affections that have not been treated in the 'particular
25 questions'.[3] What we say about their position must be
followed with the help of the figure. For clearness' sake
we have drawn the circle of the horizon, which is round, but
it represents[4] the zone in which we live[5]; for that can be
30 divided in the same
way. Let us also be-
gin by laying down
that those things are
locally contrary which
are locally most dis-
tant from one another,
just as things speci-
fically most remote
from one another are
specific contraries.
Now things that face

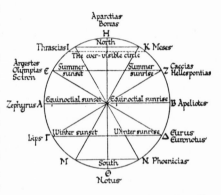

one another from opposite ends of a diameter are locally
most distant from one another.

Let A be the point where the sun sets at the equinox and
B, the point opposite, the place where it rises at the
363ᵇ equinox. Let there be another diameter cutting this at
right angles, and let the point H on it be the north and its
diametrical opposite Θ the south. Let Z be the rising of
the sun at the summer solstice and E its setting at the
5 summer solstice ; Δ its rising at the winter solstice, and Γ
its setting at the winter solstice. Draw a diameter from Z
to Γ and from Δ to E. Then since those things are locally
contrary which are most distant from one another in space,
and points diametrically opposite are most distant from one

---

[1] i. e. north and south winds.
[2] This chapter should be compared with the *Ventorum Situs et Cognomina* (vol. vi. of this translation).
[3] Not in the existing *Problems*, however.
[4] Read αὐτόν in l. 28 with F₁HN Al.   [5] Which is not round.

another, those winds must necessarily be contrary to one
another that blow from opposite ends of a diameter.   10

The names of the winds according to their position are
these. Zephyrus is the wind that blows from A, this being
the point where the sun sets at the equinox. Its contrary
is Apeliotes blowing from B the point where the sun rises
at the equinox. The wind blowing from H, the north, is
the true north wind, called Aparctias [1] : while Notus blow- 15
ing from Θ is its contrary ; for this point is the south and
Θ is contrary to H, being diametrically opposite to it.
Caecias blows from Z, where the sun rises at the summer
solstice. Its contrary is not the wind blowing from E but
Lips blowing from Γ. For Lips blows from the point
where the sun sets at the winter solstice and is diametrically
opposite to Caecias : so it is its contrary. Eurus blows 20
from Δ, coming from the point where the sun rises at the
winter solstice. It borders on Notus, and so we often find
that people speak of 'Euro-Noti'. Its contrary is not
Lips blowing from Γ but the wind that blows from E which
some call Argestes, some Olympias, and some Sciron. This 25
blows from the point where the sun sets at the summer
solstice, and is the only wind that is diametrically opposite
to Eurus. These are the winds that are diametrically
opposite to one another and their contraries.

There are other winds which have no contraries. The
wind they call Thrascias, which lies between Argestes and
Aparctias, blows from I ; and the wind called Meses, which 30
lies between Caecias and Aparctias, from K. (The line IK
nearly coincides with the ever visible circle,[2] but not quite.)
These winds have no contraries. Meses [3] has not, or else
there would be a wind blowing from the point M which is
diametrically opposite. Thraskias corresponding to the 364^a
point I has not, for then there would be a wind blowing
from N, the point which is diametrically opposite. (But
perhaps a local wind which the inhabitants of those parts
call Phoenicias blows from that point.)

[1] Omit καί after βορέας δέ in l. 14 with E₁JFHN Al., cp. Capelle, *N. JB.
f. d. klass. Alt.*, 1905, p. 542, n. 1.
[2] Cp. 362^b 3. Müllenhoff, *D. A.*, p. 257 ; Berger, *Geschichte*, p. 304.
[3] Omit οὔτε τῷ θρασκίᾳ in l. 33 with JF₁H₁N Al.

These are the most important and definite winds and these their places.

5 There are more winds from the north than from the south. The reason for this is that the region in which we live lies nearer to the north. Also, much more water and snow is pushed aside into this quarter because the other lies
10 under the sun and its course. When this thaws and soaks into the earth and is exposed to the heat of the sun and the earth it necessarily causes evaporation to rise in greater quantities and over a greater space.[1]

Of the winds we have described Aparctias is the north wind in the strict sense.[2] Thrascias and Meses are north
15 winds too. (Caecias is half north and half east.) South are that which blows from due south and Lips. East, the wind from the rising of the sun at the equinox and Eurus. Phoenicias is half south and half east. West, the wind from the true west and that called Argestes. More generally these winds are classified as northerly or southerly. The
20 west winds are counted as northerly, for they blow from the place of sunset and are therefore colder; the east winds as southerly, for they are warmer because they blow from the place of sunrise. So the distinction of cold and hot or warm is the basis for the division of the winds into northerly and southerly. East winds are warmer than west winds because
25 the sun shines on the east longer, whereas it leaves the west sooner and reaches it later.[3]

Since this is the distribution of the winds it is clear that contrary winds cannot blow simultaneously. They are diametrically opposite to one another and one of the two must be overpowered and cease. Winds that are not diametrically opposite to one another may blow simultane-
30 ously: for instance the winds from *Z* and from *Δ*. Hence it sometimes happens that both of them, though different winds and blowing from different quarters, are favourable to sailors making for the same point.

---

[1] Cp. 363ª 3, 13.
[2] Read μέσης (l. 15) and omit κοινὸς ἀργέστου (l. 14) with EHN Ol.
[3] A poor argument even for a flat-earth man; and for Aristotle with his round earth lamentable. Perhaps the sentence should be condemned.

Contrary winds commonly blow at opposite seasons. Thus Caecias and in general the winds north of the summer **364**^b solstice blow about the time of the spring equinox, but about the autumn equinox Lips; and Zephyrus about the summer solstice, but about the winter solstice Eurus.

Aparctias, Thrascias, and Argestes are the winds that fall on others most and stop them. Their source is so close 5 to us that they are greater and stronger than other winds. They bring fair weather most of all winds for the same reason, for, blowing as they do, from close at hand,[1] they overpower the other winds and stop them; they also blow away the clouds that are forming and leave a clear sky— unless they happen to be very cold. Then they do not 10 bring fair weather, but being colder than they are strong they condense the clouds before driving them away.

Caecias does not bring fair weather because it returns upon itself. Hence the saying : ' Bringing it on himself as Caecias does clouds.'

When they cease, winds are succeeded by their neigh- bours in the direction of the movement of the sun. For an 15 effect is most apt to be produced in the neighbourhood of its cause, and the cause of winds moves with the sun.

Contrary winds have either the same or contrary effects. Thus Lips and Caecias, sometimes called Hellespontias, are both rainy.[2] Argestes and Eurus are dry : the latter being 20 dry at first and rainy afterwards. Meses and Aparctias are coldest and bring most snow. Aparctias, Thrascias, and Argestes bring hail. Notus, Zephyrus, and Eurus are hot. Caecias covers the sky with heavy clouds, Lips with lighter ones. Caecias does this because it returns upon itself and 25 combines the qualities of Boreas and Eurus. By being cold it condenses and gathers the vaporous air, and because

---

[1] But cp. 361^b 3.

[2] Omit καὶ εὖρος, ὃν ἀπηλιώτην in l. 19. The clause is introduced by οἶον and should contain illustrations of contrary winds and their effects. So the words καὶ . . . ἀπηλιώτην have no place in it. They may have intruded from a marginal note suggested by the next sentence (τελευτῶν δὲ ὑδατώδης) or else καὶ εὖρος is due to the line below and ὃν ἀπηλ. was added, perhaps, if due east wind is meant, with the idea of avoiding contradiction with the first part of the next sentence. Ol. seems to omit the words. F₁ deletes ὃν ἀπηλιώτην.

it is easterly it carries with it and drives before it a great
quantity of such matter. Aparctias, Thrascias, and Argestes
bring fair weather for the reason we have explained before.¹
30 These winds and Meses are most commonly accompanied by
lightning. They are cold because they blow ² from the
north, and lightning is due to cold, being ejected when the
clouds contract.³ Some of these same winds bring hail
365ᵃ with them for the same reason; namely, that they cause
a sudden condensation.

Hurricanes⁴ are commonest in autumn, and next in
spring: Aparctias, Thrascias, and Argestes give rise to
them most. This is because hurricanes are generally formed
when some winds are blowing and others fall on them; and
these are the winds which are most apt to fall on others
5 that are blowing; the reason for which, too, we have
explained before.⁵

The Etesiae veer round: they begin from the north, and
become for dwellers in the west Thrasciae, Argestae, and
Zephyrus (for Zephyrus belongs to the north⁶). For
dwellers in the east they veer round as far as Apeliotes.
10 So much for the winds, their origin and nature and the
properties common to them all or peculiar to each.

We must go on to discuss earthquakes next, for their 7
cause is akin to our last subject.
15 The theories that have been put forward up to the present
date are three, and their authors three men, Anaxagoras of

---

¹ b 6.
² Read ἐκεῖθεν in l. 31 after Thurot, with ed. Camotiana (Ven. 1551),
and one MS. of Al.
³ Cp. c. 9.
⁴ ἐκνεφίας, a storm-wind bursting from a cloud, has been rendered
throughout as 'hurricane'. Cp. iii. 1, 370ᵇ 3-17; though this passage
agrees more closely with the account of ecnephiae in Theophr. *De Sign.
Temp.* ii. 36, 37 (cp. Gilbert, p. 559 sq.) than with iii. 1.
⁵ 364ᵇ 3.
⁶ Read ὁ γὰρ ζέφυρος ἀρκτικός ἐστιν in l. 8 with Ideler (E's reading
with ζέφυρος and ἀρκτικός transposed): the Madrid MS. reads ὁ γὰρ
ζέφυρος ἀπαρκτίας ἐστίν, the Ambrosian MS. ὁ γὰρ ζέφυρος ἐστὶν ὁ ἀπαρκτίας. Then omit the clause as an interpolation. Bekker's text makes
no sense, as emerges from Alexander's explanation of it. Ideler's conjecture would be a reminiscence of 364ᵃ 20 introduced by a confused
mind as a gloss.
Omit ἀρχόμενοι . . . πόρρω, which seems to have come in from
Alexander's commentary (113. 27).

Clazomenae, and before him Anaximenes of Miletus, and later Democritus of Abdera.

Anaxagoras[1] says that the ether, which naturally moves upwards, is caught in hollows below the earth and so shakes 20 it, for though the earth is really all of it equally porous, its surface is clogged up by rain.[2] This implies that part of the whole sphere[3] is 'above' and part 'below': 'above' being the part on which we live, 'below' the other.

This theory is perhaps too primitive to require refutation. 25 It is absurd to think of up and down otherwise than as meaning that heavy bodies move to the earth from every quarter, and light ones, such as fire, away from it; especially as we see that, as far as our knowledge of the earth goes, 30 the horizon always changes with a change in our position, which proves that the earth is convex and spherical. It is absurd, too, to maintain that the earth rests on the air because of its size, and then to say that impact upwards from below shakes it right through. Besides he gives no account of the circumstances attendant on earthquakes: for not every country or every season is subject to them. 35

Democritus[4] says that the earth is full of water and that 365^b when a quantity of rain-water is added to this an earthquake is the result. The hollows in the earth being unable to admit the excess of water it forces its way in and so causes an earthquake. Or again, the earth as it dries draws the water from the fuller to the emptier parts, and the inrush of the 5 water as it changes its place causes the earthquake.

Anaximenes[5] says that the earth breaks up when it grows wet or dry, and earthquakes are due to the fall of these masses as they break away. Hence earthquakes take place in times of drought and again of heavy rain, since, as we 10 have explained, the earth grows dry in time of drought and breaks up, whereas the rain makes it sodden and destroys its cohesion.

But if this were the case the earth ought to be found to be sinking in many places. Again, why do earthquakes

---

[1] Cp. Diels, 46 A. 1, § 9; 42, § 12; 89.
[2] ἐπεί . . . σομφήν (l. 22) is parenthetical.
[3] For Anaxagoras it is not a sphere. [4] Diels, 55 A. 97, 98.
[5] Diels, 3 A. 7, § 8; 21; 2. 28 (Anaximander).

frequently occur in places which are not excessively subject
15 to drought or rain, as they ought to be on the theory? Besides, on this view, earthquakes ought always to be getting
fewer, and should come to an end entirely some day: the
notion of contraction by packing together implies this. So
20 if this is impossible the theory must be impossible too.

[1] We have already shown [2] that wet and dry must both **8**
give rise to an evaporation: earthquakes are a necessary
consequence of this fact. The earth is essentially dry, but
25 rain fills it with moisture. Then the sun and its own fire
warm it and give rise to a quantity of wind both outside
and inside it. This wind sometimes flows outwards in
a single body, sometimes inwards, and sometimes it is
divided. All these are necessary laws. Next we must find
30 out what body has the greatest motive force. This will
certainly be the body that naturally moves farthest and is
most violent. Now that which has the most rapid motion
is necessarily the most violent; for its swiftness gives its
impact the greatest force. Again, the rarest body, that
which can most readily pass through every other body, is
35 that which naturally moves farthest. Wind satisfies these
366^a conditions in the highest degree [3] (fire only becomes flame

---

[1] The word πνεῦμα plays a large part in this chapter and is difficult
to render in a way that will make its relations to ἀήρ, the dry ἀναθυμίασις,
and ἄνεμος clear. πνεῦμα generally is equivalent to dry ἀναθυμίασις;
that is, all πνεῦμα is dry ἀναθυμίασις, and all dry ἀναθυμίασις is πνεῦμα.
But the word πνεῦμα is used by preference when the dry ἀναθυμίασις is
being regarded as the material cause of wind. Again, πνεῦμα is closely
related to ἄνεμος; for all ἄνεμος is dry ἀναθυμίασις (and therefore
πνεῦμα) in motion. We cannot quite say that all πνεῦμα is ἄνεμος; for
πνεῦμα often denotes the dry exhalation before it has assumed that
definite motion which constitutes it an ἄνεμος. But 'a πνεῦμα' or
πνεύματα in the plural, or 'the πνεῦμα' of a definite one (as distinct
from πνεῦμα in general), are used as exact equivalents for 'an ἄνεμος' or
ἄνεμοι, or 'the ἄνεμος'. ἀήρ is properly quite distinct from the other
three: it is a combination of the dry and the moist exhalations—wind
is *not* ἀήρ in motion. But twice in this chapter if the text is sound ἀήρ
is used as an equivalent for πνεῦμα (367^a 11 and 20).
As we cannot fall back on spiritus for πνεῦμα with the later translators, the word wind has been used throughout this chapter both for
πνεῦμα and for ἄνεμος, but the passages in which it stands for ἄνεμος have
been noted.   [2] 341^b 6.
[3] Omit τὸ πνεῦμα κινητικόν in l. 1 with E₁ and apparently Al. Remove
the comma after τοιαύτη and read a comma instead of a full stop after
ταχέως (l. 3).

and moves rapidly when wind accompanies it): so that not
water nor earth is the cause of earthquakes but wind—that
is, the inrush of the external evaporation into the earth.

Hence, since the evaporation generally follows in a con- 5
tinuous body in the direction in which it first started, and
either all of it flows inwards or all outwards, most earthquakes and the greatest are accompanied by calm. It is
true that some take place when a wind is blowing, but this
presents no difficulty. We sometimes find several winds [1]
blowing simultaneously. If one of these enters the earth 10
we get an [2] earthquake attended by wind. Only these
earthquakes are less severe because their source and cause
is divided.

Again, most earthquakes and the severest occur at night
or, if by day, about noon, that being generally the calmest
part of the day. For when the sun exerts its full power (as 1
it does about noon) it shuts the evaporation into the earth.
Night, too, is calmer than day. The absence of the sun
makes the evaporation return into the earth like a sort of
ebb tide, corresponding to the outward [3] flow; especially
towards dawn, for the winds, as a rule, begin to blow then, 20
and if their source changes about like the Euripus and flows
inwards the quantity of wind in the earth is greater and
a more violent earthquake results.

The severest earthquakes take place where the sea is full 25
of currents or the earth spongy and cavernous: so they
occur near the Hellespont and in Achaea and Sicily, and
those parts of Euboea which correspond to our description—
where the sea is supposed to flow in channels below the
earth. The hot springs, too, near Aedepsus [4] are due to
a cause of this kind. It is the confined character of these
places that makes them so liable to earthquakes. A great 30
and therefore violent wind is developed, which would
naturally blow away from the earth : but the onrush of the
sea in a great mass thrusts it back into the earth. The
countries that are spongy below the surface are exposed to 366ᵇ
earthquakes because they have room for so much wind.

---

[1] ἄνεμοι.   [2] Omit ὁ with E Al. in l. 11.
[3] Read ἔξω with JFHN Al. in l. 20.   [4] In Euboea.

For the same reason earthquakes usually take place in spring and autumn and in times of wet and of drought—because these are the windiest seasons. Summer with its
5 heat and winter with its frost cause calm: winter is too cold, summer too dry for winds to form. In time of drought the air is full of wind; drought is just the predominance of the dry over the moist evaporation. Again, excessive rain
10 causes more of the evaporation to form in the earth. Then this secretion is shut up in a narrow compass and forced into a smaller space by the water that fills the cavities. Thus a great wind[1] is compressed into a smaller space and so gets the upper hand, and then breaks out and beats against the earth and shakes it violently.

15 We must suppose the action of the wind in the earth to be analogous to the tremors and throbbings caused in us by the force of the wind contained in our bodies. Thus some earthquakes are a sort of tremor, others a sort of throbbing. Again, we must think of an earthquake as something like the tremor that often runs through the body after passing
20 water as the wind returns inwards from without in one volume.[2]

The force wind can have may be gathered not only from what happens in the air (where one might suppose that it owed its power to produce such effects to its volume), but
25 also from what is observed in animal bodies. Tetanus and spasms are motions of wind, and their force is such that the united efforts of many men do not succeed in overcoming the movements of the patients. We must suppose, then (to compare great things with small), that what happens in the earth is just like that.[3]

30 Our theory has been verified by actual observation in many places. It has been known to happen that an earthquake has continued until the wind[4] that caused it burst through the earth into the air and appeared visibly like

---

[1] ἄνεμος.
[2] Read γὰρ γίνεται for γίνεται γάρ with JF₁ (cp. Thurot's Latin translation) and begin the parenthesis at διὰ τοῦ.
[3] Read τοιοῦτον δὴ δεῖ in l. 29 with JHN for τὸ αὐτὸ δεῖ. Thurot's Latin translation also read δή.
[4] ἄνεμος.

a hurricane.[1] This happened lately near Heracleia in 367ᵃ
Pontus and some time past at the island Hiera, one of the
group called the Aeolian islands. Here a portion of the
earth swelled up and a lump like a mound rose with a noise :
finally it burst, and a great wind came out of it and threw up 5
live cinders and ashes which buried the neighbouring town
of Lipara and reached some of the towns in Italy. The
spot where this eruption occurred is still to be seen.

Indeed, this must be recognized as the cause of the fire
that is generated in the earth : the air [2] is first broken up in 10
small particles and then the wind is beaten about and
so catches fire.

A phenomenon in these islands affords further evidence
of the fact that winds move below the surface of the earth.
When a south wind [3] is going to blow there is a premonitory
indication : a sound is heard in the places from which the
eruptions issue. This is because the sea is being pushed on 15
from a distance and its advance thrusts back into the earth
the wind that was issuing from it. The reason why there
is a noise and no earthquake is that the underground spaces
are so extensive in proportion to the quantity of the air that
is being driven on [4] that the wind slips away into the void
beyond.[5]

Again, our theory is supported by the facts that the sun 20
appears hazy and is darkened in the absence of clouds, and
that there is sometimes calm and sharp frost before earthquakes at sunrise. The sun is necessarily obscured and
darkened when the evaporation which dissolves and rarefies
the air begins to withdraw into the earth. The calm, too,
and the cold towards sunrise and dawn follow from the 25
theory. The calm we have already explained. There
must as a rule be calm because the wind flows back into the
earth : again, it must be most marked before the more

---

[1] Cp. 370ᵇ 3-17.
[2] ἀέρος is being used very loosely (cp. l. 20 below) ; this mechanical
breaking up can hardly stand for the dissolution of the true air into its
constituents.
[3] ἄνεμος.
[4] ἀέρος again used loosely for ἀναθυμίασις or πνεῖμα, cp. l. 11 above.
[5] Read ὑπέρχεται (EHN₁) in l. 19.

violent earthquakes, for when the wind is not part outside
30 the earth, part inside, but moves in a single body, its
strength must be greater. The cold comes because the
evaporation which is naturally and essentially hot enters
the earth. (Wind[1] is not recognized to be hot, because it
sets the air[2] in motion, and that is full of a quantity of cold
367ᵇ vapour. It is the same with the breath we blow from our
mouth : close by it is warm, as it is when we breathe out
through the mouth, but there is so little of it that it is
scarcely noticed, whereas at a distance it is cold for the same
reason as wind.[3]) Well, when this evaporation disappears
5 into the earth the vaporous exhalation concentrates[4] and
causes cold in any place in which this disappearance
occurs.

A sign which sometimes precedes earthquakes can be explained in the same way. Either by day or a little after
sunset, in fine weather, a little, light, long-drawn cloud is
10 seen, like a long very straight line. This is because the
wind[5] is leaving the air and dying down. Something
analogous to this happens on the sea-shore. When the sea
breaks in great waves the marks left on the sand are very
15 thick and crooked, but when the sea is calm they are slight
and straight (because the secretion is small).[6] As the sea
is to the shore so the wind is to the cloudy air ; so, when the
wind drops, this very straight and thin cloud is left, a sort
of wave-mark in the air.

20 An earthquake sometimes coincides with an eclipse of the
moon for the same reason. When the earth is on the point
of being interposed, but the light and heat of the sun has
not quite vanished from the air but is dying away, the wind
which causes the earthquake before the eclipse, turns off in-
25 to the earth, and calm ensues. For there often are winds[7]

---

[1] οἱ ἄνεμοι.   [2] Here ἀήρ is used in its proper sense.
[3] οἱ ἄνεμοι.
[4] Omit δι' ὑγρότητα in l. 5—presumably a gloss and a wrong one :
moisture is not for Aristotle a cause of concentration of the ἀτμίς.
[5] Which would otherwise disturb it.
[6] Omit διὰ τὸ μικρὰν ποιεῖσθαι τὴν ἔκκρισιν, which looks like a misguided
gloss on γαλήνη. Vicomercato's conjecture ἔκρυσιν for ἔκκρισιν will
hardly express the breaking of waves on the shore ; for the word
cp. 351ª 5.   [7] ἄνεμοι.

before eclipses: at nightfall if the eclipse is at midnight, and
at midnight if the eclipse is at dawn. They are caused by
the lessening of the warmth from the moon when its sphere
approaches the point at which [1] the eclipse is going to take
place. So the influence which restrained and quieted the 30
air weakens and the air moves again and a wind rises, and
does so later, the later the eclipse.[2]

A severe earthquake does not stop at once or after
a single shock, but first the shocks go on, often for about
forty days; after that, for one or even two years it gives
premonitory indications in the same place. The severity of 368[a]
the earthquake is determined by the quantity of wind and
the shape of the passages through which it flows. Where
it is beaten back and cannot easily find its way out the
shocks are most violent, and there it must remain in
a cramped space like water that cannot escape. Any 5
throbbing in the body does not cease suddenly or quickly,
but by degrees according as the affection passes off. So
here the agency which created the evaporation and gave it
an impulse to motion clearly does not at once exhaust the
whole of the material from which it forms the wind [3] which 10
we call an earthquake. So until the rest of this is exhausted
the shocks must continue, though more gently, and they
must go on until there is too little of the evaporation left to
have any perceptible effect on the earth at all.

Subterranean noises, too, are due to the wind; sometimes
they portend earthquakes but sometimes they have been 15
heard without any earthquake following. Just as the air
gives off various sounds when it is struck, so it does when it
strikes other things; for striking involves being struck and
so the two cases are the same. The sound precedes the
shock because sound is thinner and passes through things 20
more readily than wind. But when the wind is too weak
by reason of thinness to cause an earthquake the absence of
a shock is due to its filtering through readily, though by
striking hard and hollow masses of different shapes it

[1] Lit. ' at which, when the moon and its sphere have got there'.
[2] Lines 25–32 are almost verbally identical with Probl. 26. 18.
Read τῆς ὀψιαίτερον ἐκλείψεως ὀψιαίτερον in l. 31 with EJ.
[3] ἄνεμος.

makes various noises, so that the earth sometimes seems to
25 'bellow' as the portent-mongers say.

Water has been known to burst out during an earthquake.
But that does not make water the cause of the earthquake.
The wind is the efficient cause whether [1] it drives the water
along the surface [2] or up from below : just as winds [3] are the
30 causes of waves and not waves of winds.[3] Else we might as
well say that earth was the cause ; for it is upset in an
earthquake, just like water (for effusion is a form of upset-
ting). No, earth and water are material causes (being
patients, not agents) : the true cause is the wind.

The combination of a tidal wave with an earthquake is
35 due to the presence of contrary winds. It occurs when the
368ᵇ wind which is shaking the earth does not entirely succeed
in driving off the sea which another wind is bringing on, but
pushes it back and heaps it up in a great mass in one place.
Given this situation it follows that when this wind gives way
5 the whole body of the sea, driven on by the other wind, will
burst out and overwhelm the land. This is what happened
in Achaea.[4] There [5] a south wind was blowing, but outside [5]
a north wind ; then there was a calm and the wind entered [6]
the earth, and then the tidal wave came on and simultaneously
there was an earthquake. This was the more violent as the
sea allowed no exit to the wind that had entered the earth,
10 but shut it in. So in their struggle with one another the
wind caused the earthquake, and the wave by its settling
down the inundation.

Earthquakes are local and often affect a small district only ;
whereas winds [7] are not local. Such phenomena are local
15 when the evaporations at a given place are joined by those
from the next and unite ; this, as we explained, is what
happens when there is drought or excessive rain locally.
Now earthquakes do come about in this way but winds [7] do
not. For earthquakes, rains, and droughts have their source

---

[1] Read ἤ for ἤ in l. 27 with EF₁HN corr. Al.
[2] Cp. l. 34 sqq.   [3] οἱ ἄνεμοι.
[4] Cp. 343ᵇ 2.
[5] Transpose ἔξω and ἐκεῖ (ll. 6, 7). The map makes it clear that the
received text is impossible.
[6] ἄνεμος.   [7] ἄνεμοι.

and origin inside the earth, so that the sun is not equally
able to direct all the evaporations in one direction. But on 20
the evaporations in the air the sun has more influence
so that, when once they have been given an impulse by its
motion, which is determined by its various positions, they
flow in one direction.[1]

When the wind is present in sufficient quantity there is
an earthquake. The shocks are horizontal like a tremor;[2]
except occasionally, in a few places, where they act vertically,
upwards from below, like a throbbing. It is the vertical 25
direction which makes this kind of earthquake so rare.
The motive force does not easily accumulate in great
quantity in the position required, since the surface of the
earth secretes far more of the evaporation than its depths.
Wherever an earthquake of this kind does occur a quantity
of stones comes to the surface of the earth (as when you
throw up things in a winnowing fan), as we see from Sipylus 30
and the Phlegraean plain and the district in Liguria, which
were devastated by this kind of earthquake.

Islands in the middle of the sea are less exposed to earthquakes than those near land. First, the volume of the sea
cools the evaporations and overpowers them by its weight 35
and so crushes them. Then, currents and not shocks are 369^a
produced in the sea by the action of the winds. Again, it
is so extensive that evaporations do not collect in it but
issue from it,[3] and these draw the evaporations from the
earth after them.[4] Islands near the continent really form
part of it : the intervening sea is not enough to make
any difference ; but those in the open sea can only be 5

---

[1] The general point of this paragraph (368^b 12-22) is clearly to contrast the local nature of earthquakes with the wide range of winds.
But there is no doubt, as Thurot saw, that the text is corrupt ; though
the corruption must be old, since Alexander plainly read very much
the same thing as we do.

διὰ τοῦτον τὸν τρόπον, l. 18, implies two variants, διὰ ταύτην τὴν αἰτίαν
and τοῦτον τὸν πρόπον. One or other of these (presumably the latter)
should be read. ἁπάσας, l. 19, sc. τὰς ἀναθυμιάσεις. In l. 20 delete the
colon and δ'.

[2] Omit μέν in l 24 with JFHN ; remove the comma after τόπους,
and omit καί after ἄνω with JFH Al.

[3] It is difficult to see the point of this.

[4] Therefore the sea cannot be shaken : and the islands cannot be
shaken without it.

shaken if the whole of the sea that surrounds them is shaken too.

We have now explained earthquakes, their nature and cause, and the most important of the circumstances attendant on their appearance.

10 Let us go on to explain lightning and thunder, and 9 further whirlwind, fire-wind, and thunderbolts : for the cause of them all is the same.

As we have said,[1] there are two kinds of exhalation, moist and dry, and the atmosphere contains them both 15 potentially. It, as we have said before,[2] condenses into cloud, and the density of the clouds is highest at their upper limit. (For[3] they must be denser and colder on the side where the heat escapes to the upper region and leaves them. This explains why hurricanes[4] and thunderbolts and all 20 analogous phenomena move downwards in spite of the fact that everything hot has a natural tendency upwards. Just as the pips that we squeeze between our fingers are heavy but often jump upwards : so these things are necessarily squeezed out away from the densest part of the cloud.) Now the heat that escapes disperses to the upper region. 25 But if any of the dry exhalation is caught in the process as the air cools, it is squeezed out as the clouds contract, and collides in its rapid course with the neighbouring[5] clouds, and the sound of this collision is what we call thunder. 30 This collision is analogous, to compare small with great, to the sound we hear in a flame which men call the laughter or the threat of Hephaestus or of Hestia. This occurs when the wood dries and cracks and the exhalation rushes on the 35 flame in a body. So in the clouds, the exhalation is pro-
369ᵇ jected[6] and its impact on dense clouds causes thunder : the variety of the sound is due to the irregularity of the clouds

---

[1] e. g. 341ᵇ6.
[2] e. g. 341ᵇ 36 sqq., 346ᵇ 23 sqq.
[3] ἦ . . . ἄνω (ll. 17–24) is parenthetical; the apodosis begins ἡ μὲν οὖν, l. 24. Read colons after σύστασιν, l. 19, and τόπον, l. 25 (Bonitz).
[4] Cp. 370ᵇ 3–17.
[5] Read περιέχουσι in l. 28.
[6] Read ἡ γιγνομένη for γιγνομένη ἡ in l. 35 with JFHN Al.

and the hollows that intervene where their density is interrupted. This, then, is thunder, and this its cause.

It usually happens that the exhalation that is ejected is 5
inflamed and burns with a thin and faint fire: this is what
we call lightning, where we see as it were the exhalation
coloured in the act of its ejection.[1] It comes into existence
after the collision and the thunder, though we see it earlier
because sight is quicker than hearing. The rowing of
triremes illustrates this: the oars are going back again 10
before the sound of their striking the water reaches us.

However, there are some who maintain that there is
actually fire in the clouds. Empedocles[2] says that it consists of some of the sun's rays which are intercepted:
Anaxagoras[3] that it is part of the upper ether (which he
calls fire) which has descended from above. Lightning, 15
then, is the gleam of this fire, and thunder the hissing noise
of its extinction in the cloud.

But this involves the view that lightning actually is prior
to thunder and does not merely appear to be so. Again,
this intercepting of the fire is impossible on either theory,
but especially when it is said to be drawn down from the 20
upper ether. Some reason ought to be given why that
which naturally ascends should descend, and why it should
not always do so, but only when it is cloudy. When the
sky is clear there is no lightning: to say that there is, is
altogether wanton.

The view that the heat of the sun's rays intercepted in the 25
clouds is the cause of these phenomena is equally unattrac-
tive: this, too, is a most careless explanation. Thunder,
lightning, and the rest must have a separate and determinate cause assigned to them on which they ensue. But this 30
theory does nothing of the sort. It is like supposing that
water, snow, and hail existed all along and were produced
when the time came and not generated at all, as if the
atmosphere brought each to hand out of its stock from time
to time. They are concretions in the same way as thunder

---

[1] Perhaps ὥσπερ should be omitted (there is no trace of it in Al.),
though it is difficult to account for its presence in the MSS.
[2] Diels, 21 A. 63.   [3] Diels, 46 A. 1, § 9; 42, § 11; 84.

35 and lightning are discretions, so that if it is true of either
that they are not generated but pre-exist, the same must be
370ᵃ true of the other.[1] Again, how can any distinction be made
about the intercepting between this case and that of interception in denser substances such as water? Water, too, is
heated by the sun and by fire: yet when it contracts again
and grows cold and freezes no such ejection as they describe
5 occurs, though it ought on their theory to take place on a proportionate scale.[2] Boiling is due to the exhalation generated
by fire: but it is impossible for it to exist in the water
beforehand; and besides they call the noise 'hissing', not
'boiling'.[3] But hissing is really boiling on a small scale[4]:
for when that which is brought into contact with moisture
and is in process of being extinguished gets the better of it,
then it boils and makes the noise in question.

10 Some—Cleidemus[5] is one of them—say that lightning is
nothing objective but merely an appearance. They compare it to what happens when you strike the sea with a rod
by night and the water is seen to shine. They say that
the moisture in the cloud is beaten about in the same way,
and that lightning is the appearance of brightness that
15 ensues.

This theory is due to ignorance of the theory of reflection,
which is the real cause of that phenomenon. The water
appears to shine when struck because our sight is reflected
from[6] it to some bright object: hence the phenomenon
20 occurs mainly by night: the appearance is not seen by day
because the daylight is too intense and obscures it.

These are the theories of others about thunder and
lightning: some maintaining that lightning is a reflection,
the others that lightning is fire shining through the cloud and

---

[1] It would therefore have to be true of snow and hail, which it is
not, if it were true (as this theory implies) of lightning (therefore it is
not true of lightning).

[2] Read colon for full stop after λέγουσιν (l. 5): full stop after μεγέ-
θους: τὴν δὲ ζέσιν (EF₁) ποιεῖ (E₁).

[3] So they cannot support their view by appealing to the phenomenon
of boiling.

[4] And therefore (although they speak of 'hissing' and not 'boiling')
the point in the first part of the last sentence does hold against them.

[5] Diels, 49. I.

[6] Read ἀπ' αὐτοῦ in l. 18 with JFN Al.

thunder its extinction, the fire not being generated in each
case but existing beforehand. We say that the same stuff 25
is wind on the earth, and earthquake under it, and in the
clouds thunder. The essential constituent of all these
phenomena is the same : namely, the dry exhalation. If it
flows in one direction it is wind, in another it causes earthquakes ; in the clouds, when they are in a process of change [1]
and contract and condense into water, it is ejected and causes 30
thunder and lightning and the other phenomena of the
same nature.

So much for thunder and lightning.

BOOK III

1   LET us explain the remaining operations of this secretion 370^b
in the same way as we have treated the rest. When this
exhalation is secreted [2] in small and scattered quantities and 5
frequently, and is transitory, and its constitution rare, it
gives rise to thunder and lightning. But if it is secreted in
a body and is denser, that is, less rare, we get a hurricane.[3]
The fact that it issues in a body explains its violence : it is
due to the rapidity of the secretion. Now when this 10
secretion issues in a great and continuous current the result
corresponds to what we get when the opposite development
takes place and rain and a quantity of water are produced.
As far as the matter from which they are developed goes [4]
both sets of phenomena are the same.[5] As soon as
a stimulus to the development of either potentiality appears,
that of which there is the greater quantity present in the 15
cloud is at once secreted from it, and there results either
rain, or, if the other exhalation prevails, a hurricane.

Sometimes the exhalation in the cloud, when it is being

---

[1] Read μεταβάλλουσι with Thurot in l. 30.
[2] From the cloud.
[3] Cp. 365ᵃ 1, 366ᵇ 33, 369ᵃ 19.   [4] The cloud.
[5] Read ταὐτά in l. 13 with the Madrid MS.

secreted, collides with another[1] under circumstances like
those found when a wind is forced from an open into
a narrow space in a gateway or a road. It often happens
20 in such cases that the first part of the moving body is
deflected because of the resistance due either to the narrowness or to a contrary current, and so the wind forms a circle
and eddy. It is prevented from advancing in a straight
line : at the same time it is pushed on from behind ; so it is
compelled to move sideways in the direction of least resis-
25 tance. The same thing happens to the next part, and the
next, and so on, till the series becomes one, that is, till
a circle is formed : for if a figure is described by a single
motion that figure must itself be one.[2] This is how eddies
are generated on the earth, and the case is the same in the
clouds as far as the beginning of them goes. Only here
(as in the case of the hurricane which shakes off[3] the cloud
30 without cessation and becomes a continuous wind) the
cloud follows the exhalation unbroken, and the exhalation,
failing to break away from the cloud because of its density,
first moves in a circle for the reason given and then
descends, because clouds are always densest on the side
371ᵃ where the heat escapes.[4] This phenomenon is called
a whirlwind when it is colourless ; and it is[5] a sort of
undigested hurricane. There is never a whirlwind when
the weather is northerly, nor a hurricane when there is
snow. The reason is that all these phenomena are

---

[1] *Sc.* another exhalation in the cloud (Gilbert), and not another cloud
(Alex.).

[2] Read ἕν for κύκλον in l. 27 with EHN Al.

[3] Read τοῦ νέφους in l. 29 with H and cod. Par. suppl. 314; cp. Al.
ad loc. and p. 136. 7, and cp. 371ᵃ 10 sq. below.
  The passage is very obscure. The translation assumes (following
Vicomercato in the main) that the chief point is the contrast of the
typhoon with the eddy generated on earth (and not as Gilbert thinks
of the typhoon with the ecnephias)—the former descends, the latter
does not. Incidentally a point of similarity between ecnephias and
typhoon is alluded to, the continuity of each of them ; and, incidentally
to that, a point which differentiates typhoon from ecnephias, its shaking
off the cloud, which is taken up again 371ᵃ 9. But all interpretations
are unsatisfactory.

[4] Cp. 369ᵃ 16.

[5] Comma after ἄνεμος (l. 2); delete commas after τυφών and ὤν.
Cp. 370ᵇ 8 ἐκνεφίας ἄνεμος. So Al.

'wind'[1], and wind is a dry and warm evaporation. Now 5 frost and cold prevail over this principle and quench it at its birth: that they do prevail is clear or there could be no snow or northerly rain, since these occur when the cold does prevail.

So the whirlwind originates in the failure of an incipient 10 hurricane to escape from its cloud: it is due to the resistance which generates the eddy, and it consists in the spiral which descends to the earth [2] and drags with it the cloud which it cannot shake off. It moves things by its wind in the direction in which it is blowing in a straight line, and whirls round by its circular motion and forcibly snatches up whatever it meets.

When the cloud burns as it is drawn downwards, 15 that is, when the exhalation becomes rarer, it is called a fire-wind, for its fire colours the neighbouring air and inflames it.

When there is a great quantity of exhalation and it is rare and is squeezed out in the cloud itself [3] we get a thunderbolt. If the exhalation is exceedingly rare this rareness 20 prevents the thunderbolt from scorching and the poets call it 'bright': if the rareness is less it does scorch and they call it 'smoky'. The former moves rapidly [4] because of its rareness, and because of its rapidity passes through an object before setting fire to it or dwelling on it so as to blacken it: the slower one does blacken the object, but passes through it before it can actually burn it.[5] Further,

---

[1] Read πνεῦμα in l. 4 with J Al.; cp. 371ª 29, and 372ª 18 πάντα γὰρ ἀνάκλασις.

[2] Read ἐπὶ γῆν in l. 11 with E₂JF Al. (Ol. ἐπὶ τὴν γῆν lemma and paraphrase).

[3] i. e. in contrast to κατασπώμενον in the account of the prester above.

[4] Some complement to φέρεται (l. 22) such as διὰ τάχους must be supplied (Thurot).

[5] This division of κεραυνοί is obscure, perhaps because Aristotle is mainly concerned with their being, or being due to, πνεῦμα (371ª 29) and less with a systematic classification of them. This may explain the fact that the contrast in this sentence is not what we expect; and that the next sentence seems to contradict this. But it may be that the next sentence is not intended as a continuation of the division begun in this, but is an independent observation confirming the *pneumatic* nature of thunderbolts, which Aristotle inserted without noticing that it involved him in at least a verbal contradiction. Or it

25 resisting substances are affected, unresisting ones are not. For instance, it has happened that the bronze of a shield has been melted while the woodwork remained intact because its texture was so loose that the exhalation filtered through without affecting it.[1] So it has passed through clothes, too, without burning them,[2] and has merely reduced them to shreds.

Such evidence is enough by itself to show that the 30 exhalation[3] is at work in all these cases, but we sometimes get direct ocular evidence as well, as in the case of the conflagration of the temple at Ephesus[4] which we lately witnessed.[5] There independent sheets of flame left the main fire and were carried bodily in many directions. Now that smoke is exhalation and that smoke burns is certain, **371ᵇ** and has been stated in another place before[6]; but when the flame moves bodily, then we have ocular proof that smoke is exhalation. On this occasion what is seen in small fires appeared on a much larger scale because of the quantity of matter that was burning. The beams which were the source 5 of the exhalation split, and a quantity of it rushed in a body from the place from which it issued forth and went up in a blaze: so that the flame was actually seen moving through the air away and falling on the houses. For[7] we must recognize that exhalation accompanies and precedes thunderbolts though it is colourless and so invisible. Hence, where 10 the thunderbolt is going to strike, the object moves before it is struck, showing that the exhalation leads the way and falls on the object first. Thunder,[8] too, splits things not by its noise but because the exhalation that strikes the object and that which makes the noise are ejected simultaneously.

---

may be supposed that our text is considerably corrupt and that something essential has been lost.

[1] Colon after διηθηθέν in l. 27 and no stop after διελθόν (Thurot).

[2] Read ἔκαυσεν (EHN Al.) in l. 28.

[3] Read πνεῦμα in l. 29 with J Al.; cp. ᵃ 4.

[4] The date is said to be 356 B.C. This passage need not necessarily be taken to imply that Aristotle was himself an eyewitness of the event.

[5] Read ἐθεωροῦμεν in l. 31 for συνέβαινε with EHN.

[6] Cp. 341ᵇ 21, 388ᵃ 2, De Gen. et Corr. 331ᵇ 25.

[7] i. e. this is natural, for . . .

[8] Omit καὶ ἀστραπαί in l. 11 with JFH₁N Al. Ol.

This exhalation splits the thing it strikes but does not scorch it at all.

We have now explained thunder and lightning and hurricane, and further fire-winds, whirlwinds, and thunder- 15 bolts, and shown that they are all of them forms of the same thing and wherein they all [1] differ.

2 Let us now explain the nature and cause of halo, rainbow, mock suns, and rods, since the same account applies to 20 them all.

We must first describe the phenomena and the circumstances in which each of them occurs. The halo often appears as a complete circle : it is seen round the sun and the moon and bright stars, by night as well as by day, and at midday or in the afternoon, more rarely about sunrise or 25 sunset.

The rainbow never forms a full circle, nor any segment greater than a semicircle. At sunset and sunrise the circle is smallest and the segment largest : as the sun rises higher the circle is larger and the segment smaller.[2] After the 30 autumn [3] equinox in the shorter days it is seen at every hour of the day, in the summer not about midday. There are never more than two rainbows at one time.[4] Each of them is three-coloured ; the colours are the same in both 372[a] and their number is the same, but in the outer rainbow they are fainter and their position is reversed. In the inner rainbow the first and largest band is red ; in the outer rainbow the band that is nearest to this one and smallest is of the same colour : the other bands correspond on the same principle. These are almost the only colours which 5 painters cannot manufacture : for there are colours which they create by mixing, but no mixing will give red, green, or purple. These are the colours of the rainbow, though between the red and the green an orange colour is often seen.

---

[1] Read πάντων αὐτῶν in l. 17 with EJF.
[2] Really the size of the circle is always the same.
[3] Read μετοπωρινήν for ὀπωρινήν in l. 30 with F Al. (μετωπορινήν J).
[4] Secondary rainbows have under experimental conditions been observed to the number of eighteen (Daniell, *Text-book of the Principles of Physics*, p. 479).

10 Mock suns and rods are always seen by the side of the sun,[1] not above or below it nor in the opposite quarter of the sky.[2] They are not seen at night but always in the neighbourhood of the sun, either as it is rising or setting but more commonly towards sunset. They have scarcely ever appeared when the sun was on the meridian, though 15 this once happened in Bosporus where two mock suns rose with the sun and followed it all through the day till sunset.

These are the facts about each of these phenomena : the cause of them all is the same, for they are all reflections. But they are different varieties, and are distinguished by 20 the surface from which and the way in which the reflection to the sun or some other bright object takes place.

The rainbow is seen by day, and it was formerly thought that it never appeared by night as a moon rainbow. This opinion was due to the rarity of the occurrence : it was not observed, for though it does happen it does so rarely. The reason is that the colours are not so easy to see in the dark 25 and that many other conditions must coincide, and all that in a single day in the month. For if there is to be one it must be at full moon,[3] and then as the moon is either rising or setting. So we have only met with two instances of a moon rainbow in more than fifty years.

We must accept from the theory of optics [4] the fact that 30 sight is reflected from air and any object with a smooth surface just as it is from water ; also that in some mirrors the forms of things are reflected, in others only their 372ᵇ colours. Of the latter kind are those mirrors which are so small as to be indivisible for sense. It is impossible that the figure of a thing should be reflected in them, for if it is the mirror will be sensibly divisible since divisibility is involved in the notion of figure. But since something must 5 be reflected in them and figure cannot be, it remains that colour alone should be reflected.[5] The colour of a bright

---

[1] i. e. east or west of it.   [2] Cp. 377ᵇ 27 sqq.
[3] Or nearly so. Scott, *Elementary Meteorology*, 202.
[4] Alexander observes that the language in which Aristotle speaks of vision in this book is not that of his theory in the *De Anima*.
[5] Cp. 373ᵃ 19-23, ᵇ 24.

object sometimes appears bright in the reflection, but it sometimes, either owing to the admixture of the colour of the mirror or to weakness of sight, gives rise to the appearance of another colour.

However, we must accept the account we have given of these things in the theory of sensation,[1] and take some 10 things for granted while we explain others.

3   Let us begin by explaining the shape of the halo ; why it is a circle and why it appears round the sun or the moon or one of the other stars : the explanation being in all these cases the same.

Sight is reflected in this way when air and vapour are 15 condensed into a cloud and the condensed matter is uniform and consists of small parts.   Hence in itself it is a sign of rain, but if it fades away, of fine weather, if it is broken up, of wind.   For if it does not fade away and is not broken 20 up but is allowed to attain its normal state, it is naturally a sign of rain since it shows that a process of condensation is proceeding which must, when it is carried to an end, result in rain.   For the same reason these haloes are the darkest.   It is a sign of wind when it is broken up because 25 its breaking up is due to a wind which exists there but has not reached us.   This view finds support in the fact that the wind blows from the quarter in which the main division appears in the halo.   Its fading away is a sign of fine weather because if the air is not yet[2] in a state to get the 30 better of the heat it contains and proceed to condense into water, this shows that the moist vapour has not yet separated from the dry and firelike exhalation : and this is the cause of fine weather.

So much for the atmospheric conditions under which the reflection takes place.   The reflection is from the mist that 373^a forms round the sun or the moon, and that is why the halo is not seen opposite the sun like the rainbow.   Since the reflection takes place in the same way from every point the result is necessarily a circle or a segment of a circle :

----

[1] Perhaps *De Sensu*, c. 3.
[2] Read πω in l. 30.

for if the lines start from the same point and end
at the same point and are equal,[1] the points where they
5 form an angle will always lie on a circle.

Let AΓB and AZB and AΔB be lines each of which goes
from the point A to the point B and forms an angle. Let
the lines AΓ, AZ, AΔ be equal and those at B, ΓB, ZB, ΔB
equal too. Draw the line AEB. Then the triangles are
10 equal; for their base AEB is equal.

Draw perpendiculars to AEB from the
angles; ΓE from Γ, ZE from Z, ΔE
from Δ. Then these perpendiculars are
equal, being in equal triangles.[2] And
they are all in one plane, being all at
15 right angles to AEB and meeting at a
single point E. So if you draw the line[3]
it will be a circle and E its centre. Now
B is[4] the sun, A the eye, and the circumference passing through the points ΓZΔ
the cloud from which the line of sight
is reflected to the sun.

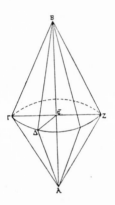

The mirrors must be thought of as contiguous: each of
20 them is too small to be visible, but their contiguity makes
the whole made up of them all to seem one. The bright
band is the sun, which is seen as a circle, appearing
successively in each of the mirrors as a point indivisible to
sense.[5] The band of cloud next to it is black, its colour
25 being intensified by contrast with the brightness of the
halo.[6] The halo is formed rather near[7] the earth because

---

[1] This begs the question and stultifies the succeeding demonstration,
cp. Poske, *Zschr. f. Math. u. Phys.*, 1883, p. 134 sqq.; Gilbert,
p. 602 sqq.

[2] Colon after τριγώνοις (l. 14).

[3] Through ΓΖΔ.

[4] Read ἔστι (EJFHN₁) for ἔστω in l. 16.

[5] Cp. 372ᵃ 32 sqq. and note; 373ᵇ 24 sqq.

[6] Transposing πρὸς δὲ τῇ γῇ . . . φανερόν (ll. 23–5) after παρὰ δὲ
τοῦτο . . . μελαντέρα with Vicomercato and others. Better, perhaps,
put these clauses after ἀέρος (l. 29): γίγνονται (αἱ ἅλῳ) will then be the
verb to πρὸς δὲ τῇ γῇ, for which it is difficult to supply a suitable verb in
the place in which Vicomercato's transposition leaves it.

[7] Or 'nearer,' i.e., than the rainbow, cp. 374ᵃ 1.

that is calmer [1]: for where there is wind it is clear that no
halo can maintain its position.[2]

Haloes are commoner round the moon because the greater
heat of the sun dissolves the condensations of the air more
rapidly.

Haloes are formed round stars for the same reasons, but 30
they are not prognostic in the same way because the
condensation they imply is so insignificant as to be
barren.

4   We have already stated that the rainbow is a reflection:
we have now to explain what sort of reflection it is, to
describe its various concomitants, and to assign their causes.

Sight is reflected from all smooth surfaces, such as are 35
air and water among others. Air must be condensed if it **373^b**
is to act as a mirror, though it often gives a reflection even
uncondensed when the sight is weak. Such was the case of
a man whose sight was faint and indistinct. He always 5
saw an image in front of him and facing him as he walked.
This was because his sight was reflected back to him. Its
morbid condition made it so weak and delicate that the air
close by acted as a mirror, just as distant and condensed air
normally does, and his sight could not push it back.[3] So [4] 10
promontories in the sea 'loom' [5] when there is a south-east
wind, and everything seems bigger, and in a mist, too,

---

[1] Cp. 340^b 33. It is difficult to be certain what part of the atmosphere
Aristotle has in mind here: his account of the various strata is obscure.
It must be inside the tops of the highest mountains, for above them
there are no clouds; and outside the innermost stratum which is
dominated by the rays of the sun reflected from the earth's surface,
and where there are also no clouds. Vicomercato thinks that we
must suppose a specially windy stratum just below the tops of the
highest mountains; our 'calm' stratum would be between that and
the innermost stratum. But it may be (in spite of his objections) that
the whole stratum between the innermost and the tops of the highest
mountains is meant, and that it is contrasted with the higher strata
which are involved in perpetual flow by the κυκλοφορία. In this case
πνεῦμα would be used rather loosely of that flow.

[2] (But they do).

[3] Read a dash after ἀπωθεῖν (l. 9).

[4] The connexion seems to be that the state of the air conditions
what is seen. Ideler thinks there is a lacuna before this sentence, or
else that the sentence itself is spurious.

[5] 'Distant objects are said to loom when they appear abnormally
elevated above their true positions.' Scott, *El. Met.*, p. 207.

things seem bigger: so, too, the sun and the stars seem
bigger when rising and setting than on the meridian. But
things are best reflected from water, and even in process of
15 formation it is a better mirror than air, for each of the
particles, the union of which constitutes a raindrop, is
necessarily a better mirror than mist. Now it is obvious
and has already been stated[1] that a mirror of this kind
renders the colour of an object only, but not its shape.
20 Hence it follows that when it is on the point of raining and
the air in the clouds is in process of forming into raindrops
but the rain is not yet actually there, if the sun is opposite, or
any other object bright enough to make the cloud a mirror
and cause the sight to be reflected to the object then[2] the
reflection must render the colour of the object without its
shape. Since each of the mirrors is so small as to be
25 invisible and what we see is the continuous magnitude made
up of them all, the reflection necessarily gives us a continuous magnitude made up of one colour; each of the mirrors
contributing the same colour to the whole.[3] We may
deduce that since these conditions are realizable there will
30 be an appearance due to reflection whenever the sun and the
cloud are related in the way described and we are between
them. But these are just the conditions under which the
rainbow appears. So it is clear that the rainbow is
a reflection of sight to the sun.

So the rainbow always appears opposite the sun whereas
35 the halo is round it. They are both reflections, but the
374^a rainbow is distinguished by the variety of its colours. The
reflection in the one case is from water which is dark and
from a distance; in the other from air which is nearer and
lighter in colour. White light through a dark medium or
on a dark surface (it makes no difference) looks red[4]. We
5 know how red the flame of green wood is: this is because
so much smoke is mixed with the bright white firelight: so,
too, the sun appears red through smoke and mist. That is
why in the rainbow reflection the outer circumference is

---

[1] 372^a 34.
[2] Omit τε (l. 24) with E$_1$JFHN.   [3] Cp.^{a} 19, 374^a 34.
[4] De Sensu, 440^a 10; De Col. 792^a 9.

red (the reflection being from small particles of water [1]), but
not in the case of the halo.　The other colours shall be ex- 10
plained later.　Again, a condensation of this kind cannot
persist in the neighbourhood of the sun : it must either turn
to rain or be dissolved, but opposite to the sun there is an
interval during which the water is formed.　If there were
not this distinction haloes would be coloured like the rain- 15
bow.　Actually no complete or circular halo presents this
colour, only small and fragmentary appearances called
'rods'.[2]　But if a haze due to water or any other dark
substance formed there we should have had, as we maintain [3], a complete rainbow like that which we do find round
lamps.　A rainbow appears round these in winter, generally 20
with southerly winds.　Persons whose eyes are moist see it
most clearly because their sight is weak and easily reflected.
It is due to the moistness of the air and the soot which the
flame gives off and which mixes with the air and makes it 25
a mirror,[4] and to the blackness which that mirror derives
from the smoky nature of the soot.　The light of the lamp
appears as a circle which is not white but purple.　It shows
the colours of the rainbow ; but because the sight that is
reflected is too weak [5] and the mirror too dark, red is
absent.　The rainbow that is seen when oars are raised out 30
of the sea involves the same relative positions as that in
the sky,[6] but its colour is more like that round the lamps,
being purple rather than red.　The reflection is from very
small particles continuous with one another, and in this case
the particles are fully formed water.　We get a rainbow, 35
too, if a man sprinkles fine drops in a room turned to the **374^b**
sun so that the sun is shining in part of the room and
throwing a shadow in the rest.　Then if one man sprinkles
in the room, another, standing outside, sees a rainbow where
the sun's rays cease and make the shadow.　Its nature and 5

---

[1] And water being dark.
[2] 'Wind galls', 'weather galls', 'wind dogs'.
[3] Cf. ^a 1 above.　Read λέγομεν in l. 19 with the MSS.
[4] Read τότε γὰρ γίνεται ἔνοπτρον (l. 25) as a parenthesis with
Thurot.
[5] It is bound to be weak by lamplight.
[6] i. e. the observer is between the sun and the bow.

colour is like that from the oars and its cause is the same, for the sprinkling hand corresponds to the oar.

That the colours of the rainbow are those we described[1] and how the other colours come to appear in it will be clear from the following considerations. We must recognize, as 10 we have said,[2] and lay down : first, that white colour on a black surface or seen through a black medium gives red ; second, that sight when strained to a distance[3] becomes weaker and less ; third, that black is in a sort the negation of sight : an object is black because sight fails ; so everything at a distance looks blacker, because sight does not 15 reach it. The theory of these matters belongs to the account of the senses, which are the proper subjects of such an inquiry ; we need only state about them what is necessary for us. At all events, that[4] is the reason why distant objects and objects seen in a mirror look darker and 20 smaller and smoother, and why the reflection of clouds in water is darker than the clouds themselves. This latter is clearly the case : the reflection diminishes the sight that reaches them. It makes no difference whether the change is in the object seen or in the sight,[5] the result being in either case the same. The following fact further is worth 25 noticing. When there is a cloud near the sun and we look at it it does not look coloured at all but white, but when we look at the same cloud in water it shows a trace of rainbow colouring. Clearly, then, when sight is reflected it is weakened and, as it makes dark look darker, so it makes 30 white look less white, changing it and bringing it nearer to black. When the sight is relatively strong the change is to red ; the next stage is green, and a further degree of weakness gives violet. No fuither change is visible, but three completes the series of colours (as we find three does in most other things[6]), and the change into the rest is imperceptible

---

[1] 372ª 7, cp. 375ª 28 below.
[2] 374ª 3.
[3] Read ἀποτεινομένη in l. 11 with JF Al. Ol.
[4] Because sight fails.
[5] i. e. whether the object is actually farther from the eye in space or whether (owing to reflection) the sight travels to it by a longer route.
[6] Cp. *De Caelo*, 268ª 9.

to sense.[1] Hence also the rainbow appears with three colours ; this is true of each of the two, but in a contrary way. **375ᵃ** The outer band of the primary rainbow is red : for the largest band reflects most [2] sight to the sun, and the outer band is largest. The middle band and the third go on the same principle. So if the principles we laid down [3] about the appearance of colours are true the rainbow necessarily has 5 three colours, and these three and no others. The appearance of yellow is due to contrast, for the red is whitened by its juxtaposition with green. We can see this from the fact that the rainbow is purest when the cloud is blackest ; and 10 then the red shows most yellow. (Yellow in the rainbow comes between red and green.) So the whole of the red shows white by contrast with the blackness of the cloud around : for it is white compared to the cloud and the green.[4] Again,[5] when the rainbow is fading away [6] and the red is dissolving, the white cloud is brought into contact 15 with the green and becomes yellow. But the moon rainbow affords the best instance of this colour contrast. It looks quite white : this is because it appears on the dark cloud and at night. So, just as fire is intensified by added fire, black 20 beside black makes that which is in some degree white look quite white.[7] Bright dyes too show the effect of contrast. In woven and embroidered stuffs the appearance of colours [8] is profoundly affected by their juxtaposition with one another (purple, for instance, appears different on white and 25 on black wool), and also by differences of illumination. Thus embroiderers say that they often make mistakes in their colours when they work by lamplight, and use the wrong ones.

[1] The meaning of this clause seems to be that no further weakening of sense gives rise to any more colours.

[2] There is no sense in this, but the nonsense is probably Aristotelian.

[3] 374ᵇ 9 above.

[4] We must apparently supply the step : white and green gives yellow ; as Al. does. The argument is : the blacker the cloud, the whiter the red and the greater the contrast with green, and therefore the more yellow the appearance of the rainbow.

[5] The red shows most yellow.

[6] Omit ἐγγυτάτω (l. 15) with E₁ Al. Ol. (lemma).

[7] Omit τοῦτο δ' ἐστὶ τὸ φοινικοῦν (l. 21) as a gloss due to someone who thought A. was referring to the outer band of the moon rainbow only. The words are incompatible with λευκὴ πάμπαν (l. 18).

[8] Omit ἔνια in l. 25 with JFHN Ol.

We have now shown why the rainbow has three colours and that these are its only colours.[1]

30 The same cause[2] explains the double rainbow and the faintness of the colours in the outer one and their inverted order. When sight is strained to a great distance the appearance of the distant object is affected in a certain way : and the same thing holds good here.[3] So the reflection

375ᵇ from the outer rainbow is weaker because it takes place from a greater distance and less of it reaches the sun, and so the colours seen are fainter. Their order is reversed because

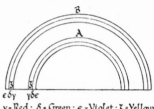

γ = Red ; δ = Green ; ε = Violet ; ʒ = Yellow

more[4] reflection reaches the sun from the smaller, inner
5 band. For that reflection is nearer to our sight which is reflected from the band which is nearest to the primary rainbow. Now the smallest band in the outer rainbow is that which is nearest, and so it will be red ; and the second and the third will follow the same principle. Let B be the outer
10 rainbow, A the inner one ; let Γ stand for the red colour, Δ for green, E for violet ; yellow appears at the point Z. Three rainbows or more are not found because even the second is fainter, so that the third reflection can have no
15 strength whatever and cannot reach the sun at all.

The rainbow can never be a circle nor a segment of 5 a circle greater than a semicircle. The consideration of the diagram[5] will prove this and the other properties of the rainbow.

[1] i. e. the only ones directly due to reflection ; any others being due to contrast.
[2] i. e. reflection and the consequent weakening of sight the remoter the reflection is. The theory (though Alexander misunderstands it) evidently is that the second bow is an indirect reflection from the first, but the whole passage to the end of the chapter is obscure and probably corrupt.
[3] Cp. 374ᵇ 22. [4] Read πλείω with E₂JF₂HN and apparently Al.
[5] The figure is incorrectly drawn : ΚΠΜ should be ⟩ a right-angle ; but it probably represents what Aristotle had in mind (Poske). The

Let A be a hemisphere resting on the circle of the horizon, let its centre be K and let H be another point 20 appearing on the horizon. Then, if the lines that fall in a cone from K have HK as their axis, and, K and M being joined, the lines KM are reflected from the hemisphere to H over the greater angle,[1] the lines from K will fall on the circumference of a circle. If the reflection takes place when 25 the luminous body is rising or setting the segment of the circle above the earth which is cut off by the horizon will be a semicircle ; if the luminous body is above the horizon it

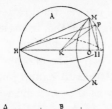

will always be less than a semicircle, and it will be smallest when the luminous body culminates.

First let the luminous body be appearing on the horizon 30 at the point H, and let KM be reflected to H, and let the plane in which A is,[2] determined by the triangle HKM,[3] be produced. Then the section of the sphere will be a great circle. Let it be A (for it makes no difference which[4] of the planes passing through the line HK and determined by the triangle KMH[5] is produced). Now **376^a** the lines drawn from H and K to a point on the semicircle A are in a certain ratio to one another, and no lines drawn from the same points to another point on that semicircle can

circle part of which is dotted stands for the meridian ; the circle HMPN for another great circle of the sphere, passing through H (the rising sun) and M (a point in the cloud) ; the curve MN for a semicircle in a plane at right angles to the plane of HMPN.

[1] HKM.

[2] A, originally a hemisphere (l. 19), is now used for a great circle of the whole sphere, and presently (376^a 2) for the half of that circle which is above the horizon.

[3] Read ἐφ' ᾧ in l. 32.

[4] Read ὁποιονοῦν in l. 34 with F H N Al. Ol.

[5] Only one plane passes through a particular triangle KMH. But the △ KMH may be imagined as rotating round HK, and the plane determined by any one of its positions would do equally well.

have the same ratio. For since both the points H and K
and the line KH are given,[1] the line MH will be given too;
consequently the ratio of the line MH to the line MK will
5 be given too. So M will touch a given circumference.
Let this be NM. Then the intersection of the circum-
ferences [2] is given, and the same ratio cannot hold between
lines in the same plane drawn from the same points to any
other circumference but MN.[3]

10 Draw a line ΔB outside of the figure and divide it so that
Δ : B = MH : MK. But MH is greater than MK since the
reflection of the cone is over the greater angle (for it sub-
tends the greater angle of the triangle KMH). Therefore
15 Δ is greater than B. Then add to B a line Z such that
B + Z : Δ = Δ : B. Then make another line KΠ having the
same ratio to B as KH has to Z, and join MΠ.

Then Π is the pole of the circle on which the lines from
20 K fall. For the ratio of Δ to ΠM is the same as that of
Z to KH and of B to KΠ. If not, let Δ be in the same
ratio to a line indifferently lesser or greater than ΠM, and
let this line be ΠP. Then HK and KΠ and ΠP will have
the same ratios to one another as Z, B, and Δ.[4] But the
ratios between Z, B, and Δ were such that Z + B : Δ = Δ : B.
25 Therefore ΠH : ΠP = ΠP : ΠK. Now, if the points K, H
be joined with the point P by the lines HP, KP, these lines
will be to one another as ΠH is to ΠP, for the sides of the
triangles HΠP, KPΠ about the angle Π are homologous.
30 Therefore, HP [5] too will be to KP as HΠ is to ΠP. But
this is also the ratio of MH to MK, for [6] the ratio both of
HΠ to ΠP and of MH to MK is the same as that of Δ to

376^b B. Therefore, from the points H, K there will have been
drawn lines with the same ratio to one another, not only to
the circumference MN but to another point as well, which
is impossible. Since then Δ cannot bear that ratio to any

---

[1] Delete the comma after δέδοται and insert a comma after KH (l. 4).
[2] i.e. of the great circle inclined to the horizon and now called A
and the circle forming the base of the cone.
[3] Read ἄλλη δέ γε (JF₁ Ol. (lemma), ἄλλη δε γη E₁) ἤ τῇ MN (E₁
Ol. (lemma)) in l. 8. Cp. [b] 2.
[4] Read ZBΔ twice with E₁ Al.
[5] Read ἡ HP with J rec. Al. Ol. (ἡ ρ̄ E₁).
[6] Read τοῦτον τὸν λόγον (JFHN Al.), ὃν γάρ (J Al.) in l. 32.

line either lesser or greater than ΠM (the proof being in
either case the same), it follows that it must stand in that 5
ratio to MΠ itself. Therefore as MΠ is to ΠK so ΠH
will be to MΠ and finally MH to MK.

If, then, a circle be described with Π as pole at the
distance MΠ it will touch all the angles which the lines
from H and K ¹ make by their reflection. If not, it can be 10
shown, as before, that lines drawn to different points in the
semicircle will have the same ratio to one another, which
was impossible. If, then, the semicircle A be revolved
about the diameter HKΠ, the lines reflected from the
points ² H, K at the point M will have the same ratio, and 15
will make the angle KMH equal, in every plane. Further,
the angle which HM ³ and MΠ make with HΠ will always
be the same. So there are a number of triangles on HΠ
and KΠ equal to the triangles HMΠ and KMΠ. Their
perpendiculars will fall on HΠ at the same point and will
be equal. Let O be the point on which they fall. Then O 20
is the centre of the circle, half of which, MN ⁴, is cut off by ⁵
the horizon.⁶

Next let the horizon be ABΓ but let H have risen above
the horizon. Let the axis now be HΠ. The proof will be 30

---

¹ Read ἀπὸ τοῦ H καὶ K in l. 10, omitting κύκλου. Al. read ἀπὸ τοῦ K
καὶ H, Bag. ἀπὸ τοῦ KH, and both, as well as Ol., omit κύκλου. By reading
H καὶ K the insertion of κύκλου is explained.

² Read τῶν HK and πρὸς τῷ in l. 14 with (apparently) Al.

³ Read HM in l. 16 after Tannery. The MSS. read HΠ: Bag.
Vic. KΠ.

⁴ τὸ περὶ τὴν MN (l. 21) implies a confusion between the horizon and
the great circle inclined to it (375ᵇ 32). Ar. may have fallen into this
confusion, but there is no trace of these words in Al. and perhaps they
are a gloss. Or perhaps we should read τοῦ περὶ τὴν MN (sc. κύκλου).

⁵ Read ὑπό in l. 22 with FHN Al.

⁶ The following passage (ll. 22–28) is found in all the MSS. except
the first hand of E and is recognized by Ol. But it is not recognized
by Al. and is not found in Bag. The transition to *oratio obliqua* is
suspicious; the passage is irrelevant to the context and incoherent in
itself and certainly an interpolation.

'For the sun does not get the better of the upper parts, but it does
of those that lie near the earth, and there it dissolves the air. This is
the reason why the rainbow does not form a complete circle. A rainbow due to the moon is found at night, but rarely. For the moon is
not always full, and its light is too weak to get the better of the air'
(read ⟨ἢ⟩ ὥστε in l. 26). 'The rainbow is most established where the
sun is most overpowered: for there then remains in it most moisture.'

the same for the rest as before, but the pole Π of the circle will be below the horizon ΑΓ since the point Η has risen
377ᵃ above the horizon. But the pole, and the centre of the circle,[1] and the centre of that circle (namely ΗΠ) which now determines the position of the sun[2] are on the same line. But since ΚΗ lies above the diameter ΑΓ, the centre[3]
5 will be at Ο on the line ΚΠ below the plane of the circle ΑΓ which determined the position of the sun before. So the segment ΨΥ[4] which is above the horizon will be less than a semicircle.[5] For ΨΥΩ was a semicircle and it has now been cut off by[6] the horizon ΑΓ. So part of it,[7] ΥΩ, will be invisible when the sun has risen above the horizon,

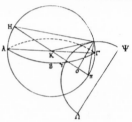

and the segment visible will be smallest when the sun is on
10 the meridian[8]; for the higher Η is the lower the pole and the centre of the circle will be.

In the shorter days after the autumn equinox there may be a rainbow at any time of the day, but in the longer days from the spring to the autumn equinox there cannot be
15 a rainbow about midday. The reason for this is that when the sun is north of the equator the visible arcs of its course are all greater than a semicircle, and go on increasing, while the invisible arc is small, but when the sun is south of the equator the visible arc is small and the invisible arc great,[9] and the farther the sun moves south of the equator the

---

[1] Which is the base of the cone.
[2] i.e. the great circle which would be the horizon if the sun were rising when it is at the point H.
[3] Of the circle which is the base of the cone.
[4] Read ΨΥ in l. 7 with EJHN.
[5] Comma after ἡμικυκλίου (l. 7).
[6] Read ὑπό in l. 8 with FHN.
[7] Read αὐτοῦ, ἐπαρθέντος in l. 9 with JFHN.
[8] Read μεσημβρίας in l. 10 with JFHN.
[9] Comma after μέγα, and colon after πορρωτέρω (l. 19) with Busse-maker.

greater is the invisible arc.   Consequently, in the days 20
near the summer solstice, the size of the visible arc is such
that before the point H reaches the middle of that arc, that
is its point of culmination, the point Π is well below the
horizon;   the reason for this being the great size of the
visible arc, and the consequent distance of the point of
culmination from the earth.   But in the days near the
winter solstice the visible arcs are small, and the contrary is 25
necessarily the case : for the sun is on the meridian before
the point H has risen far.

6   Mock suns, and rods too, are due to the causes we have
described.   A mock sun is caused by the reflection of sight 30
to the sun.   Rods are seen when sight reaches the sun
under circumstances like those which we described,[1] when
there are clouds near the sun and sight is reflected from some
liquid surface to the cloud.   Here the clouds themselves
are colourless when you look at them directly, but in the **377ᵇ**
water they are full of rods.   The only difference is that in
this latter case the colour of the cloud seems to reside in
the water, but in the case of rods on the cloud itself.   Rods
appear when the composition of the cloud is uneven, dense 5
in part and in part rare, and more and less watery in different
parts.   Then the sight is reflected to the sun : the mirrors
are too small for the shape of the sun to appear, but, the
bright white light of the sun, to which the sight is reflected,
being seen on the uneven mirror, its colour appears partly
red, partly green or yellow.   It makes no difference 10
whether sight passes through or is reflected from a medium
of that kind ; the colour is the same in both cases ; if
it is red in the first case it must be the same in the
other.

Rods then are occasioned by the unevenness of the
mirror—as regards colour, not form.   The mock sun, on the 15
contrary, appears when the air is very uniform, and of the
same density throughout.   This is why it is white :
the uniform character of the mirror gives the reflection
in it a single colour, while the fact that the sight is reflected

[1] 374ᵇ 24.

in a body and is thrown on the sun all together by the mist,
20 which is dense and watery though not yet quite water,
causes the sun's true colour to appear just as it does when
the reflection is from the dense, smooth surface of copper.
So the sun's colour being white, the mock sun is white too.
This, too, is the reason why the mock sun is a surer sign of
25 rain than the rods; it indicates,[1] more than they do, that
the air is ripe for the production of water. Further a mock
sun to the south is a surer sign of rain than one to the
north, for the air in the south is readier to turn into water
than that in the north.

Mock suns and rods are found, as we stated,[2] about
sunset and sunrise, not above the sun nor below it, but
30 beside it. They are not found very close to the sun, nor
very far from it, for the sun dissolves the cloud if it is near,
but if it is far off the reflection cannot take place, since
sight weakens when it is reflected from a small mirror to
a very distant object. (This is why a halo is never found
378ᵃ opposite to the sun.) If the cloud is above the sun and
close to it the sun will dissolve it: if it is above the sun
but at a distance the sight is too weak for the reflection to
take place, and so it will not reach the sun. But at the
side of the sun,[3] it is possible for the mirror to be at such
an interval that the sun does not dissolve the cloud, and
5 yet sight reaches it undiminished because it moves close to
the earth[4] and is not dissipated[5] in the immensity of space.
It cannot subsist below the sun because close to the earth
the sun's rays would dissolve it, but if it were high up and
the sun in the middle of the heavens, sight would be
dissipated. Indeed, even by the side of the sun, it is not found
when the sun is in the middle of the sky, for then the line of
10 vision is not close to the earth,[6] and so but little sight reaches
the mirror and the reflection from it is altogether feeble.

Some account has now been given of the effects of the
15 secretion above the surface of the earth; we must go on

[1] Read σημαίνει in l. 25 with E₁ Al. Bag.   [2] 372ᵃ 10.
[3] Omit ὑπὸ τὸν ἥλιον in l. 3 with JFHN Al.
[4] Read τῇ γῇ in l. 5 with Al. (τη γῆν E₁).
[5] Read διασπᾶσθαι in l. 6 with E₁JF₁.
[6] Read πρὸς τῇ γῇ in l. 10 with (perhaps) Al.

to describe its operations below, when it is shut up in the parts of the earth.

Just as its twofold nature gives rise to various effects in the upper region, so here it causes two varieties of bodies. We maintain that there are two exhalations, one vaporous the other smoky, and there correspond two kinds of bodies that originate in the earth, 'fossiles' and metals. The heat 20 of the dry exhalation is the cause of all 'fossiles'. Such are the kinds of stones that cannot be melted, and realgar, and ochre, and ruddle, and sulphur, and the other things of that kind, most 'fossiles' being either coloured lye or, 25 like cinnabar, a stone compounded of it. The vaporous exhalation is the cause of all metals, those bodies which are either fusible or malleable such as iron, copper, gold. All these originate from the imprisonment of the vaporous exhalation in the earth, and especially in stones. Their 30 dryness compresses it, and it congeals just as dew or hoar-frost does when it has been separated off, though in the present case the metals are generated before that segregation occurs. Hence, they are water in a sense, and in a sense not. Their matter was that which might have become water, but it can no longer do so:[1] nor are they, like savours, due to a qualitative change in actual water. Copper **378^b** and gold are not formed like that, but in every case the evaporation congealed before water was formed. Hence, they all (except gold) are affected by fire, and they possess an admixture of earth; for they still contain the dry exhalation.

This is the general theory of all these bodies, but we 5 must take up each kind of them and discuss it separately.

BOOK IV

1   WE have explained that the qualities that constitute the 10 elements are four, and that their combinations determine the number of the elements to be four.

Two of the qualities, the hot and the cold, are active; two, the dry and the moist, passive. We can satisfy

---

[1] Read a colon after οὐκέτι (l. 34) with Ideler.

ourselves of this by looking at instances. In every case
15 heat and cold determine, conjoin, and change things of the
same kind and things of different kinds, moistening, drying,
hardening, and softening them. Things dry and moist,
on the other hand, both in isolation and when present
together in the same body are the subjects of that deter-
20 mination and of the other affections enumerated. The
account we give of the qualities when we define their
characters shows this too. Hot and cold we describe as
active, for 'congregating' is essentially [1] a species of 'being
active': moist and dry are passive, for it is in virtue of its
being acted upon in a certain way that a thing is said to
25 be 'easy to determine' or 'difficult to determine'.[2] So it
is clear that some of the qualities are active and some
passive.

Next we must describe the operations [3] of the active
qualities and the forms taken by the passive. First of all,
true becoming, that is, natural change,[4] is always the work
of these powers and so is the corresponding natural destruc-
30 tion; and this becoming and this destruction are found in
plants and animals and their parts.[5] True natural becoming
is a change introduced by these powers into the matter
underlying a given thing when they are in a certain ratio
to that matter,[6] which is the passive qualities we have
379[a] mentioned. When the hot and the cold are masters of the
matter they generate a thing: if they are not, and the
failure is partial, the object is imperfectly boiled [7] or otherwise unconcocted. But the strictest general opposite of
true becoming is putrefaction. All natural destruction is on
the way to it, as are, for instance, growing old or growing
5 dry. Putrescence is the end of all these things,[8] that is of

---

[1] Read ὅπερ in l. 23 with E Al. Vic.
[2] Colon after αὐτῶν in l. 25 (Bonitz). ἡ . . . αὐτῶν (ll. 13–25) is
parenthetical. Colon after συνέστηκεν (l. 20).
[3] Read ἅς in l. 27 with HN and perhaps Al.
[4] As distinguished from the making of artificial objects.
[5] But not only in them. The statement is universally true of homogeneous μικτά; cp. the reference to sea-water 379[b] 4.
[6] There should be a comma after λόγον (l. 33).
[7] Read μόλυνσις in l. 2 with E₂JFHN Al.
[8] Read τούτων ἁπάντων with E₂ and cod. Par. suppl. 314 in l. 5 for
τῶν ἄλλων ἁπάντων. Bag. read ἁπάντων τούτων. JFHN read τούτων as

all natural objects, except such as are destroyed by violence:[1] you can burn, for instance, flesh, bone, or anything else, but the natural course of their destruction ends in putrefaction. Hence things that putrefy begin by being moist and end by being dry. For the moist and the dry were their matter, and the operation of the active qualities 10 caused the dry to be determined by the moist.

Destruction supervenes when the determined gets the better of the determining by the help of the environment (though in a special sense the word putrefaction is applied to partial destruction, when a thing's nature is perverted). Hence everything, except fire, is liable to putrefy ; for earth, water, 15 and air putrefy, being all of them matter relatively to fire. The definition of putrefaction is : the destruction of the peculiar and natural heat in any moist subject by external heat, that is, by the heat of the environment. So since lack of heat is the ground of this affection and everything in as far [2] as it lacks heat is cold, both heat and cold will 20 be the causes of putrefaction, which will be due indifferently to cold in the putrefying subject or to heat in the environment.

This explains why everything that putrefies grows drier and ends by becoming earth or dung. The subject's own heat departs and causes the natural moisture to evaporate with it, and then there is nothing left to draw in moisture, for it is a thing's peculiar heat that attracts moisture and 25 draws it in. Again, putrefaction takes place less in cold than in hot seasons, for in winter the surrounding air and water contain but little heat and it has no power, but in summer there is more. Again, what is frozen does not putrefy, for its cold is greater than the heat of the air and 30 so is not mastered, whereas what affects a thing does master it. Nor does that which is boiling or hot putrefy, for the heat in the air being less than that in the object does not

well as τῶν ἄλλων, and Vic. shows traces of the same reading. τῶν ἄλλων and τούτων are alternatives. ἄλλων implies a contrast which is wanting and Al. apparently did not read it. τῶν ἄλλων seems to be due to some one who thought that σαπρότης was something contrasted with σῆψις.

[1] There should be a comma after φθαρῇ (l. 6).

[2] Read ᾗ δὲ ἐνδεές in l. 19 with E₁ Bag and probably Al.

prevail over it or set up any change. So too anything that
is flowing or in motion is less apt to putrefy than a thing
35 at rest, for the motion set up by the heat in the air is
379ᵇ weaker than that pre-existing in the object, and so it causes
no change. For the same reason a great quantity of a thing
putrefies less readily than a little, for the greater quantity
contains too much proper fire and cold foɪ the corresponding
qualities in the environment to get the better of. Hence,
5 the sea putrefies quickly when broken up into parts, but
not as a whole; and all other waters likewise. Animals
too are generated in putrefying bodies, because the heat
that has been secreted, being natural, organizes the particles
secreted with it.

So much for the nature of becoming and of destruction.

10 We must now describe the next kinds of processes which **2**
the qualities already mentioned set up in actually existing
natural objects as matter.

Of these concoction is due to heat; its species are
ripening, boiling, broiling.[1] Inconcoction is due to cold
and its species are rawness, imperfect boiling,[2] imperfect
broiling. (We must recognize that the things are not
15 properly denoted by these words: the various classes of
similar objects have no names universally applicable to
them; consequently we must think of the species enumerated as being not what those words denote but something like it.) Let us say what each of them is. Concoction
is a process in which the natural and proper heat of an
object perfects the corresponding passive qualities, which
20 are the proper matter of any given object.[3] For when
concoction has taken place we say that a thing has been
perfected and has come to be itself. It is the proper heat
of a thing that sets up this perfecting, though external
influences may contribute in some degree to its fulfilment.
Baths, for instance, and other things of the kind contribute

---

[1] For uniformity these words are used throughout the following
chapters to render πέπανσις, ἕψησις, ὄπτησις, though in various places
other English words would be more appropriate.

[2] Read μόλυνσις in l. 14 with E₂FHN₂ Al. Ol.

[3] Read ἑκάστῳ in l. 20 with EJF₁ Al. Bag.

to the digestion of food, but the primary cause is the
proper heat of the body.   In some cases of concoction 25
the end of the process is the nature[1] of the thing—nature,
that is, in the sense of the formal cause and essence.   In
other cases it leads to some *presupposed state* which is
attained when the moisture has acquired certain properties
or a certain magnitude in the process of being broiled or
boiled or of putrefying,[2] or however else it is being heated.
This state is the end, for when it has been reached the
thing has some use and we say that concoction has taken
place.   Must is an instance of this,[3] and the matter in boils 30
when it becomes purulent, and tears when they become
rheum, and so with the rest.[4]

Concoction ensues whenever the matter, the moisture,
is mastered.   For the matter is what is determined by the
heat connatural to the object, and as long as the ratio 35
between them exists in it a thing maintains its nature.
Hence things like the liquid and solid excreta and ejecta in **380**[a]
general are signs of health, and concoction is said to have
taken place in them, for they show that the proper heat has
got the better of the indeterminate matter.

Things that undergo a process of concoction necessarily
become thicker and hotter, for the action of heat is to make
things more compact, thicker, and drier.   5

This then is the nature of concoction : but inconcoction is
an imperfect state due to lack of proper heat, that is, to cold.
That *of* which the imperfect state is, is the corresponding
passive qualities which are the natural matter of anything.

So much for a definition of concoction and inconcoction. 10

3   Ripening is a sort of concoction ; for we call it ripening
when there is a concoction of the nutriment in fruit.   And
since concoction is a sort of perfecting, the process of ripening
is perfect when the seeds in fruit are able to reproduce the

---

[1] Digestion proper or the ripening of fruit (380[a] 25) subserves the
perfecting of what is a ' natural ' organic thing in a sense in which
pus and rheum are not ' natural ' organic things.   This is the distinction
which A. is trying to draw.

[2] We should expect πεπαινόμενον ' ripening ', as Thurot points out.

[3] i. e. when it ' ripens ' and becomes wine.   [4] Cp. n. I.

15 fruit in which they are found ; for in all other cases as well
this is what we mean by 'perfect'. This is what 'ripening'
means when the word is applied to fruit. However, many
other things that have undergone concoction are said to be
'ripe', the general character of the process being the same,
though the word is applied by an extension of meaning.
The reason for this extension is, as we explained before,[1]
that the various modes in which natural heat and cold perfect the matter[2] they determine have not special names
20 appropriated to them. In the case of boils and phlegm, and
the like, the process of ripening is the concoction of the
moisture in them by their natural heat, for only that which
gets the better of matter can determine it.[3] So everything
that ripens is condensed from a spirituous into a watery
state, and from a watery into an earthy state, and in general
25 from being rare becomes dense. In this process the nature
of the thing that is ripening incorporates some of the matter
in itself,[4] and some it rejects. So much for the definition of
ripening.

Rawness is its opposite and is therefore an imperfect
concoction of the nutriment in the fruit, namely, of the undetermined moisture. Consequently a raw thing is either
spirituous or watery or contains both spirit and water.
30 Ripening being a kind of perfecting, rawness will be an imperfect state, and this state[5] is due to a lack of natural heat
and its disproportion to the moisture that is undergoing the
process of ripening. (Nothing moist ripens without the
admixture of some dry matter : water alone of liquids[6]
380ᵇ does not thicken.)[7] This disproportion may be due either
to defect of heat or to excess of the matter to be determined :
hence the juice of raw things is thin, cold rather than hot,
and unfit for food or drink. Rawness, like ripening, is used
5 to denote a variety of states. Thus the liquid and solid
excreta and catarrhs are called raw for the same reason, for

---

[1] 379ᵇ 14. [2] i.e. the moist and the dry.
[3] And the natural heat is that which can master the moist.
[4] Read αὐτήν in l. 26. [5] Read δ' ἡ ἀτέλεια in l. 31 with JFHN.
[6] Cp. 383ᵃ 12 and note, and 382ᵇ 13.
[7] This sentence interrupts the connexion and would be more in
place at l. 3 (Vic.).

in every case the word is applied to things because their
heat has not got the mastery in them and compacted them.
If we go further, brick is called raw and so is milk and
many other things too when they are such as to admit of
being changed and compacted by heat but have remained
unaffected.   Hence, while we speak of ' boiled ' water, we 10
cannot speak of raw water, since it does not thicken.   We
have now defined ripening and rawness and assigned their
causes.

Boiling is, in general, a concoction by moist heat of the
indeterminate matter contained in the moisture of the thing
boiled, and the word is strictly applicable only to things
boiled in the way of cooking.   The indeterminate matter, 15
as we said,[1] will be either spirituous or watery.   The cause
of the concoction is the fire contained in the moisture ; [2] for
what is cooked in a frying-pan is broiled : it is the heat outside that affects it and, as for the moisture in which it is
contained, it dries this up and draws it into itself.   But
a thing that is being boiled behaves in the opposite way :
the moisture contained in it is drawn out of it by the heat 20
in the liquid outside.   Hence boiled meats are drier than
broiled ; for, in boiling, things do not draw the moisture into
themselves, since the external heat gets the better of the
internal : if the internal heat had got the better it would
have drawn the moisture to itself.   Not every body admits
of the process of boiling : if there is no moisture in it, it does 25
not (for instance, stones), nor does it if there is moisture in it
but the density of the body is too great for it to be mastered,
as in the case of wood.   But only those bodies can be boiled
that contain moisture which can be acted on by the heat contained in the liquid outside.   It is true that gold and wood
and many other things are said to be ' boiled ': but this is
a stretch of the meaning of the word, though the kind of
thing intended is the same,[3] the reason for the usage being 30
that the various cases have no names appropriated to them.
Liquids too, like milk and must, are said to undergo a process of ' boiling ' when the external fire that surrounds and

---

[1] a 29.   [2] In the moisture external to the thing boiled.
[3] Omit οὐ with E₁ (οὐ supra add. E₁) Bag.   Cp. a 17.

heats them changes the savour in the liquid into a given
form, the process being thus in a way like what we have
called boiling.

381ᵃ   The end of the things that undergo boiling, or indeed any
form of concoction, is not always the same : some are meant
to be eaten, some drunk, and some are intended for other
uses; for instance dyes, too, are said to be 'boiled '.[1]

All those things then admit of ' boiling' which can grow
5 denser, smaller, or heavier; also those which do that with
a part of themselves and with a part do the opposite, dividing
in such a way that one portion thickens while the other
grows thinner, like milk when it divides into whey and curd.[2]
Oil by itself is affected in none of these ways, and therefore
cannot be said to admit of ' boiling'. Such then is the
10 species of concoction known as ' boiling ', and the process is
the same in an artificial and [3] in a natural instrument, for
the cause will be the same in every case.

Imperfect boiling [4] is the form of inconcoction opposed to
boiling. Now the opposite of boiling properly so called [5] is
an inconcoction of the undetermined matter in a body due
to lack of heat in the surrounding liquid. (Lack of heat
15 implies, as we have pointed out, the presence of cold.) [6] The
motion which causes imperfect boiling is different from that
which causes boiling, for the heat which operates the concoction is driven out. The lack of heat is due either to the
amount of cold in the liquid or to the quantity of moisture [7]
in the object undergoing the process of boiling. Where
either of these conditions is realized the heat in the surrounding liquid is too great to have no effect at all, but too small

---

[1] This sentence interrupts the connexion, as Thurot points out, and
is at least out of place, and οὔτε πεττομένοις is not easy to explain.

[2] Read πυετίαν in l. 7 with JF₂HN, as in *H. A.* 522ᵇ 5, 8, 9, 11;
P. A. 676ᵃ 6, 8, 11, 15, 18; *G. A.* 739ᵇ 22, 772ᵃ 25. πυετία properly
means rennet, but Ar. also uses it of the milk coagulated by rennet.
Cp. *P. A.* 676ᵃ 8 and Ogle's note.

[3] Read καί for ἤ in l. 10 with EJFHN.

[4] Read μόλυνσις in l. 12 with J₂FHN Al. Vic.

[5] Read ἐναντία τῇ πρώτῃ λεχθείσῃ in l. 13. Bag. read τῇ πρώτῃ and
Vic. records the same reading as a variant.

[6] ἡ δ' ἔνδεια . . . εἴρηται (ll. 14, 15) should be in a parenthesis (Thurot).
The reference is to 379ᵃ 19.

[7] Cp. ᵇ 18.

to carry out the process of concoction uniformly and
thoroughly. Hence things are harder when they are imper- 20
fectly boiled [1] than when they are boiled, and the moisture
in them more distinct from the solid parts. So much for the
definition and causes of boiling and imperfect boiling.[2]

Broiling is concoction by dry foreign heat. Hence if
a man were to boil a thing but the change and concoction
in it were due, not to the heat of the liquid but to that of 25
the fire, the thing will have been broiled and not boiled
when the process has been carried to completion : if the
process has gone too far we use the word ' scorched ' to
describe it. If the process leaves the thing drier at the end
the agent has been dry heat. Hence the outside is drier
than the inside, the opposite being true of things boiled.
Where the process is artificial, broiling is more difficult than 30
boiling, for it is difficult to heat the inside and the outside
uniformly, since the parts nearer to the fire are the first to
get dry and consequently get more intensely dry. In this 381ᵇ
way the outer pores contract and the moisture in the thing
cannot be secreted but is shut in by the closing of the pores.
Now broiling and boiling are artificial processes, but the
same general kind of thing, as we said,[3] is found in nature
too. The affections produced are similar though they lack 5
a name ; for art imitates nature. For instance, the concoction
of food in the body is like boiling, for it takes place in a hot
and moist medium and the agent is the heat of the body.
So, too, certain forms of indigestion are like imperfect boiling. And it is not true that animals are generated in the
concoction of food, as some say. Really they are generated 10
in the excretion which putrefies in the lower belly, and they
ascend afterwards. For concoction goes on in the upper
belly but the excretion putrefies in the lower : the reason
for this has been explained elsewhere.[4]

---

[1] Read μεμολυσμένα in l. 21 with E rec. FHN Al.
[2] Read μόλυνσις in l. 22 with E rec. FHN.
[3] 379ᵇ 14, 380ᵃ 16.
[4] Alexander thinks the reference is to the *Problems* ; Heitz thinks it is
to a lost work, περὶ τροφῆς. The connexion seems to be this : if animals
were generated in digestion, digestion would be σῆψις, and then it
would be quite different from ἕψησις : so it is necessary to show that
digestion is not σῆψις.

We have seen that the opposite of boiling is imperfect boiling: now there is something correspondingly opposed to 15 the species of concoction called broiling, but it is more difficult to find a name for it. It would be the kind of thing that would[1] happen if there were imperfect broiling instead of broiling proper through lack of heat due to deficiency in the external fire or to the quantity of water in the thing undergoing the process. For then we should get too much heat for no effect to be produced, but too little for concoction to take place.

20 We have now explained concoction and inconcoction, ripening and rawness, boiling and broiling, and their opposites.

We must now describe the forms taken by the passive **4** qualities the moist and the dry. The elements of bodies, 25 that is, the passive ones, are the moist and the dry; the bodies themselves are compounded of them and whichever predominates determines the nature of the body; thus some bodies partake more of the dry, others of the moist. All the forms to be described will exist either actually, or potentially and in their opposite: for instance, there is actual melting and on the other hand that which admits of being melted. Since the moist is easily determined and the dry deter- 30 mined with difficulty, their relation to one another is like that of a dish and its condiments. The moist is what makes the dry determinable, and each serves as a sort of glue to the **382ᵃ** other—as Empedocles said in his poem on Nature,[2] 'glueing meal together by means of water'. Thus the determined body involves them both. Of the elements earth is especially representative of the dry, water of the moist,[3] and therefore all determinate bodies in our world[4] involve earth and 5 water. Every body shows the quality of that element which predominates in it. It is because earth and water are the material elements of all bodies that animals live in them alone and not in air or fire.

Of the qualities of bodies hardness and softness are those 10 which must primarily belong to a determined thing, for

---

[1] Read in l. 16 οἷον εἰ γένοιτο with FHN.   [2] Diels, 21 B. 34.
[3] Contrast *De Gen. et Corr.* 331ᵃ 4.   [4] i.e. the sublunary region.

anything made up of the dry and the moist is necessarily either hard or soft. Hard is that the surface of which does not yield into itself; soft that which does yield but not[1] by interchange of place : water, for instance, is not soft, for its surface does not yield to pressure or sink in but there is an interchange of place. Those things are absolutely hard and soft which satisfy the definition absolutely, and those things 15 relatively so which do so compared with another thing. Now relatively to one another hard and soft are indefinable, because it is a matter of degree, but since all the objects of sense are determined by reference to the faculty of sense it is clearly the relation to touch which determines that which is hard and soft absolutely, and touch is that which we use as a standard or mean. So we call that which exceeds it 20 hard and that which falls short of it soft.

5 A body determined by its own boundary[2] must be either hard or soft ; for it either yields or does not.

It must also be concrete : or it could not be so determined. So since everything that is determined and solid is either hard or soft and these qualities are due to concretion, all 25 composite[3] and determined bodies must involve concretion. Concretion therefore must be discussed.

Now[4] there are two causes besides[5] matter, the agent and the quality brought about, the agent being the efficient cause, the quality the formal cause. Hence concretion and disaggregation, drying and moistening, must have these two 30 causes.

But since concretion is a form of drying let us speak of 382ᵇ the latter first.[6]

As we have explained, the agent operates by means of 382ᵃ two qualities and the patient is acted on in virtue of two

---

[1] Read μὴ τῷ for τῷ μή in l. 12.
[2] As contrasted with a liquid determined by the form of the vessel containing it.
[3] As distinct from *elementary*.
[4] Read δή in l. 27 with E₂JHN Ol. (lemma).
[5] Read παρά in l. 28 with E₁JFHN Al. Ol.
[6] ἐπεὶ... πρῶτον (ᵇ 1, 2) is clearly out of place. Transpose ἐπεὶ... πρῶτον to follow ὑγραίνεσθαι (ᵃ 31) ; and read τὸ δὲ πάσχον in ᵇ 2 with var. J₁. The contrast to ποιεῖ μέν (ᵃ 32) comes in τὸ δὲ πάσχον, and τὸ δὲ πάθος ... ψυχροῦ (ᵃ 33) is more or less parenthetical.

qualities : action takes place by means of heat or cold, and
the quality is produced either by the presence or by the
382ᵇ absence of heat or cold ; but that which is acted upon is
moist or dry or a compound of both. Water is the element
characterized by the moist, earth that characterized by the
dry, for these among the elements that admit the qualities
moist and dry are passive. Therefore cold, too, being found
5 in water and earth (both of which we recognize to be cold),
must be reckoned rather as a passive quality. It is active
only as contributing to destruction or incidentally in the
manner described before [1] ; for cold is sometimes actually
said to burn and to warm, but not in the same way as heat
does, but by collecting and concentrating heat.

10 The subjects of drying are water and the various watery
fluids and those bodies which contain water either foreign
or connatural. By foreign I mean like the water in wool,
by connatural, like that in milk. The watery fluids are
wine, urine, whey, and in general those fluids which have no
sediment or only a little, except where this absence of sedi-
15 ment is due to viscosity. For in some cases,[2] in oil and
pitch for instance, it is the viscosity which prevents any
sediment from appearing.

It is always a process of heating or cooling that dries
things, but the agent in both cases is heat, either internal or
external. For even when things are dried by cooling, like
20 a garment, where the moisture exists separately it is the
internal heat that dries them. It carries off the moisture in
the shape of vapour (if there is not too much of it), being itself
driven out by the surrounding cold. So everything is dried,
as we have said, by a process either of heating or cooling,
but the agent is always heat, either internal or external,
25 carrying off the moisture in vapour. By external heat
I mean as where things are boiled : by internal where the
heat breathes out and takes away and uses up its moisture.[3]
So much for drying.

---

[1] i. e. by ἀντιπερίστασις. Cp. 347ᵇ 4-9.
[2] Omit μέν in l. 15 with JFHN.
[3] ἀφαιρεθέντος (l. 26) as a genitive absolute, where the nominative
would be more regular, is difficult. Perhaps we should read ἀφαιρεθέντος
⟨τοῦ ἐκτός⟩, sc. θερμοῦ. So perhaps Al. 204. 7.

6   Liquefaction is, first, condensation into water ; second,
the melting of a solidified body.   The first, condensation,
is due to the cooling of vapour : [1] what melting is will 30
appear from the account of solidification.

Whatever solidifies is either water or a mixture of earth
and water, and the agent is either dry heat or cold. Hence
those of the bodies solidified by heat or cold which are
soluble[2] at all are dissolved by their opposites.   Bodies 383^a
solidified by the dry-hot are dissolved by water, which is the
moist-cold, while bodies solidified by cold are dissolved by
fire, which is hot.   Some things seem to be solidified by
water, e. g. boiled honey,[3] but really it is not the water but 5
the cold in the water which effects the solidification. Aqueous
bodies are not solidified by fire : for it is fire that dissolves
them, and the same cause in the same relation cannot have
opposite effects upon the same thing.   Again, water solidifies owing to the departure of heat ; so it will clearly be
dissolved by the entry into it of heat : cold, therefore, must
be the agent in solidifying it.

Hence aqueous bodies do not thicken when they soli- 10
dify ; for thickening occurs when the moisture goes off and
the dry matter comes together, but water is the only liquid
that does not thicken.[4]   Those bodies that are made up of
both earth and water are solidified both by fire and by cold
and in either case are thickened.   The operation of the two
is in a way the same and in a way different.   Heat acts by 15
drawing off the moisture, and as the moisture goes off in
vapour the dry matter thickens and collects.   Cold acts by

---

[1] Omit εἰς ὕδωρ in l. 30 with EJF₁HN Ol. (lemma).

[2] Aristotle does not distinguish in this or the next chapter between
solution (λύεσθαι) and melting (τῆξις) : they are treated indifferently
as the correlate of πῆξις.

[3] But cp. 385^b 1.

[4] Two points are confusedly intended : (1) because thickening =
removal of moisture, solidification of aqueous bodies by cold (not
involving removal of moisture) does not involve thickening ; (2) thickening involves dry matter that comes together ; aqueous bodies have no
such matter (or too little, though Aristotle does not say this) ; . ˙ . aqueous
bodies do not thicken. ὕδωρ in the last clause (l. 12) must be taken
to = τὰ ὕδατος and to include οἶνος οὖρον ὀρρός (382^b 13), and is contrasted with τὰ ὑγρά, e.g. milk, blood (cp. 384^a 11–19), as containing
(little or) no dry matter. The first line of thought is implied by διό
(l. 10), the second by τοιαῦτα (l. 11). Cp. 380^a 33.

driving out the heat, which is accompanied by the moisture
as this goes off in vapour with it. Bodies that are soft but
20 not liquid do not thicken but solidify when the moisture
leaves them, e. g. potter's clay in process of baking : but
those mixed bodies that are liquid thicken besides solidifying, like milk. Those bodies which have first been thickened
or hardened by cold often begin by becoming moist : thus
potter's clay at first in the process of baking steams and
25 grows softer, and is liable to distortion in the ovens for that
reason.

Now of the bodies solidified by cold which are made up
both of earth and water but in which the earth preponderates,
those which solidify by the departure of heat melt by heat
when it enters into them again ; this is the case with frozen
30 mud. But those which solidify by refrigeration, where all
the moisture has gone off in vapour with the heat,[1] like iron
and horn, cannot be dissolved except by excessive heat, but
they can be softened—though manufactured iron does
melt, to the point of becoming fluid and then solidifying
again. This is how steel is made. The dross sinks to the
383ᵇ bottom [2] and is purged away : when this has been done often
and the metal is pure we have steel. The process is not
repeated often because the purification of the metal involves
great waste and loss of weight. But the iron that has less
5 dross is the better iron. The stone *pyrimachus*,[3] too,
melts and forms into drops and becomes fluid ; after having
been in a fluid state it solidifies and becomes hard again.
Millstones,[4] too, melt and become fluid: when the fluid
mass begins to solidify it is black but its consistency comes
to be like that of lime. [Mud and earth, too, melt].[5]

[1] Read ὑγροῦ for θερμοῦ in l. 30 with E₂.
[2] It does not, but Aristotle may have thought that it did, especially
as the iron would be of the nature of earth. It is hard to make the
text mean the opposite, which is true, with Ideler. Cp. *Aetna* 478
'qualem purgato cernes desidere ferro'.
[3] Perhaps a sort of silex: 'silex pyromaque' in Daremberg and
Saglio, s.v. *ferrum*.
[4] Millstones were often made of various kinds of lava, especially
basaltic lava.
[5] This sentence should be rejected with Thurot. It is disconnected :
πηλός repeats ᵃ 29 ; γῆ without qualification is senseless in this connexion.

Of the bodies which are solidified by dry heat some are 10
insoluble, others are dissolved by liquid. Pottery and some
kinds of stone that are formed out of earth burnt up by fire,
such as millstones,[1] cannot be dissolved. Natron and salt
are soluble by liquid, but not all liquid but only such as is
cold.[2] Hence water and any of its varieties melt them, but
oil does not. For the opposite of the dry-hot is the cold-moist 15
and what the one solidified the other will dissolve, and so
opposites will have opposite effects.

7   If a body contains more water than earth fire only thickens
it : if it contains more earth fire solidifies it. Hence natron
and salt and stone and potter's clay must contain more earth.

The nature of oil presents the greatest problem.[3] If 20
water preponderated in it, cold ought to solidify it ; if
earth preponderated, then fire ought to do so.[4] Actually
neither solidifies, but both thicken it. The reason is that it
is full of air (hence it floats on the top of water, since air 25
tends to rise). Cold thickens it by turning the air in it into
water, for any mixture of oil and water is thicker than
either. Fire and the lapse of time thicken and whiten it.
The whitening follows on the evaporation of any water that
may have been in it ; the thickening is due to the change of 30
the air into water as the heat in the oil is dissipated. The
effect in both cases is the same and the cause is the same,
but the manner of its operation is different. Both heat
and cold thicken it, but neither dries it (neither the sun nor
cold dries oil), not only because it is glutinous but because it 384[a]

---

[1] This seems to contradict l. 7. The word there is αἱ μύλαι, here
οἱ μυλίαι. Since millstones were made of a great variety of kinds of
stone it is possible that Aristotle here meant by οἱ μυλίαι an entirely
different kind of stone from the lava to which αἱ μύλαι referred. If so,
he expressed his meaning in a very clumsy way ; for he has given no
means of finding out what sort of stone οἱ μυλίαι is meant to denote.
But perhaps the word is corrupt. ? οἱ Μήλιοι. Cp. Theophr. *De Lap.*
ii. 14, iii. 21. The difficulty cannot be met by distinguishing τήκεσθαι
and λύεσθαι with Ideler.

[2] Warm water, of course, is 'cold' for the purpose of the argument.

[3] Cp. *De Gen. An.* 735[b] 13 sqq.

[4] Omit ἔχει πλέον in l. 21 with E₁JHN Vic. Bag. ; omit ὡς οἱ πάγοι and
ὡς ὁ κέραμος with EHN Al.

contains air. Its glutinous nature prevents it from giving off vapour and so fire does not dry it or boil it off.[1]

Those bodies which are made up of earth and water may be classified according to the preponderance of either. There is a kind of wine, for instance, which both solidifies[2]
5 and thickens by boiling—I mean, must. All bodies of this kind lose their water as they dry. That it is their water may be seen from the fact that the vapour from them condenses into water when collected. So wherever some sediment[3] is left this is of the nature of earth. Some of these bodies, as we have said,[4] are also thickened and dried
10 by cold. For cold not only solidifies but also dries water, and thickens things by turning air into water. (Solidifying, as we have said,[5] is a form of drying.) Now those things that are not thickened by cold, but solidified, belong rather to water, e.g. wine, urine, vinegar, lye,[6] whey. But those things that are thickened (not by evaporation due to fire)[7]
15 are made up either of earth or of water and air : honey of earth, while oil contains air. Milk and blood, too, are made up of both water and earth, though earth generally[8] predominates in them. So, too, are the liquids out of which natron and salt are formed ; and stones are also formed from some mixtures of this kind. Hence, if the whey has not been separated, it burns away if you boil it over a fire.
20 But the earthy element in milk can also be coagulated by the help of fig-juice, if you boil it in a certain way as

---

[1] Omitting τὸ ὕδωρ (l. 1): this and the variant τὸ ἔλαιον are rival glosses.

[2] And therefore comes under the heading of earth, whereas wine in general is 'water' (382ᵇ 13). You would expect the order to be 'thickens and solidifies', but ἐψεται is a sort of afterthought to make it clear that the πῆξις is by heat and not by cold. But Aristotle is rather uncertain on the point. Cp. 385ᵇ 1, 387ᵇ 9, 388ᵇ 1.

[3] Some sediment worth speaking of is meant as distinct from the 'little or none' of 382ᵇ 14. Aristotle is unsuccessfully trying to clear up the difficulty he has created by sometimes treating whey, wine, &c., as water (species of water, 382ᵇ 13), which really involves their having no admixture of earth, when he knows that really they have some sediment, though not much. Cp. 388ᵇ 1.

[4] 383ᵃ 13.
[5] 382ᵇ 1.
[6] κονία, a lye of wood ashes.
[7] i. e. that are thickened by cold.
[8] Exceptions in 384ᵃ 24-9.

doctors do when they treat it with fig-juice,[1] and this is
how the whey and the cheese are commonly separated.
Whey, once separated, does not thicken, as the milk did,
but boils away like water. Sometimes, however, there is
little or no cheese in milk, and such milk is not nutritive
and is more like water. The case of blood is similar : cold 25
dries and so solidifies it. Those kinds of blood that do not
solidify, like that of the stag, belong rather to water and
are very cold. Hence they contain no fibres : for the fibres
are of earth and solid, and blood from which they have been
removed does not solidify. This is [2] because it cannot dry ;
for what remains is water, just as what remains of milk 30
when cheese has been removed is water. The fact that
diseased blood will not solidify is evidence of the same thing,
for such blood is of the nature of serum and that is phlegm
and water, the nature of the animal having failed to get the
better of it and digest it.

Some of these bodies [3] are soluble, e. g. natron, some in-
soluble, e. g. pottery : of the latter, some, like horn, can be **384^b**
softened by heat, others, like pottery and stone, cannot. The
reason is that opposite causes have opposite effects : consequently, if solidification is due to two causes, the cold and
the dry, solution must be due to the hot and the moist,
that is, to fire and to water (these being opposites) : water 5
dissolving what was solidified by fire alone, fire what was
solidified by cold alone. Consequently, if any things [4]
happen to be solidified by the action of both, these are least
apt to be soluble. Such a case we find where things have
been heated and are then solidified by cold. When the
heat in leaving them has caused most of the moisture [5] to
evaporate, the cold so compacts these bodies together again
as to leave no entrance even for moisture.[6] Therefore heat 10
does not dissolve them (for it only dissolves those bodies
that are solidified by cold alone), nor does water (for it does

---

[1] Cp. Dioscorides, ii. 77.
[2] Read ἐστίν in l. 29 with JFHN Bag.
[3] Those made up of earth and water.
[4] Read εἴ τι for εἰ in l. 6 with F and Henricus (εἴτ' εἰ J₁).
[5] Delete the comma after ἐξιών (l. 9) and read a comma after ὑγρόν.
[6] Cp. 383ª 13, 26.

not dissolve what cold solidifies, but only what is solidified by dry heat).[1] But iron is melted by heat and solidified by 15 cold.[2] Wood consists of earth and air and is therefore combustible but cannot be melted or softened by heat. (For the same reason it floats in water—all except ebony. This does not, for other kinds of wood contain a preponderance of air, but in black ebony the air has escaped and so earth preponderates in it.) Pottery consists of earth alone because 20 it solidified gradually in the process of drying.[3] Water cannot get into it, for the pores were only large enough to admit of vapour escaping : and seeing that fire solidified it, that cannot dissolve it either.

So solidification and melting, their causes, and the kinds of subjects in which they occur have been described.

All this makes it clear that bodies are formed by heat **8** 25 and cold and that these agents operate by thickening and solidifying. It is because these qualities fashion bodies that we find heat in all of them, and in some cold in so far as heat is absent. These qualities, then, are present as active, and the moist and the dry as passive, and consequently 30 all four are found in mixed bodies. So water and earth are the constituents of homogeneous bodies both in plants and in animals and of metals such as gold, silver, and the rest—water and earth and their respective exhalations shut up in the compound bodies, as we have explained elsewhere.[4]

385ᵃ All these mixed bodies are distinguished from one another, firstly by the qualities special to the various senses, that is, by

---

[1] This sentence should perhaps be omitted. There is an anacolution—οὔθ' ὑπὸ ὕδατος—and the general explanation given entirely ignores the more special account of the preceding sentence. The 'therefore' is pointless (so Thurot). Further ὁ δὲ σίδηρος . . . πήγνυται (l. 14) follows much better on the sentence before. Ll. 11–14 are really an alternative to ll. 7–11 and ll. 14, 15.

[2] Omit ὥστε . . . ἄλυτον (ll. 14, 15). There is no MS. authority for it, and it seems to have found its way into the texts through a misinterpretation of Alexander, who certainly did not read it. The clause runs : 'hence both are involved in its solidification : therefore it is insoluble' (i. e. difficult to dissolve). This gloss may give the correct interpretation of the remark about iron. Iron is quoted as an instance of the process described in ll. 7, 8. Cp. 385ᵃ 31.

[3] And therefore is insoluble.

[4] e. g. 378ᵃ 15–ᵇ6 in relation to metals.

their capacities of action.[1] (For a thing is white, fragrant, sonant, sweet, hot, cold in virtue of a power of acting on sense.)[2] Secondly by other more characteristic affections which express their aptitude to be affected: I mean, for 5 instance, the aptitude to melt or solidify or bend and so forth, all these qualities, like moist and dry, being passive. These are the qualities that differentiate bone, flesh, sinew, wood, bark, stone and all other homogeneous natural bodies. Let us begin by enumerating these qualities ex- 10 pressing the aptitude or inaptitude of a thing to be affected in a certain way. They are as follows: to be apt or inapt to solidify, melt, be softened by heat, be softened by water, bend, break, be comminuted, impressed, moulded, squeezed ; 15 to be tractile or non-tractile, malleable or non-malleable, to be fissile or non-fissile, apt or inapt to be cut ; to be viscous or friable, compressible or incompressible, combustible or incombustible ; to be apt or inapt to give off fumes. These affections differentiate most bodies from one another. Let us go on to explain the nature of each of them.

We have already given a general account of that which is 20 apt or inapt to solidify or to melt, but let us return to them again now. Of all the bodies that admit of solidification and hardening, some are brought into this state by heat, others by cold. Heat does this by drying up their moisture, cold by driving out their heat. Consequently some bodies 25 are affected in this way by defect of moisture, some by defect of heat : watery bodies by defect of heat, earthy bodies of moisture. Now those bodies that are so affected by defect of moisture are dissolved by water, unless like pottery they have so contracted that their pores are too small for the particles of water to enter. All those bodies in which 30 this is not the case are dissolved by water, e.g. natron, salt, dry mud. Those bodies that solidified through defect of heat are melted by heat, e.g. ice, lead, copper. So much for the bodies that admit of solidification and of melting, and those that do not admit of melting.

---

[1] Omit καί before τῷ in l. 2 with E (original reading) and HN₁.
[2] Delete the colon after δύνασθαι (l. 2). λευκόν . . . ἐστι is a parenthesis (Ideler).

385ᵇ   The bodies which do not admit of solidification are those
which contain no aqueous moisture and are not watery, but
in which heat and earth preponderate, like honey[1] and
must[2] (for these are in a sort of state of effervescence), and
those which do possess some water but have a preponderance
5 of air, like oil and quicksilver, and all viscous substances
such as pitch and birdlime.[3]

Those bodies admit of softening[4] which are not (like ice)[5] 9
made up of water, but in which earth predominates. All
their moisture must not have left them (as in the case of
natron and salt), nor must the relation of dry to moist in
10 them be incongruous (as in the case of pottery).[6] They
must be tractile (without admitting water) or malleable
(without consisting of water), and the agent in softening
them is fire. Such are iron and horn.[7]

Both of bodies that can melt and of bodies that cannot,
some do and some do not admit of softening in water.
Copper, for instance, which can be melted, cannot be
softened in water, whereas wool and earth can be softened
in water, for they can be soaked. (It is true that though
15 copper can be melted the agent in its case is not water, but
some of the bodies that can be melted by water too such
as natron and salt cannot be softened in water: for nothing
is said to be so affected unless the water soaks into it and
makes it softer.) Some things, on the other hand, such as
wool and grain, can be softened by water though they cannot
be melted. Any body that is to be softened by water must
be of earth and must have its pores larger than the particles
20 of water, and the pores themselves must be able to resist
the action of water, whereas bodies that can be ' melted '
by water must have pores throughout.[8]

---

[1] Cp. 383ᵃ 5.
[2] Cp. 384ᵃ 5, 387ᵇ 9, 388ᵇ 1.
[3] Reading ⟨πίττα καὶ⟩ ἰξός in l. 5 with Al. Ol.
[4] μαλακτός, that which can be softened by heat, as opposed to τεγκτός, that which can be softened by water.
[5] Omit πᾶς γὰρ κρύσταλλος in l. 7 with E (original reading) JHN₁.
[6] Cp. ᵃ 28 and Theophr. de Igne, v. 42.
[7] Omit καὶ ξύλα in l. 12 with Gesner. Cp. 384ᵇ 15.
[8] ὄντων δὲ σκληροτέρων (l. 20) must be corrupt, but the contrast intended is clear. If a body is τεγκτόν (can be softened by water)

[Why is it that earth is both 'melted' and softened by moisture, while natron is 'melted' but not softened? Because natron is pervaded throughout by pores so that [1] the parts are immediately divided by the water, but earth 25 has also pores [2] which do not connect [3] and is therefore differently affected according as the water enters by one or the other set of pores. [4]]

Some bodies [5] can be bent or straightened, like the reed or the withy, some cannot, like pottery and stone. Those bodies are apt to be bent and straightened which can change from being curved to being straight and from being 30 straight to being curved, and bending and straightening consist in the change or motion to the straight or to a curve, for a thing is said to be in process of being bent whether it is being made to assume a convex or a concave shape. So 386^a bending is defined as motion to the convex or the concave without a change of length. For if we added 'or to the straight', we should have a thing bent and straight at once, and it is impossible for that which is straight to be bent. And if all bending is a bending back or a bending down, the former being a change to the convex, the latter to the 5 concave, a motion that leads to the straight cannot be called bending, but bending and straightening are two different things. These, then, are the things that can, and those that cannot be bent, and be straightened.

Some things can be both broken and comminuted, others admit only one or the other. Wood, for instance, can be broken but not comminuted, ice and stone can be com- 10 minuted but not broken, while pottery may either be com-

---

it must admit the water by certain pores or passages, the passages themselves remaining intact ; if it is τηκτόν (soluble) the pores themselves yield to the action of the water: this is expressed rather illogically by saying that it has pores throughout. Obviously if it had pores in *every* direction it would already be dissolved into its ultimate particles. Read ὄντας σκληροτέρους with E rec. N rec. and perhaps Al. Ol.

[1] Omit γε in l. 24 with JFHN.
[2] Omit οἱ in l. 25 with EJHN₁.
[3] i. c. are not in a straight line with one another, cp. *Probl.* 905^a 40.
[4] Aristotle might have contrasted hard and soft pores, or partial pores and pores throughout; he mixes the two contrasts in the text we have.
[5] Omit τῶν σωμάτων in l. 27 with E₁ Ol. (lemma).

minuted or broken. The distinction is this: breaking is
a division and separation into large parts, comminution into
parts of any size, but there must be more of them than two.
Now those solids that have many pores not communicating
15 with one another are comminuible (for the limit to their subdivision is set by the pores), but those whose pores stretch
continuously for a long way are breakable, while those
which have pores of both kinds are both comminuible and
breakable.

Some things, e. g. copper and wax, are impressible, others,
e. g. pottery and water, are not. The process of being
impressed[1] is the sinking of a part of the surface of a thing
in response to pressure or a blow, in general to contact.
20 Such bodies are either soft,[2] like wax, where part of the
surface is depressed while the rest remains, or hard, like
copper. Non-impressible[3] bodies are either hard, like
pottery (its surface does not give way and sink in), or liquid,
like water (for though water does give way it is not in
a part of it, for there is a reciprocal change of place of all its
25 parts). Those impressibles that retain the shape impressed
on them and are easily moulded by the hand are called
'plastic'; those that are not easily moulded, such as stone
or wood,[4] or are easily moulded but do not retain the shape
impressed, like wool or a sponge, are not plastic. The last
group are said to be 'squeezable'. Things are 'squeezable'
when they can contract into themselves under pressure,
30 their surface sinking in without being broken and without[5]
the parts interchanging position as happens in the case of
water. (We speak of pressure when there is movement and
386ᵇ the motor remains in contact with the thing moved, of
impact when the movement is due to the local movement of
the motor.) Those bodies are subject to squeezing which
have empty pores—empty, that is, of the stuff of which the
body itself consists—and that can sink in upon the void
spaces within them, or rather upon their pores. For some-

---

[1] Omit μέν in l. 19 with all the MSS.
[2] Read μαλακά in l. 20 with E (original reading) Ol. Bag.
[3] Read καὶ ⟨τὰ⟩ ἄθλαστα in l. 22 with Thurot, and a full stop after χαλκός.   [4] Cp. ᵇ23.
[5] Read καὶ ⟨μή⟩ in l. 31 with Par. suppl. 314.

times the pores upon which a body sinks in are not empty
(a wet sponge, for instance, has its pores full). But the 5
pores, if full, must be full of something softer than the body
itself which is to contract.[1] Examples of things squeezable
are the sponge, wax, flesh. Those things are not squeezable
which cannot be made to contract upon their own pores by
pressure, either because they have no pores or because their
pores are full of something too hard. Thus iron, stone, 10
water and all liquids are incapable of being squeezed.

Things are tractile when their surface can be made to
elongate, for being drawn out is a movement of the surface,
remaining unbroken, in the direction of the mover. Some
things are tractile, e. g. hair, thongs, sinew, dough, birdlime,
and some are not, e. g. water, stone. Some things are both 15
tractile and squeezable, e. g. wool; in other cases the two
qualities do not coincide; phlegm, for instance, is tractile but
not squeezable, and a sponge squeezable but not tractile.

Some things are malleable, like copper. Some are not,
like stone and wood. Things are malleable when their
surface can be made to move (but only in part)[2] both down- 20
wards and sideways with one and the same blow: when
this is not possible a body is not malleable. All malleable
bodies are impressible, but not all impressible bodies are
malleable, e.g. wood, though on the whole the two go
together. Of squeezable things some are malleable and
some not: wax and mud are malleable, wool is not.[3]

Some things are fissile, e.g. wood, some are not, e.g. 25
potter's clay. A thing is fissile when it is apt to divide in
advance of the instrument dividing it, for a body is said to
split when it divides to a further point than that to
which the dividing instrument divides it and the act of
division advances: which is not the case with cutting.
Those bodies which cannot behave like this are non-fissile. 30
Nothing soft is fissile (by soft I mean absolutely soft and
not relatively: for iron itself may be relatively soft); nor
are all hard things fissile, but only such as are neither liquid 387^a

---

[1] Read αὐτό in l. 7 (αὐτό E corr. N, ἑαυτά J₁H₁, ἑαυτό J rec.).
[2] To exclude ἀντιπερίστασις. Cp. ^a 24.
[3] Omit οὐδ' ὕδωρ in l. 25 after Vic.

nor impressible nor comminuible. Such are the bodies that have the pores along which they cohere lengthwise and not crosswise.

Those hard or soft solids are apt to be cut which do not
5 necessarily either split in advance of the instrument or break into minute fragments when they are being divided. Those that necessarily do so and liquids cannot be cut. Some things can be both split and cut, like wood, though generally it is lengthwise that a thing can be split and crosswise that it can be cut. For, a body being divided into many parts,
10 in so far as its unity is made up of many lengths it is apt to be split, in so far as it is made up of many breadths it is apt to be cut.

A thing is viscous when, being moist or soft, it is tractile. Bodies owe this property to the interlocking of their parts when they are composed like chains, for then they can be drawn out to a great length and contracted again. Bodies that are not like this are friable.
15 Bodies are compressible when they are squeezable and retain the shape they have been squeezed into[1]; incompressible when they are either inapt to be squeezed at all or do not retain the shape they have been squeezed into.

Some bodies are combustible and some are not. Wood, wool, bone are combustible ; stone, ice are not. Bodies are
20 combustible when their pores are such as to admit fire and their longitudinal pores contain moisture weaker than fire. If they have no moisture, or if, as in ice or very green wood, the moisture is stronger than fire, they are not combustible.

Those[2] bodies give off fumes which contain moisture, but in such a form that it does not go off separately in vapour when they are exposed to fire. For vapour is a moist
25 secretion tending to the nature of air[3] produced from

---

[1] Cp. πλαστά 386ª 27 : the only difference seems to be that the ' plasta ' must be easily moulded while there is no such limitation to the πιλητά here.

[2] The text for the remainder of this chapter is particularly corrupt and uncertain.

[3] Omit καὶ πνεῦμα (l. 25) as a gloss due to a mistaken inference from l. 29. The words are inconsistent with Aristotle's theory of πνεῦμα.

a liquid by the agency of burning heat. Bodies that give
off fumes give off secretions of the nature of air by the lapse
of time : as they perish away they dry up or become earth.
But the kind of secretion we are concerned with now differs
from others in that it is not moist nor does it become wind [1]
(which is a continuous flow of air in a given direction).
Fumes are a common secretion of dry and moist together 30
caused by the agency of burning heat. Hence they do not
moisten things but rather colour them.

The fumes of a woody body are called smoke. (I mean 387[b]
to include bones and hair and everything of this kind in the
same class. For there is no name common to all the
objects that I mean, but, for all that, these things are all in
the same class by analogy. Compare what Empedocles
says : They are one and the same, hair and leaves and the
thick wings of birds and scales that grow on stout limbs.[2]) 5
The fumes of fat are a sooty smoke and those of oily substances a greasy steam. Oil does not boil away or thicken
by evaporation [3] because it does not give off vapour but
fumes. Water on the other hand does not give off fumes,
but vapour. Sweet wine [4] does give off fumes, for it contains
fat and behaves like oil. It does not solidify under the in- 10
fluence of cold and it is apt to burn. Really it is not wine
at all in spite of its name : for it does not taste like wine
and consequently does not inebriate as ordinary wine does.
It contains but little fumigable stuff and consequently is inflammable.[5]

All bodies are combustible that dissolve into ashes, and
all bodies do this that solidify under the influence either of 15
heat or of both heat and cold ; for we find that all these
bodies are mastered by fire. Of stones the precious stone
called carbuncle [6] is least amenable to fire.[7]

Of combustible bodies some are inflammable and some

[1] i. e. it is different both from the moist and from the dry ἀναθυμίασις.
[2] Diels, 21 B. 82. [3] Cp. 383[b] 20.
[4] Cp. 380[b] 32, 384[a] 5, 388[b] 1.
[5] Read δ' ἔχει in l. 13 with J₁FHN Bag. Al., and θυμίασιν with EJHN
Al. Ol. The line of thought would be : θυμίασις implies moisture, [a] 23 ;
so having little of it may = being dry and therefore inflammable.
[6] Cp. Theophr. De Lap. iii. 18. [7] Cp. [a] 19.

are not, and some of the former are reduced to coals. Those
20 are called 'inflammable' which produce flame and those
which do not are called 'non-inflammable'. Those fumigable bodies that are not liquid are inflammable, but pitch,
oil, wax are inflammable in conjunction with other bodies
rather than by themselves. Most inflammable are those
bodies that give off smoke.[1] Of bodies of this kind [2] those
that contain more earth than smoke are apt to be reduced
to coals. Some bodies that can be melted are not in-
25 flammable, e. g. copper; and some bodies that cannot be
melted are inflammable, e. g. wood; and some bodies can
be melted and are also inflammable, e. g. frankincense. The
reason is that wood has its moisture all together and this is [3]
continuous throughout and so it burns up: whereas copper
has it in each part but not continuous, and insufficient in
30 quantity to give rise to flame. In frankincense it is disposed in both of these ways. Fumigable bodies are
inflammable when earth predominates in them and they are
consequently such as to be unable to melt. These are in-
388ᵃ flammable because they are dry like fire. When this dry
comes to be hot there is fire. This is why flame is burning
smoke or dry exhalation. The fumes of wood are smoke,
those of wax and frankincense and such-like, and pitch and
whatever contains pitch or such-like, are sooty smoke, while
5 the fumes of oil and oily substances are a greasy steam; so
are those of all substances which are not at all combustible by
themselves because there is too little of the dry in them (the
dry being the means by which the transition to fire is
effected), but burn very readily in conjunction with something else. (For the fat is [4] just the conjunction of the oily
with the dry.) So those bodies [5] that give off fumes, like
oil and pitch, belong rather to the moist, but those that
burn to the dry.[6]

---

[1] Because flame is burning smoke, 388ᵃ 2.
[2] Inflammable bodies.
[3] Read συνεχές ἐστιν in l. 28 with the MSS.
[4] Which does burn readily, *P. A.* 649ᵃ 28.
[5] Omit τῶν ὑγρῶν (l. 8), which is an alternative to ὑγροῦ.
[6] Both classes are thought of as falling within the fumigables in the
wide sense of 387ᵃ 23, ᵇ 1.

10   Homogeneous bodies differ to touch by these affections 10
and differences, as we have said.[1] They also differ in
respect of their smell, taste, and colour.

By homogeneous bodies I mean, for instance,[2] ' metals ',
gold, copper, silver, tin, iron, stone, and everything else of
this kind and the bodies that are extracted from them ; 15
also the substances found in animals and plants, for instance,
flesh, bones, sinew, skin, viscera, hair, fibres, veins (these are
the elements of which the non-homogeneous bodies like the
face, a hand, a foot, and everything of that kind are made up),
and in plants, wood, bark, leaves, roots,[3] and the rest like
them.

The homogeneous bodies, it is true, are constituted by 20
a different cause,[4] but the matter of which they are composed is the dry and the moist, that is, water and earth (for
these bodies exhibit those qualities most clearly).   The
agents are the hot and the cold, for they constitute and make
concrete the homogeneous bodies out of earth and water
as matter.   Let us consider, then, which of the homogeneous 25
bodies are made of earth and which of water, and which of
both.

Of organized bodies some are liquid, some soft, some
hard.   The soft and the hard are constituted by a process
of solidification,[5] as we have already explained.

Those liquids that go off in vapour are made of water,
those that do not are either of the nature of earth, or a 30
mixture either of earth and water, like milk, or of earth
and air, like wood,[6] or of water and air, like oil.   Those
liquids which are thickened by heat are a mixture.   (Wine
is a liquid which raises a difficulty : for it is both liable to 388^b
evaporation and it also thickens ; for instance new wine

---

[1] 385^a 8.
[2] Read οἷον τά τε in l. 13 with EJN Bag., and omit οἷον after μεταλλευόμενα with all the MSS. and Bag.
[3] According to Aristotle's doctrine elsewhere, however, while wood
and bark are homoeomerous (385^a 9), leaves and roots are anomoeo-
merous (De An. 412^b 2, 3). τἆλλα l. 19 . . . καί l. 20 should perhaps be
omitted with H, but this looks like an error due to homoeoteleuton.
Aristotle is probably writing carelessly.
[4] sc. their εἶδος.
[5] Read ⟨ὅτι⟩ πήξει in l. 28 after Gessner.   Cp. 382^a 25.
[6] Cp. 384^b 15.

does. The reason is that the word 'wine' is ambiguous [1] and different 'wines' behave in different ways. New wine is more earthy than old, and for this reason it is more apt to be thickened by heat and less apt to be congealed by 5 cold. For it contains much heat and a great proportion of earth, as in Arcadia, where it is so dried up in its skins by the smoke that you scrape it to drink. If all wine has some sediment in it then it will belong to earth or to water according to the quantity of the sediment it possesses.) The liquids that are thickened by cold are of the nature of earth; those that are thickened either by heat or by cold consist of more than one element, like oil and honey and 'sweet wine '.

10 Of solid bodies those that have been solidified by cold are of water, e. g. ice, snow, hail, hoar-frost. Those solidified by heat are of earth, e. g. pottery, cheese, natron, salt. Some bodies are solidified by both heat and cold.[2] Of this kind are those solidified by refrigeration, that is by the privation both of heat and of the moisture which departs with the 15 heat. For salt and the bodies that are purely of earth solidify by the privation of moisture only, ice by that of heat only, these bodies by that of both. So both the active qualities and both kinds of matter were involved in the process. Of these bodies those from which all the moisture has gone are all of them of earth, like pottery [3] or amber. (For amber, also, and the bodies called 'tears' are 20 formed by refrigeration, like myrrh, frankincense, gum. Amber, too, appears to belong to this class of things : the animals enclosed in it show that it is formed by solidification. The heat is driven out of it by the cold of the river and causes the moisture to evaporate with it, as in the case of honey when it has been heated and is immersed in water.) 25 Some of these bodies cannot be melted or softened ; for instance, amber and [4] certain stones, e.g. the stalactites in caves.

---

[1] Read ⟨ἐν⟩ ἐνί in l. 2 with JFN.
[2] Cp. 383ª 13. Bekker's punctuation is misleading. ὅσα δ' ὑπ' ἀμφοῖν (l. 13) is taken up by ὅσων μὲν οὖν ἅπαν (l. 18) and ὅσα δὲ μὴ ὅλα (l. 30). From τοιαῦτα δ' (l. 13) to καὶ εἶχεν ἄμφω (l. 17) is a parenthesis.
[3] The words καὶ γάρ to ἐξατμίζει τὸ ὑγρόν (ll. 19–24) are a parenthesis and there should therefore be no full stops after κόμμι and ὑγρόν.
[4] Reading καί for ἤ in l. 25 with JFH Al.

(For these stalactites, too, are formed in the same way : the agent is not fire, but cold which drives out the heat, which, as it leaves the body,[1] draws out the moisture with it : in the other class of bodies[2] the agent is external fire.) In those from which the moisture has not wholly gone earth 30 still preponderates, but they admit of softening by heat, e.g. iron and horn.[3]

Now since we must include among 'meltables' those bodies which are melted by fire, these contain some water : indeed some of them, like wax, are common to earth and water alike. But those that are melted by water are of 389^a earth. Those that are not melted either by fire or water are of earth, or of earth and water.

Since, then, all bodies are either liquid or solid, and since the things that[4] display the affections we have enumerated belong to these two classes and there is nothing intermediate, it follows that we have given a complete account of the criteria for distinguishing whether a body consists of 5 earth or of water or of more elements than one, and whether fire was the agent in its formation, or cold, or both.

Gold, then, and silver and copper and tin and lead and glass and many nameless stones are of water : for they are 10 all melted by heat. Of water, too, are some wines and urine and vinegar and lye and whey and serum : for they are all congealed by cold. In iron, horn, nails, bones, sinews, wood, hair, leaves, bark, earth preponderates. So, too, in amber, myrrh, frankincense, and all the substances called 'tears', and stalactites, and fruits, such as leguminous 15 plants and corn. For things of this kind are, to a greater or less degree, of earth. For of all these bodies some admit of softening by heat, the rest give off fumes and are formed

---

[1] Read αὐτῶν for αὐτοῦ in l. 29.

[2] e.g. salt, natron.

[3] Omit λιβανωτὸς ... ἀτμίζει (ll. 31, 32) ['Frankincense and bodies of that kind give off vapour in the same sense in which wood does']. The sentence is quite irrelevant to the context and may have been absent from Alexander's text.

[4] Alexander's paraphrase ταῦτα δέ for τούτων δὲ τά (l. 3) suggests that the true reading may be τούτων δ' ἕκαστα or τούτων δὲ τὰ εἴδη, 'and the varieties of these are determined by the aforesaid qualities'.

by refrigeration. So again in natron, salt, and those kinds of stones that are not formed by refrigeration and cannot be melted. Blood, on the other hand, and semen [1] are made
20 up of earth and water and air. If the blood contains fibres, earth preponderates in it: consequently it solidifies by refrigeration and is melted by liquids ; if not, it is of water and therefore does not solidify. Semen solidifies by refrigeration, its moisture leaving it together with its heat.

We must investigate in the light of the results we have **II** arrived at what solid or liquid bodies are hot and what cold.
25 Bodies consisting of water are commonly cold, unless (like lye, urine, wine) they contain foreign heat. Bodies consisting of earth, on the other hand, are commonly hot because heat was active in forming them: for instance lime and ashes.

We must recognize that cold is in a sense the matter of bodies. For the dry and the moist are matter (being
30 passive) and earth and water are the elements that primarily embody them, and they are characterized by cold. Con-
389[b] sequently cold must predominate in every body that consists of one or other of the elements simply, unless such a body contains foreign heat as water does when it boils or when it has been strained through ashes. This latter, too, has acquired heat from the ashes, for everything that has been
5 burnt contains more or less heat. This explains the generation of animals in putrefying bodies : the putrefying body contains the heat which destroyed its proper heat.[2]

Bodies made up of earth and water are hot, for most of them derive their existence from concoction and heat, though some, like the waste products of the body,[3] are the products of putrefaction. Thus blood, semen, marrow, fig-juice, and all things of the kind are hot as long as they are
10 in their natural state, but when they perish and fall away from that state they are so no longer. For what is left of them is their matter and that is earth and water.[4] Hence

---

[1] Cp. *De Gen. An.* 735[a] 29 sqq.
[2] Cp. 379[a] 3–[b] 8.   [3] Cp. *De Gen. An.* 724[b] 27 and Platt's note.
[4] Read καί for ἤ in l. 12 with FN Al.

both views are held about them, some people maintaining
them to be cold and others to be warm ; for they are
observed to be hot when they are in their natural state, but
to solidify [1] when they have fallen away from it.   That, then, 15
is the case of mixed bodies.   However, the distinction we
laid down holds good : if its matter is predominantly water
a body is cold (water being the complete opposite of fire),
but if earth or air it tends to be warm.

It sometimes happens that the coldest bodies can be
raised to the highest temperature by foreign heat ; for the
most solid and the hardest bodies are coldest when deprived 20
of heat and most burning after exposure to fire : thus water
is more burning than smoke [2] and stone than water.

12   Having explained all this we must describe the nature of
flesh, bone, and the other homogeneous bodies severally.

Our account of the formation of the homogeneous bodies
has given us the elements out of which they are compounded
and the classes into which they fall, and has made it clear 25
to which class each of those bodies belongs.   The homogeneous bodies are made up of the elements, and all the
works of nature in turn of the homogeneous bodies as
matter.   All the homogeneous bodies consist of the elements
described, [3] as matter, but their essential nature is determined
by their definition.   This fact is always clearer in the case of
the later products, of those, in fact, that are instruments, as 30
it were, and have an end : it is clearer, for instance, that
a dead man is a man only in name.   And so the hand of
a dead man, too, will in the same way be a hand in name
only, just as stone flutes might still be called [4] flutes : for 390[a]
these members, too, are instruments of a kind.   But in the
case of flesh and bone the fact is not so clear to see, and in
that of fire and water [5] even less.   For the end is least obvious there where matter predominates most.   If you take
the extremes, matter is pure matter and the essence is pure 5
definition ; but the bodies intermediate between the two are

---

[1] Cp. [a] 19.   [2] i. e. burning smoke = flame.
[3] i. e. earth and water.
[4] Read λεχθείησαν ⟨ἄν⟩ in l. 1 with Thurot.
[5] Omit γῆς in l. 3 with JFHN and probably Al.

matter or definition in proportion as they are near to either.[1] For each of those elements has an end and is not water or fire in any and every condition of itself, just as flesh is not flesh nor viscera viscera, and the same is true 10 in a higher degree with face and hand. What a thing is is always determined by its function: a thing really is itself when it can perform its function; an eye, for instance, when it can see. When a thing cannot do so it is that thing only in name, like a dead eye or one made of stone, just as a wooden saw is no more a saw than one in a picture.[2] The same, then, is true of flesh, except that its function is less 15 clear than that of the tongue. So, too, with fire; but its function is perhaps even harder to specify by physical inquiry[3] than that of flesh. The parts of plants, and inanimate bodies like copper and silver, are in the same case. They all are what they are in virtue of a certain power of action or passion—just like flesh and sinew. But 20 we cannot state their form accurately, and so it is not easy to tell when they are really there and when they are not unless the body is thoroughly corrupted and its shape only remains. So ancient corpses suddenly become[4] ashes in 390[b] the grave and very old fruit preserves its shape only but not its taste: so, too, with the solids that form from milk.

Now heat and cold and the motions they set up[5] as the bodies are solidified by the hot and the cold are sufficient to 5 form all such parts as are the homogeneous bodies, flesh, bone, hair, sinew, and the rest. For they are all of them differentiated by the various qualities enumerated above, tension, tractility, comminuibility, hardness, softness, and the rest of them: all of which are derived from the hot and the cold and the mixture of their motions. But no one would go as far as to[6] consider them sufficient in the case of

---

[1] And therefore the form, though it is there, is hard to see in those bodies which 'are near' to matter, like the elements.

[2] Read ἀλλ' ἢ ὡς ἡ εἰκών in l. 13 with E.

[3] φυσικῶς, l. 16, of which there is no trace in Al., should perhaps be omitted.

[4] Read οἷον in l. 22 with JFHN Al. and omit ἄ with the MSS. and Al.

[5] Read ταῖς ὑπὸ τούτων in l. 3 with JFHN (ταῖς ἀπὸ τούτων Al. paraphrase).

[6] Read ἂν ἔτι δόξειε (l. 10) with JFN Al. (H too supports ἔτι).

the non-homogeneous parts (like the head, the hand, or the foot) which these homogeneous parts go to make up. Cold and heat and their motion[1] would be admitted to account for the formation of copper or silver, but not for that of a saw, a bowl, or a box. So here, save that in the examples given the cause is art, but in the non-homogeneous bodies nature or some other cause.

Since, then, we know to what element each of the homogeneous bodies belongs, we must now find the definition of each of them, the answer, that is, to the question, 'what is' flesh, semen, and the rest? For we know the cause of a thing and its definition when we know the material or the formal or, better, both the material and the formal conditions of its generation and destruction, and the efficient cause of it.[2]

After the homogeneous bodies have been explained we must consider the non-homogeneous too, and lastly the bodies made up of these, such as man, plants, and the rest.

---

[1] Read ψυχρότης καὶ θερμότης καὶ κίνησις with E₂JHN Al. Bag. (supported by F).

[2] Cp. *De Gen. et Corr.* 335ᵃ 24 sqq.

INDEX

$$38^a—90^b = 338^a—390^b$$

INDEX

DE MUNDO

BY

E. S. FORSTER

OXFORD
AT THE CLARENDON PRESS

FIRST EDITION 1914

PREFACE

This interesting little treatise has no claim to be regarded as a genuine work of Aristotle. In his careful examination of it (*Neue Jahrbücher*, xv (1905), pp. 529-68) Wilhelm Capelle has traced most of its doctrines to Poseidonius, and comes to the conclusion that it is a popular philosophic treatise founded on two works of Poseidonius, the Μετεωρολογικὴ στοιχείωσις and the Περὶ κόσμου.

The treatise is addressed to Alexander, who must either be Alexander the Great (in which case the author doubtless wished to have his work attributed to Aristotle, and therefore addressed it to Aristotle's most distinguished pupil), or else some other Alexander must be intended. From the fact that he is spoken of in 391ᵇ 6 as ἡγεμόνων ἄριστος, it has been supposed that Tiberius Claudius Alexander, nephew of Philo Judaeus and Procurator of Judaea, and in A. D. 67 Prefect of Egypt, is intended. In this case the treatise must be dated early in the second half of the first century A. D. Capelle, however (l. c. p. 567), dates it in the first half of the second century A. D.

The description of the natural phenomena of the universe is the most Aristotelian portion of the work, and many close parallels are to be found in the *Meteorologica*. It has been thought better not to multiply references to the *Meteorologica* in this part of the treatise, but a certain number of references have been added in other places.

The text used for this translation is that of Bekker in the Berlin edition. A complete account of the literature upon the *De Mundo* will be found in Capelle's article (l. c. p. 532). I have to thank Mr. W. D. Ross, who read the translation in manuscript and in proof, and my colleague, Professor W. C. Summers, who read the greater part of it in manuscript, both of whom made a number of valuable suggestions.

E. S. F.

The University, Sheffield,
Dec. 2, 1913.

CONTENTS

DE MUNDO

1 MANY a time, Alexander [1], has Philosophy seemed to me **391ᵃ**
a thing truly divine and supernatural, especially when in
solitude she soars to the contemplation of things universal
and strives to recognize the truth that is in them, and
while all others abstain from the pursuit of this truth
owing to its sublimity and vastness, she has not shrunk 5
from the task nor thought herself unworthy of the fairest
pursuits, but has deemed the knowledge of such things at
once most natural to herself and most fitting. For seeing
that it was not possible (as once the foolish Aloadae [2]
attempted) by means of the body to reach the heavenly
region and leaving the earth behind to spy out that 10
heavenly country, the soul by means of philosophy, taking
the intellect as her guide, finding an easy path has traversed the intervening space and fared forth on its pilgrim-
age, and by intelligence comprehended things very far
removed in space from one another, easily, methinks,
recognizing those things which have kinship with one
another, and by the divine eye of the soul apprehending 15
things divine and interpreting them to mankind. This
she felt, being desirous, as far as in her lay, freely to give
to all men a share of her treasures. And so men who
have laboriously described to us either the nature of a
single region or the plan of a single city or the dimensions
of a river or the scenery of a mountain, as some ere now 20
have done,—telling of Ossa or Nysa or the Corycian
cave [3] or giving us some other limited description,—such
men one should pity for their small-mindedness in admir-
ing ordinary things and making much of some quite
insignificant spectacle. They are thus affected because they
have never contemplated what is nobler—the Universe 25

---

[1] See preface.   [2] Otus and Ephialtes.   [3] Paus. x. 32. 2.

and the greatest things of the Universe; for if they had really given attention to these things, they would

391^b never marvel at anything else, but all else would appear insignificant and, compared to the surpassing excellence of those other things, of no account. Let us therefore treat of all these matters and, as far as possible, inquire into their divine nature, and discuss the nature and position
5 and movement of each of them. And I think that it is but fitting that even you, who are the noblest of rulers, should pursue the inquiry into the greatest of all subjects and in philosophy entertain no trivial thoughts, and make the noblest among men welcome to these only of her gifts.

The Universe then is a system made up of heaven and 2
10 earth and the elements which are contained in them. But the word is also used in another sense of the ordering and arrangement of all things, preserved by and through God.[1] Of this Universe the centre, which is immovable and fixed, is occupied by the life-bearing earth, the home and the mother of diverse creatures. The upper portion
15 of the Universe has fixed bounds on every side, the highest part of it being called Heaven, the abode of the gods. Heaven is full of divine bodies, which we usually call stars, and moves with a continual motion in one orbit, and revolves in stately measure with all the heavenly bodies unceasingly for ever. The whole heaven and universe being
20 spherical and moving, as I have said, continually, there must of necessity be two points which do not move, exactly opposite to one another (as in the revolving wheel of a turner's lathe), points which remain fixed and hold the sphere together and round which the whole universe moves. The universe therefore revolves in a circle and the points
25 are called poles. If we imagine a straight line drawn so as to join them (the axis, as it is sometimes called), it will form the diameter of the Universe, occupying the centre
392^a of the earth, with the two poles as its extremities. Of

---

[1] Reading with W. Capelle, *Neue Jahrb.* xv (1905), p. 535, ὑπὸ θεοῦ καὶ διὰ θεόν: Bekker's reading, ὑπὸ θεῶν τε καὶ διὰ θεῶν, contradicts the pantheistic character of the treatise. R reads διὰ θεόν, Q διὰ θεοῦ.

these fixed poles the one is always visible, being at the summit of the axis in the northern region of the sky, and is called the Arctic Pole[1]; the other is always hidden beneath the earth to the south and is called the Antarctic Pole.

The substance of the heaven and stars we call Ether,[2] not because it blazes, owing to its fiery nature (as some explain the word, mistaking its nature, which is very far removed from fire), but because it is in continual motion,[3] revolving in a circle, being an element other than the four indestructible and divine. Of the stars which are contained in it, those called 'fixed' revolve only with the whole heaven, always occupying the same positions. A belt is formed through their midst by the so-called Circle of the Zodiac, which passes crosswise through the tropics, being divided up into the twelve regions of the Signs of the Zodiac. Others, which are called 'planets', do not naturally move with the same velocity as those stars of which I have already spoken, nor with the same velocity as one another, but each in a different course, so that one will be nearer the earth, another higher in the heavens. Now the number of the fixed stars cannot be ascertained by man, although they move in one surface, which is that of the whole heaven. But the planets fall into seven divisions in seven successive circles, so situated that the higher is always greater than the lower, and the seven circles are successively encompassed by one another and are all surrounded by the sphere containing the fixed stars. The position nearest to this sphere is occupied by the so-called circle of the 'Shining star', or Cronos; next is that of the 'Beaming star', which also bears the name of Zeus; then follows the circle of the 'Fiery star', called by the names both of Heracles and of Ares; next comes the 'Glistening star', which some call sacred to Hermes, others sacred

---

[1] 'Arctic' and 'Antarctic' are not Aristotelian terms; cp. *Meteor.* 362[a] 32, 33, 363[a] 34, [b] 4, 31.

[2] Cp. *Meteor.* 339[b] 19 ff.

[3] i.e. αἰθήρ, 'ether', is here derived not from αἴθεσθαι, 'to blaze', but from ἀεὶ θεῖν, 'to be in continual motion'; cp. Plat. *Crat.* 410 B, and *de Caelo* 270[b] 22.

to Apollo ; after that is the circle of the ' Light-bearing
star', which some call the star of Aphrodite, others the
star of Hera ; then comes the circle of the Sun, and lastly
that of the Moon, which borders on the Earth. The ether
30 encompasses the heavenly bodies and the area over which
they are ordained to move.

After the Ethereal and Divine Element, which we have
shown to be governed by fixed laws and to be, moreover,
free from disturbance, change, and external influence, there
follows immediately an element which is subject throughout to external influence and disturbance and is, in a word,
35 corruptible and perishable. In the outer portion of this
occurs the substance which is made up of small particles
392ᵇ and is fiery, being kindled by the ethereal element owing
to its superior size and the rapidity of its movement. In
this so-called Fiery and Disordered Element flashes shoot
and fires dart, and so-called ' beams ' ¹ and ' pits ' ² and
comets have their fixed position and often become extin-
5 guished.

Next beneath this spreads the air, which is in its nature
murky and cold as ice, but becomes illuminated and set
on fire by motion,³ and thus grows brighter and warm.
And since the air too admits of influence and undergoes
10 every kind of change, clouds form in it, rain-storms beat
down, and snow, hoar-frost, hail with blasts of winds and
of hurricanes, and thunder too and lightning and falling
bolts, and the crashing together of countless opaque bodies.

Next to the aerial element the earth and sea have **3**
15 their fixed position, teeming with plant and animal life,
and fountains and rivers, either winding over the earth or
discharging their waters into the sea. The earth is diver-
sified by countless kinds of verdure and lofty mountains
and densely wooded copses and cities, which that intelligent animal man has founded, and islands set in the

---

¹ *trabes* of Seneca, *Quaest. Nat.* i. 1. 5, vii. 4. 3, *Epp.* 94. 56 ; Plin. ii.
26. 26.
² Cp. Seneca, *Quaest. Nat.* i. 14. 1.
³ Q reads ἐκείνης for κινήσεως : Capelle, *l.c.*, p. 536, adopts ἐκείνης,
but cp. above, l. 2.

sea and continents. Now the usual account divides the 20
inhabited world into islands and continents, ignoring the
fact that the whole of it forms a single island round which
the sea that is called Atlantic flows. But it is probable
that there are many other continents separated from ours
by a sea that we must cross to reach them, some larger and
others smaller than it, but all, save our own, invisible to
us. For as our islands are in relation to our seas, so is 25
the inhabited world in relation to the Atlantic, and so
are many other continents in relation to the whole sea;
for they are as it were immense islands surrounded by
immense seas. The general element of moisture, covering
the earth's surface and allowing the so-called inhabited 30
countries to rise in patches as it were of dry land, may
be said to come immediately after the aerial element. Next
to it the whole earth has been formed, firmly fixed in the
lowest position at the midmost centre of the Universe,
closely compacted, immovable and unshakable. This [1]
forms the whole of what we call the lower portion of the 35
Universe.

Thus then five elements, situated in spheres in five **393ᵃ**
regions,[2] the less being in each case surrounded by the
greater—namely, earth surrounded by water, water by
air, air by fire, and fire by ether—make up the whole
Universe. All the upper portion represents the dwelling
of the gods, the lower the abode of mortal creatures. Of 5
the latter, part is moist, to which we are accustomed to give
the names of rivers, springs, and seas; while part is dry,
which we call land and continents and islands.

Of the islands, some are large, like the whole of what we
call the inhabited world (and there are many other such 10
surrounded by mighty seas); other islands are smaller,
which are visible to us and in our own sea. Of these
some are of considerable size, Sicily, Sardinia, Corsica,
Crete, Euboea, Cyprus, and Lesbos; others are less extensive, such as the Sporades and Cyclades and others 15
bearing various names.

Again, the sea which lies outside the inhabited world

[1] i.e. the earth and sea.   [2] Cp. *Meteor.* 340ᵇ 19 ff., 341ᵃ 2 ff.

is called the Atlantic or Ocean, flowing round us. Opening in a narrow passage towards the West, at the so-called
Pillars of Heracles, the Ocean forms a current into the
20 inner sea, as into a harbour ; then gradually expanding it
spreads out, embracing great bays adjoining one another,
opening into other seas by narrow straits and then
widening out again. First, then, on the right as one sails
in through the Pillars of Heracles it is said to form two
25 bays, the so-called Syrtes, the Greater and the Lesser
as they are called ; on the other side it does not make
such bays, but forms three seas, the Sardinian, the Gallic,
and the Adriatic. Next to these comes the Sicilian sea,
lying crosswise, and after it the Cretan. Continuing it
come the Egyptian, Pamphylian, and Syrian seas in one
30 direction, and the Aegean and Myrtoan seas in the other.
Over against the seas already mentioned extends the
Pontus, which is made up of several parts; the innermost
portion is called Maeotis, while the outer portion in the
393^b direction of the Hellespont is connected by a strait with
the so-called Propontis. Towards the East the Ocean
again flows in and opens up the Indian[1] and Persian
Gulfs, and displays the Erythraean sea[2] continuous with
these, embracing all three.[3] With its other branch it passes
5 through a long narrow strait and then expands again bounding the Hyrcanian and Caspian country. Beyond this
it occupies the large tract beyond the Lake of Maeotis ;
then beyond the Scythians and the land of the Celts
it gradually confines the width of the habitable world, as
10 it approaches the Gallic Gulf and the Pillars of Heracles
already mentioned, outside which the Ocean flows round
the earth. In this sea are situated two very large islands,
the so-called British Isles, Albion and Ierne, which are
greater than any which we have yet mentioned and lie
beyond the land of the Celts. (The island of Taprobane[4]
15 opposite India, situated at an angle to the inhabited world,
is quite as large as the British Isles, as also is the island

---

[1] The Gulf of Cutch or the Gulf of Cambay.
[2] The Arabian Sea.
[3] For the use of διειληφώς cp. 396^b 31 and L. and S., *s. v.*, ii. 1, 2.
[4] Ceylon, cp. Strabo, xv. 14 (p. 690).

called Phebol[1] which lies over against the Arabian Gulf.[2])
There is a large number of small islands round the British
Isles and Iberia, forming a belt round the inhabited world,
which as we have already said is itself an island. The
width of the inhabited world at the greatest extent of its
mainland is rather less than 40,000 stades, so the best [20]
geographers say, and its length about 70,000 stades. It
is divided into Europe, Asia, and Libya.

Europe is the tract bounded in a circle by the Pillars
of Heracles, the inner recesses of the Pontus, and the
Hyrcanian sea, where a very narrow isthmus stretches to
the Pontus. Some have held that the river Tanais carries [25]
on the boundary from this isthmus. Asia extends from
the said isthmus and the Pontus and the Hyrcanian sea
to the other isthmus which lies between the Arabian Gulf[2]
and the inner sea, being surrounded by the inner sea and
the Ocean which flows round the world. Some, however,
define the bounds of Asia as from the Tanais to the [30]
mouths of the Nile. Libya extends from the Arabian
isthmus to the Pillars of Heracles; though some describe
it as stretching from the Nile to the Pillars; Egypt, which **394[a]**
is surrounded by the mouths of the Nile, is given by some
to Asia, by others to Libya; some exclude the islands
from both continents, others attach them to their nearest
neighbour.

Such is our account of the nature of land and sea and [5]
their position—the inhabited world as we call it.

4   Let us now deal with the most remarkable conditions
which are produced in and around the earth, summarizing
them in the barest outline. There are two kinds of exhalation[3] which rise continually from the earth into the air above
us, namely, those[4] composed of small particles and entirely [10]
invisible, except when they occur in the east, and those
which rise from rivers and streams and are visible. Of
these the former kind being given off from the earth is
dry and resembles smoke, while the latter being exhaled
from the element of moisture is damp and vaporous. From

---

[1] Capelle, l. c., p. 539, suggests Madagascar.   [2] The Red Sea.
[3] Cp. *Meteor.* 341[b] 6 ff.   [4] Reading ⟨αἱ⟩ λεπτομερεῖς.

15 the latter are produced mist and dew and the various
forms of frost, clouds and rain and snow and hail; while
from the dry exhalation come the winds and the different
kinds of breezes, and thunder and lightning, and hurricanes
and thunderbolts, and all other cognate phenomena. Mist
20 is a vaporous exhalation which does not produce water,
denser than air but less dense than cloud; it arises either
from the first beginnings of a cloud or else from the
remnant of a cloud. The contrary of this is what is called
a clear sky, being simply air free from cloud and mist.
Dew is moisture minute in composition falling from a clear
25 sky; ice is water congealed in a condensed form from
a clear sky; hoar-frost is congealed dew, and 'dew-frost'
is dew which is half congealed. Cloud is a vaporous mass,
concentrated and producing water. Rain is produced
from the compression of a closely condensed cloud, varying according to the pressure exerted on the cloud; when
30 the pressure is slight it scatters gentle drops; when it is
great it produces a more violent fall, and we call this
a shower, being heavier than ordinary rain, and forming
continuous masses of water falling over earth. Snow is
produced by the breaking up of condensed clouds, the
cleavage taking place before the change into water; it
is the process of cleavage which causes its resemblance to
35 foam and its intense whiteness, while the cause of its coldness
is the congelation of the moisture in it before it is dis-
394[b] persed or rarefied. When snow is violent and falls heavily
we call it a blizzard. Hail is produced when snow becomes
densified and acquires impetus for a swifter fall from its
close mass; the weight becomes greater and the fall more
5 violent in proportion to the size of the broken fragments
of cloud. Such then are the phenomena which occur as
the result of moist exhalation.

From dry exhalation, impelled into motion by cold, is
produced wind; for wind is merely a quantity of air set in
motion in a mass. Wind is also called breath, a word
10 used in another sense of the vital and generative substance
which is found in plants and living creatures, and permeates
all things; but with this we need not deal here. The

breath which breathes in the air we call wind, while to the
expirations from moisture we give the name of breezes.
The winds which blow from moist land we call 'land-
winds', those which spring up from gulfs we call 'gulf- 15
winds'; somewhat similar to these are those which blow
from rivers and lakes. Winds which are produced by the
bursting of a cloud causing an expansion of its density in
their own direction,[1] are called 'cloud-winds'. Those
which are accompanied by a mass of water breaking forth
are called 'rain-winds'.

The winds [2] which blow continuously from the rising sun
are called Euri; those from the north, Boreae; those from 20
the setting sun, Zephyri; those from the south, Noti. Of
the east winds, that which blows from the region of the
summer sunrise is called Caecias; that which blows from
the region of the equinoctial sunrise is known as Apeliotes;
while the name of Eurus is given to the wind which blows
from the quarter of the winter sunrise. Of the west winds,
on the other hand, that which blows from the summer 25
setting is Argestes, though some call it Olympias,[3] others

[1] Lit. 'which cause a dissolution of its density against themselves'.
[2] The chart of the winds as given here is almost identical with that
given in *de Vent. Sit. et Appellat.* (973[a-b]).

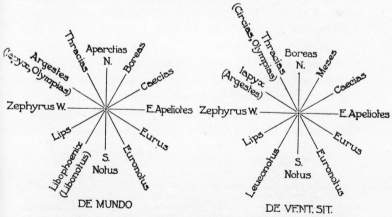

DE MUNDO   DE VENT. SIT.

The following are the other principal passages describing the winds
in classical authors : Aristot. *Meteor.* 363[a] 2–365[a] 13 ; Seneca, *Quaest.
Nat.* v. 16 ; Pliny, ii. 119 ff.; Ioannes Lydus, *de Mensibus* iv. 119.
[3] In *de Vent. Sit.* 973[b] 21 Olympias is given as a synonym for
Thracias, not for Argestes as here.

Iapyx; that which blows from the equinoctial setting is
Zephyrus, and that which blows from the winter setting
is Lips. Of the north winds (Boreae) that which is next
to Caecias is called Boreas in the specific sense of the
word.[1] Aparctias[2] is next to it, and blows in a southerly
30 direction from the pole. Thracias[3] is the wind which
blows next to Argestes; by some it is called Circias.[4] Of
the south winds, that which comes from the invisible pole
and immediately faces Aparctias is called Notus; that
between Notus and Eurus is called Euronotus. The wind
on the other side between Lips and Notus is called by some
Libonotus, by others Libophoenix.

35 Some winds are direct, those, that is, which blow along
a straight line; others follow a bending course, as for
395ᵃ instance the wind called Caecias.[5] Some winds hold sway
in the winter, the south winds for example; others in the
summer, such as the Etesian winds (Trade winds), which
are a mixture of northerly and westerly winds. The
so-called Ornithian[6] winds, which occur in the spring, are
a northerly type of wind.

5 Of violent blasts of wind, a squall is one which suddenly
strikes down from above; a gust is a violent blast which
springs up in a moment; a whirlwind, or tornado, is a
wind which revolves in an upward direction from below.
An eruption of wind from the earth is a blast caused by
the emission of air from a deep hole or cleft; when it
10 comes forth in a whirling mass it is called an 'earth-storm'.
A wind which is whirled along in a dense watery cloud
and being driven forth[7] through it violently breaks up the
continuous masses of the cloud, causes a roar and crash,
which we call thunder, similar to the noise made by wind

---

[1] Called Meses in *de Vent. Sit.* 973ᵃ 3-7, where see note.
[2] Called Boreas in *de Vent. Sit.*
[3] Reading Θρακίας (R Θρακίας): cp. *de Vent. Sit.* 973ᵇ 17.
[4] Καικίας, the MS. reading, cannot possibly be right here, the name
having been already given to the N. E. wind (394ᵇ 22). I therefore
read Κιρκίας: cp. *de Vent. Sit.* 973ᵇ 20 Θρακίας . . . ἐν δὲ Ἰταλίᾳ καὶ
Σικελίᾳ Κιρκίας (emended by Rose for Κίρκας).
[5] Cp. *Meteor.* 364ᵇ 12.
[6] i.e. the winds which bring the birds of passage.
[7] Reading ἐξωσθέν for ἔξωθεν.

driven violently through water. When the wind in breaking forth from a cloud catches fire and flashes it is called 15
lightning. The lightning reaches our perception sooner
than the thunder, though it actually occurs after it, since it
is the nature of that which is heard to travel less quickly
than that which is seen; for the latter is visible at a
distance, while the former is only heard[1] when it reaches
the ear, especially since the one, the fiery element, travels
faster than anything else, while the other, being of the nature 20
of air, is less swift and only reaches the ear by actually
striking upon it.[2] If the flashing body is set on fire and
rushes violently to the earth it is called a thunderbolt; if
it be only half of fire, but violent also and massive, it is
called a meteor; if it is entirely free from fire, it is called
a smoking bolt.[3] They are all called 'swooping bolts', 25
because they swoop down upon the earth. Lightning[4]
is sometimes smoky, and is then called 'smouldering
lightning'; sometimes it darts quickly along, and is then
said to be 'vivid'; at other times it travels in crooked
lines, and is called 'forked lightning'; when it swoops
down upon some object it is called 'swooping lightning'.

To sum up, some of the phenomena which occur in the
air are merely appearances, while others have actual sub- 30
stance and reality. Rainbows and streaks in the sky and
the like are only appearances, while flashes and shooting-
stars and comets and the like have real substance. A rainbow is the reflection of a segment of the sun or of the moon,
seen, like an image in a mirror, in a cloud which is moist,
hollow, and continuous in appearance, and taking a circular 35

---

[1] ὁρωμένου is used in its proper sense in the clause in which it
stands, and by a sort of *zeugma* for ἀκουομένου in the next clause.
[2] Lightning is immediately seen by the eye, thunder can only be
perceived by the ear when the original movement has set up other
movements which eventually strike upon the ear. (Cp. *de Aud.*
800ᵃ 6–12.)
[3] τυφών cannot here be used (as in 400ᵃ 29) of a 'violent storm',
'hurricane'; as applied to a thunderbolt, it seems to mean one which
smokes, and to be connected with the verb τύφειν, 'to smoke'.
[4] The word κεραυνός is used in Greek to mean either (1) 'a thunderbolt', or (2) 'lightning', which were more or less identified by the
Greeks. The context seems to show that it has the former meaning
in 395ᵃ 22, the latter in this passage.

form. A streak is a rainbow appearing in the form of a
straight line. A halo is an appearance of brightness shining
395ᵇ round a star; it differs from a rainbow, because the latter
appears opposite the sun and moon, while the halo is formed
all round a star. A light in the sky is caused by the kindling
of a dense fire in the air; some lights shoot along, others
5 are fixed. The shooting is the generation of fire by
friction, when the fire moves quickly through the air and
by its quickness produces an impression of length; the
fixture is a prolonged extension without movement, an
elongated star as it were. A light which broadens out
towards one end is called a comet. Some heavenly lights
10 often last a considerable time, others are extinguished
immediately. There are numerous other peculiar kinds
of appearances seen in the sky, the so-called 'torches',
'beams',[1] 'barrels', and 'pits',[1] which derive their names
from their similarity to these objects. Some of them
appear in the west, others in the east, others in both
15 these quarters, but rarely in the north or south. None of
them are subject to fixed laws; for none of them have
been discovered to be always visible in a fixed position.
Such are the phenomena of the air.

As the earth contains many sources of water, so also it
contains many sources of wind and fire. Of these some
20 are subterranean and invisible, but many have vents and
spiracles, as Lipara, Etna, and the volcanoes of the Aeolian
islands. Some of them frequently flow like rivers and cast
up red-hot lumps. Some, which are under the earth near
springs of water, warm them and cause some streams to
25 flow tepid, others very hot, others tempered to a pleasant
heat. Similarly, many vent-holes for wind open in every
part of the earth; some of them cause those who draw
near to them to become frenzied, others cause them to
waste away, others inspire them to utter oracles, as at
Delphi and Lebadia,[2] others utterly destroy them, as the
30 one in Phrygia.[3] Often, too, a moderate wind engendered

---

[1] Cp. 392ᵇ 4.
[2] Paus. ix. 39. 5; Strabo, ix. 2. 38 (p. 414); Philostratus, *Vit. Apoll.*
viii. 19.
[3] Strabo, xiii. 4. 11 (p. 628).

in the earth, being driven aside into distant holes and
crannies of the earth and displaced from its proper locality,
causes shocks in many parts. Often, too, a strong current
from without becomes involved in the hollows of the earth,
and, its exit being cut off, it shakes the earth violently,
seeking an exit, and sets up the condition which we com- 35
monly call an earthquake. Earthquakes of which the
shock is oblique, at a sharp angle, are known as 'horizontal 396^a
earthquakes'; those which lift the earth up and down at
right angles are known as 'heaving earthquakes'; those
which cause the earth to settle down into hollows are called
'gaping earthquakes'; those which open up chasms and
break up the earth's surface are called 'rending earthquakes'. Some of them also emit winds, others stones or 5
mud, while others cause springs to appear which did not
exist before. Some earthquakes cause a disturbance by
means of a single shock and are known as 'thrusting earthquakes'. Others which swing to and fro and by inclinations
and waves in each direction remedy the effect of their
shock, are called 'vibrating earthquakes', setting up a 10
condition which resembles trembling. There are also
'bellowing earthquakes', which shake the earth with a roar.
Underground bellowing, however, is often heard unaccom-
panied by shocks, when the wind, though insufficient
to cause a shock, is compressed together in the earth and
beats with the force of its impetus. Blasts which penetrate
into the earth are materialized also from moisture con- 15
cealed underground.

We find analogous phenomena occurring in the sea.
Chasms form in it and its waters often retire or the waves
rush in ; this is sometimes followed by a recoil and sometimes there is merely a forward surge of water, as is said to 20
have occurred at Helice and Bura.[1] Often, too, there are
exhalations of fire from the sea, and springs gush out and
river-mouths are formed and trees suddenly grow up, and
currents and eddies appear, like those caused in the air by

---

[1] An account of this tidal wave in northern Achaea in 373 B.C.
is given by Strabo, viii. 7. 2 (p. 384), and Pausanias (vii. 25. 8) ;
cp. also *Meteor.* 343^b 1, 17, 344^b 34, 368^b 6.

²⁵ blasts of wind, sometimes in the middle of the sea, sometimes in straits and channels. Many tides and tidal waves
are said always to accompany the periods of the moon at
fixed intervals. In short, owing to the mingling of the
elements together, similar conditions are produced in the
³⁰ air and in the earth and in the sea, causing decay and
generation in detail, but preserving the whole free from
destruction and generation.

Yet some have wondered how it is that the Universe, 5
if it be composed of contrary principles—namely, dry and
³⁵ moist, hot and cold—has not long ago perished and been
396ᵇ destroyed.[1] It is just as though one should wonder how
a city continues to exist, being, as it is, composed of
opposing classes—rich and poor, young and old, weak and
strong, good and bad. They fail to notice that this has
always been the most striking characteristic of civic con-
5 cord, that it evolves unity out of plurality, and similarity
out of dissimilarity, while it admits every kind and variety.
It may perhaps be that nature has a liking for contraries
and evolves harmony out of them and not out of similarities
(just as she joins the male and female together and not
10 members of the same sex), and has devised the original harmony by means of contraries and not similarities.
The arts, too, apparently imitate nature in this respect.
The art of painting, by mingling in the picture the
elements of white and black, yellow and red, achieves
15 representations which correspond to the original object.
Music, too, mingling together notes, high and low, short
and prolonged, attains to a single harmony amid different
voices; while writing, mingling vowels and consonants,
composes of them all its art. The saying found in Hera-
20 cleitus 'the obscure' was to the same effect: 'Junctions
are: wholes and not wholes, that which agrees and that
which differs, that which produces harmony and that which
produces discord ; from all you get one and from one you
get all.'[2]

---

[1] Cf. Seneca, *Quaest. Nat.* vii. 27. 3 ff.
[2] Reading συνάψιες (O R) ὅλα καὶ οὐχ ὅλα (P) with Diels, *Vorsokr.*[3]
i, p. 80, l. 2.

Thus then a single harmony orders the composition of the whole—heaven and earth and the whole Universe—by the mingling of the most contrary principles. The dry 25 mingling with the moist, the hot with the cold, the light with the heavy, the straight with the curved, all the earth, the sea, the ether, the sun, the moon, and the whole heaven are ordered by a single power extending through all, which has created the whole universe out of separate and different elements—air, earth, fire, and water—embracing[1] them all 30 on one spherical surface and forcing the most contrary natures to live in agreement with one another in the universe, and thus contriving the permanence of the whole. The cause of this permanence is the agreement of the elements, and the reason of this agreement is their equal proportion and the fact that no one of them is more 35 powerful than any other, for the heavy is equally balanced **397^a** with the light and the hot with the cold. Thus nature teaches us in the greater principles of the world that equality somehow tends to preserve harmony, whilst harmony preserves the universe which is the parent of all things and itself the fairest thing of all. For what created thing is more excellent? Any that one can name is but 5 a part of the ordered Universe. All that is beauteous bears its name, and all that which is arranged well, for it is said to be well ‘ordered’, being thus called after the ‘ordered’ Universe.[2] And what subordinate phenomenon could be likened to the ordered system of the heavens and the march of the stars and the sun and the moon, which move 10 on in unvarying measure through age after age? Where else could be found such regularity as is observed by the goodly seasons, which produce all things and bring in due order summer and winter, day and night, to the accomplishment of the month and the year? Moreover, in greatness the universe is pre-eminent, in motion swiftest, in radiance 15 most bright, and in might it knows not old age or corruption. It has divided the various creatures that live in the sea, on the earth, and in the air, and regulated their lives by its

---

[1] For this use of διαλαμβάνω cp. 393^b 4 and note.
[2] Cp. 391^b 10–11.

movements. Of it all living things breathe and have their
20 life. Even all the unexpected changes which occur in it are
really accomplished in an ordered sequence—diverse winds
conflicting together, thunderbolts falling from heaven, and
violent storms bursting forth. The expulsion of moisture
and the exhalation of fire by these means restores the
whole to harmony and stability. The earth, too, clothed
25 with diverse vegetation, gushing forth with streams and
trodden by the feet of living creatures, in due season
bringing forth, nurturing, and receiving back all things,
producing countless varieties and changes, none the less
always preserves its nature untouched by age, though
shaken by earthquakes, washed by floods, and in parts
30 burnt up by fires. All these things seem to work its
welfare and to ensure its eternal permanence. For when
it is shaken by earthquakes, the winds which have been
diverted into it escape forth, finding vents through the
clefts, as we have already said ; [1] when it is washed by rain,
it is cleansed of all that is unhealthy : and when the breezes
35 blow about it, it is purified above and beneath. Again,
397ᵇ the fires soften that which is frost-bound, while the frosts
abate the fires. Of individual things upon the earth some
are coming into being, others are at their prime, others are
decaying ; and birth checks decay and decay lightens birth.
5 Thus an unbroken permanence, which all things conspire to
secure, counteracting one another—at one time dominating,
at another being dominated—preserves the whole unim-
paired through all eternity.

There still remains for us to treat briefly, as we have 6
10 discussed the other subjects, of the cause which holds all
things together. For in dealing with the universe, not
perhaps in exact detail, yet at any rate so as to give a
general idea of the subject, it would be wrong to omit that
which is the most important thing in the universe. The
old explanation which we have all inherited from our
fathers, is that all things are from God and were framed
15 for us by God, and that no created thing is of itself sufficient

---

[1] Cp. 395ᵇ 20.

for itself, deprived of the permanence which it derives from him. Therefore some of the ancients went so far as to say that all those things are full of God which are presented to us through the eyes and the hearing and all the other senses, thus propounding a theory which, though it accords with the divine power, does not accord with the [20] divine nature. For God is in very truth the preserver and creator of all that is in any way being brought to perfection in this universe; yet he endures not all the weariness of a being that administers and labours, but exerts a power which never wearies; whereby he prevails even over things which seem far distant from him. He hath himself obtained the first and highest place and is therefore called [25] Supreme, and has, in the words of the poet,

Taken his seat in heaven's topmost height;[1]

and the heavenly body which is nighest to him most enjoys his power, and afterwards the next nearest, and so on successively until the regions wherein we dwell are reached. Wherefore the earth and the things upon the earth, being farthest removed from the benefit which [30] proceeds from God, seem feeble and incoherent and full of much confusion; nevertheless, inasmuch as it is the nature of the divine to penetrate to all things, the things also of our earth receive their share of it, and the things above us according to their nearness to or distance from [35] God receive more or less of divine benefit. It is therefore 398[a] better, even as it is more seemly and befitting God, to suppose that the power which is stablished in the heavens is the cause of permanence even in those things which are furthest removed from it—in a word, in all things,— rather than to hold that it passes forth and travels to and [5] fro to places which become and befit it not, and personally administers the affairs of this earth. For indeed, to superintend any and every operation does not become even the rulers among mankind—the chief, for example, of an army or a city, or the head of a household, if it were necessary to bind up a sack of bedding or perform any other some-

---

[1] *Il.* i. 499, &c.

10 what menial task, such as in the days of the Great King would not be performed by any ordinary slave. Nay, we are told that the outward show observed by Cambyses and Xerxes and Darius was magnificently ordered with the utmost state and splendour. The king himself, so the story goes, established himself at Susa or Ecbatana, invisible to
15 all, dwelling in a wondrous palace within a fence gleaming with gold and amber and ivory. And it had many gateways one after another, and porches many furlongs apart from one another, secured by bronze doors and mighty walls. Outside these the chief and most distinguished men had their appointed place, some being the king's
20 personal servants, his bodyguard and attendants, others the guardians of each of the enclosing walls, the so-called janitors and 'listeners', that the king himself, who was called their master and deity, might thus see and hear all things. Besides these, others were appointed as stewards of
25 his revenues and leaders in war and hunting, and receivers of gifts, and others charged with all the other necessary functions. All the Empire of Asia, bounded on the west by the Hellespont and on the east by the Indus, was apportioned according to races among generals and satraps
30 and subject-princes of the Great King; and there were couriers and watchmen and messengers and superintendents of signal-fires. So effective was the organization, in particular the system of signal-fires, which formed a chain of beacons from the furthest bounds of the empire to Susa and Ecbatana, that the king received the same day the
35 news of all that was happening in Asia. Now we must
398ᵇ suppose that the majesty of the Great King falls as far short of that of the God who possesses the universe, as that of the feeblest and weakest creature is inferior to that of the king of Persia. Wherefore, if it was beneath the dignity of Xerxes to appear himself to administer all things and
5 to carry out his own wishes and superintend the government of his kingdom, such functions would be still less becoming for a god. Nay, it is more worthy of his dignity and more befitting that he should be enthroned in the highest region, and that his power, extending through the

whole universe, should move the sun and moon and make
the whole heaven revolve and be the cause of permanence
to all that is on this earth.   For he needs no contrivance 10
or the service of others, as our earthly rulers, owing to their
feebleness, need many hands to do their work ; but it is most
characteristic of the divine to be able to accomplish diverse
kinds of work with ease and by simple movement, even as
past masters of a craft by one turn of a machine accomplish 15
many different operations.   And just as puppet-showmen
by pulling a single string make the neck and hand and
shoulder and eye and sometimes all the parts of the figure
move with a certain harmony ; so too the divine nature,
by simple movement of that which is nearest to it, imparts 20
its power to that which next succeeds, and thence further
and further until it extends over all things.   For one thing,
moved by another, itself in due order moves something
else, each acting according to its own constitution, and not
all following the same course but different and various and 25
sometimes even contrary courses ; although the first impulse, as it may be called, was directed to a single form of
motion.   It is just as though one should cast from one
vessel at the same time a sphere, a cube, a cone, and a
cylinder ; each of them will move according to its particular
shape.   Or if one should hold in the folds of a garment 30
a water-animal, a land-animal, and a bird, and let them go ;
clearly the animal that swims will leap into its own element
and swim away, the land-animal will creep away to its
own haunts and pastures, the bird of the air will raise itself
aloft from the earth and fly away, though one original
cause gave each its aptitude for movement.   So is it with 35
the universe; by a single revolution of the whole within **399ᵃ**
the bounds of day and night, the different orbits of all the
heavenly bodies are produced, though all are enclosed in
a single sphere, some moving more quickly, others more
slowly, according to the distances between them and the 5
individual composition of each.   For the moon accomplishes
her circuit in a month, waxing and waning and disappearing ;
the sun and the heavenly bodies whose course is of equal
length, namely those called the 'Lightbearer' and Hermes,

perform their revolution in a year; the 'Fiery star' in
10 double that period; the star of Zeus in six years; and
lastly the so-called star of Cronos in a period two and a
half times as long as the heavenly body next below it.
The single harmony produced by all the heavenly bodies
singing and dancing together springs from one source and
ends by achieving one purpose, and has rightly bestowed
the name not of 'disordered' but of 'ordered universe'
15 upon the whole.   And just as in a chorus, when the leader
gives the signal to begin, the whole chorus of men, or it
may be of women, joins in the song, mingling a single
studied harmony among different voices, some high and
some low; so too is it with the God that rules the whole
world.   For at the signal given from on high by him who
20 may well be called their chorus-leader, the stars and the
whole heaven always move, and the sun that illumines all
things travels forth on his double course, whereby he both
divides day and night by his rising and setting, and also
brings the four seasons of the year, as he moves forwards
towards the north and backwards towards the south.   And
in their own due season the rain, the winds, and the dews,
25 and all the other phenomena which occur in the region
which surrounds the Earth, are produced by the first,
primaeval cause.   These are followed by the flowing of
rivers, the swelling of the sea, the growth of trees, the
ripening of fruits, the birth of animals, the nurturing and
the prime and decay of all things, to which, as I have said,
30 their individual composition contributes.   When, therefore,
the ruler and parent of all, invisible save to the mind of the
eye, gives the word to all nature that moves betwixt heaven
and earth, the whole revolves unceasingly in its own circuits
and within its own bounds, sometimes unseen and sometimes appearing, revealing and again hiding diverse manners
35 of things, from one and the same cause.   Very like is it to
399ᵇ that which happens in times of war, when the trumpet
sounds to the army; then each soldier hears its note, and
one takes up his shield, another dons his breast-plate;
another puts on his greaves or his helmet or his sword-
5 belt; one puts the bit in his horse's mouth, another mounts

his chariot, another passes along the watchword; the
captain betakes himself straightway to his company, the
commander to his division, the horseman to his squadron,
the light-armed warrior hastens to his appointed place; all
is hurry and movement in obedience to one word of command, to carry out the orders of the leader who is supreme
over all. Even so must we suppose concerning the universe; 10
by one impelling force, unseen and hidden from our eyes,
all things are stirred and perform their individual functions.
That this force is unseen stands in the way neither of its
action nor of our belief in it. For the spirit of intelligence
whereby we live and dwell in houses and communities,
though invisible, is yet seen in its operations; for by it the 15
whole ordering of life has been discovered and organized
and is held together—the ploughing and planting of the
earth, the discovery of the arts, the use of law, the ordering
of constitutions, the administration of home affairs and war
outside our borders and peace. Thus, too, must we think of
God, who in might is most powerful, in beauty most fair, 20
in time immortal, in virtue supreme; for, though he is
invisible to all mortal nature, yet is he seen in his very
works. For all that happens in the air, on the earth, and
in the water, may truly be said to be the work of God,
who possesses the universe; from whom, in the words of 25
Empedocles, the natural philosopher,

Whatsoever hath been and is now and shall be hereafter,
All alike hath its birth—men, women, trees of the forest,
Beasts of the field and fowls of the air and fish in the water.[1]

To use a somewhat humble illustration, we might with
truth compare the ordering of the universe to the so-called
'key-stones' in arches, which, placed at the junction of the 30
two sides, ensure the balance and arrangement of the whole
structure of the arch and give it stability. Moreover, they
say that the sculptor Pheidias, when he was setting up the
Athena on the Acropolis, represented his own features in
the centre of her shield, and so attached it to the statue by 35
a hidden contrivance, that any one who tried to cut it out, **400**[a]

---

[1] Diels, *Vorsokr.*[3] i, p. 233, 9–11.

thereby necessarily shattered and overthrew the whole statue.[1] The position of God in the universe is analogous to this, for he preserves the harmony and permanence of all things; save only that he has his seat not in the midst, 5 where the earth and this our troubled world is situated, but himself pure he has gone up into a pure region, to which we rightly give the name of heaven, for it is the furthest boundary[2] of the upper world, and the name of Olympus, because it is all-bright[3] and free from all gloom and disordered motion, such as is caused on our earth by 10 storms and the violence of the wind. Even thus speaks the poet Homer —

Unto Olympus' height, where men say that the gods have their dwelling,
Alway safe and secure; no wind ever shaketh its stillness,
Nor is it wet with the rain; no snow draweth nigh; but unclouded,
Ever the air is outspread, and a white sheen floateth about it.[4]

15 This, too, is borne out by the general habit of mankind, which assigns the regions above to God; for we all stretch up our hands to heaven when we offer prayers. Wherefore these words of the poet are not spoken amiss,

Heaven belongeth to Zeus, wide spread mid the clouds and the ether.[5]

20 Therefore also the objects of sense which are held in the highest esteem occupy the same region, to wit the stars and the sun and moon. For this cause the heavenly bodies alone are so arranged that they ever preserve the same order, and never alter or move from their course, while the things of earth, being mutable, admit of many changes 25 and conditions. For ere now mighty earthquakes have rent the earth in diverse places, and violent rains have burst forth and flooded it, and the inroads and withdrawals

---

[1] Cp. *de Mir. Ausc.* 846ᵃ 19 ff.; Plut. *Pericles* 31 ; Cic. *Tusc.* i. 15, 34 ; Val. Max. viii. 14. 6 ; and for the Strangford shield, which is a copy of the shield of the Athena Parthenos, see A. H. Smith, *Cat. of Gk. Sculpture in the Brit. Mus.* i, no. 302.
[2] οὐρανός is here derived from ὄρος, 'boundary'.
[3] Ὄλυμπος is here derived from ὅλος and λάμπειν, 'to shine'.
[4] *Od.* vi. 42–45.   [5] *Il.* xv. 192.

of waves have often turned the dry land into sea and sea into dry land, and the might of winds and hurricanes has sometimes overthrown whole cities, and fires and flames have consumed the earth, either coming forth from heaven in 30 former times, even as men say that in the days of Phaethon they burnt up the eastern regions of the earth, or else gushing forth and breathing from the earth in the west, as when the craters of Etna burst and flowed like a torrent over the earth. (There also the favour of heaven bestowed **400**[b] especial honour upon the generation of the pious, when they were overtaken by the fiery stream, because they were carrying their aged parents upon their shoulders and seeking to save them. For when the river of fire drew near to them, it was parted asunder and turned part of its flame this way and part that way, and preserved the young men 5 and their parents unscathed.[1])

To sum up the matter, as is the steersman in the ship, the charioteer in the chariot, the leader in the chorus, law in the city, the general in the army, even so is God in the Universe; save that to them their rule is full of weariness and disturbance and care, while to him it is without toil or 10 labour and free from all bodily weakness. For, enthroned amid the immutable, he moves and revolves all things, where and how he will, in different forms and natures; just as the law of a city, fixed and immutable in the minds of those who are under it, orders all the life of the state. For 15 in obedience to it, it is plain, the magistrates go forth to their duties, the judges to their several courts of justice, the councillors and members of the assembly to their appointed places of meeting, and one man proceeds to his meals in the prytaneum, another to make his defence before 20 the jury, and another to die in prison. So too the customary public feasts and yearly festivals take place. and sacrifices to the gods and worship of heroes and libations in honour of the dead. The various activities of the citizens in obedience to one ordinance or lawful authority are well expressed in the words of the poet,

> And all the town is full of incense smoke,   25
> And full of cries for aid and loud laments.[2]

[1] Cp. Lycurg. *in Leocr.* 95-96.   [2] Soph. *O. T.* 4, 5.

So must we suppose to be the case with that greater city, the universe. For God is to us a law, impartial, admitting not of correction or change, and better, me-
30 thinks, and surer than those which are engraved upon tablets. Under his motionless[1] and harmonious rule the whole ordering of heaven and earth is administered, extending over all created things through the seeds of life in each both to plants and to animals, according to genera and
401^a species. For vines and date-palms and peach-trees and 'sweet fig-trees and olives'[2], as the poet says, and trees which, though they bear no fruits, have other uses, plane-trees and pines and box-trees,

Alder and poplar-tree and cypress breathing sweet odours,[3]

5 and trees which produce autumn crops pleasant but also difficult to store,

Pear-trees and pomegranate-trees and apple-trees glorious-fruited,[4]

and animals, both wild and tame, feeding in the air or on the earth or in the water, all are born and come to
10 their prime and decay in obedience to the ordinances of God ; for, in the words of Heraclitus, 'every creeping thing grazes at the blow of God's goad'.[5]

God being one yet has many names, being called after **7** all the various conditions which he himself inaugurates. We call him Zen and Zeus, using the two names in the
15 same sense, as though we should say 'him through whom we live'.[6] He is called the son of Kronos and of Time, for he endures from eternal age to age. He is God of Lightning and Thunder, God of the Clear Sky and of Ether, God of the Thunderbolt and of Rain, so called after the rain and the thunderbolts and other physical phenomena. Moreover, after the fruits he is called the Fruitful God,
20 after cities the City-God : he is God of Birth, God of the House-court, God of Kindred and God of our Fathers

---

[1] Reading ἀκινήτως with O. [2] *Od.* xv. 116.
[3] ib. v. 64. [4] ib. xi. 589.
[5] Reading πληγῇ for τὴν γῆν with Diels, *Vorsokr.*[3] i, p. 80, l. 8.
[6] i.e. Zeus is here derived from ζῆν, 'to live', and its accusative Δία, apparently, from the preposition διά.

from his participation in such things. He is God of Comradeship and Friendship and Hospitality, God of Armies and of Trophies, God of Purification and of Vengeance and of Supplication and of Propitiation, as the poets name him, and in very truth the Saviour and God of Freedom, and to complete the tale of his titles, God of Heaven and 25 of the World Below, deriving his names from all natural phenomena and conditions, inasmuch as he is himself the cause of all things. Wherefore it is well said in the Orphic Hymns,

> Zeus of the flashing bolt was the first to be born and the latest,
> Zeus is the head and the middle; of Zeus were all things created;
> Zeus is the stay of the earth and the stay of the star- 401ᵇ spangled heaven;
> Zeus is male and female of sex, the bride everlasting;
> Zeus is the breath of all and the rush of unwearying fire;
> Zeus is the root of the sea, and the sun and the moon in the heavens;
> Zeus of the flashing bolt is the king and the ruler of 5 all men,
> Hiding them all away, and again to the glad light of heaven
> Bringing them back at his will, performing terrible marvels.[1]

I think also that God and nought else is meant when we speak of Necessity, which is as it were invincible[2] being; and Fate, because his action is continuous[3] and he cannot be stayed in his course; and Destiny,[4] because all 10 things have their bounds, and nothing which exists is infinite; and Lot,[5] from the fact that all things are allotted; and Nemesis,[6] from the apportionment which is made to every individual; and Adrasteia,[7] which is a cause ordained by nature which cannot be escaped; and Dispensation,[8] so

---

[1] Kaibel, *Orphica*, 46.
[2] Ἀνάγκη, 'necessity', is here derived from ἀνίκητος, 'invincible'.
[3] Εἱμαρμένη, 'fate', from εἴρειν, 'to plait together'.
[4] Πεπρωμένη, 'destiny', from περατοῦν, 'to bound'.
[5] Μοῖρα, 'lot', from μερίζειν, 'to allot'.
[6] Νέμεσις, from νέμειν, 'to apportion'.
[7] Ἀδράστεια, from ἀ-, 'not', and διδράσκειν, 'to run away'.
[8] Αἶσα, 'dispensation', from ἀεὶ οὖσα, 'ever existing'.

called because it exists for ever. What is said of the Fates
15 and their spindle tends to the same conclusion; for they
are three, appointed over different periods of time, and the
thread on the spindle is part of it already spent, part
reserved for the future, and part in the course of being
spun. One of the Fates is appointed to deal with the
past, namely, Atropos, for nothing that is gone by can be
20 changed [1]; Lachesis is concerned with the future, for cessation [2] in the course of nature awaits all things; Clotho
presides over the present, accomplishing and spinning [3] for
each his own particular destiny. This fable is well and
duly composed. All these things are nought else but God,
even as worthy Plato tells us.[4]

25 God, then, as the old story has it, holding the beginning
and the end and the middle of all things that exist, proceeding by a straight path in the course of nature brings
them to accomplishment; and with him ever follows
Justice, the avenger of all that falls short of the Divine
Law—Justice, in whom may he that is to be be happy, be
from the very first a blessed and happy partaker!

----

[1] Ἄτροπος, from ἀ-, 'not', and τρέπειν, 'to turn'.
[2] Λάχεσις, from λήγειν, 'to cease'.
[3] Κλωθώ, from κλώθειν, 'to spin'.
[4] The reference appears to be to the account of the Fates given in
the Vision of Er (Plato, *Rep.* 617 c).

INDEX

INDEX

INDEX

DE ANIMA

BY

J. A. SMITH, M.A., Hon. LL.D. (Edin.)

WAYNFLETE PROFESSOR OF MORAL AND METAPHYSICAL PHILOSOPHY
FELLOW OF MAGDALEN COLLEGE
HONORARY FELLOW OF BALLIOL COLLEGE

OXFORD
AT THE CLARENDON PRESS

FIRST EDITION 1931

CONTENTS

BOOK I

BOOK II

BOOK III

BOOK I

1   HOLDING as we do that, while knowledge of any kind is a thing to be honoured and prized, one kind of it may, either by reason of its greater exactness or of a higher dignity and greater wonderfulness in its objects, be more honourable and precious than another, on both accounts we should naturally be led to place in the front rank the study of the soul. The knowledge of the soul admittedly contributes greatly to the advance of truth in general, and, above all, 5 to our understanding of Nature, for the soul is in some sense the principle of animal life. Our aim is to grasp and understand, first its essential nature, and secondly its properties; of these some are thought to be affections proper to the soul itself, while others are considered to attach to the animal[1] owing to the presence within it of soul.

To attain any assured knowledge about the soul is one 10 of the most difficult things in the world. As the form of question which here presents itself, viz. the question ' What is it ? ', recurs in other fields, it might be supposed that there was some single method of inquiry applicable to all objects whose essential nature we are endeavouring to ascertain (as 15 there *is* for derived properties the single method of demonstration); in that case what we should have to seek for would be this unique method. But if there is no such single and general method for solving the question of essence, our task becomes still more difficult; in the case of each different subject we shall have to determine the appropriate process of investigation. If to this there be a clear answer, e.g. that the process is demonstration or division, or some other known method, difficulties and hesitations still beset 20 us—with what facts shall we begin the inquiry? For the facts which form the starting-points in different subjects must be different, as e. g. in the case of numbers and surfaces.

First, no doubt, it is necessary to determine in which of the *summa genera* soul lies, what it *is*; is it 'a this-somewhat', a substance, or is it a quale or a quantum, or

[1] i.e. the complex of soul and body.

some other of the remaining kinds of predicates which we
25 have distinguished? Further, does soul belong to the class
of potential existents, or is it not rather an actuality?
Our answer to this question is of the greatest importance.
402ᵇ   We must consider also whether soul is divisible or is without parts, and whether it is everywhere homogeneous or not;
and if not homogeneous, whether its various forms are different
specifically or generically : up to the present time those who
have discussed and investigated soul seem to have confined
5 themselves to the human soul. We must be careful not to ignore
the question whether soul can be defined in a single unam-
biguous formula, as is the case with animal, or whether we
must not give a separate formula for each sort of it, as we
do for horse, dog, man, god (in the latter case the ' universal' animal—and so too every other ' common predicate '
—being treated either as nothing at all or as a later product[1]).
Further, if what exists is not a plurality of souls, but a
plurality of parts of one soul, which ought we to investigate
10 first, the whole soul or its parts? (It is also a difficult problem
to decide which of these parts are in nature distinct from
one another.) Again, which ought we to investigate first,
these parts or their functions, mind or thinking, the faculty
or the act of sensation, and so on? If the investigation of
the functions precedes that of the parts, the further question
suggests itself: ought we not before either to consider the
15 correlative objects, e. g. of sense or thought?[2] It seems not
only useful for the discovery of the causes of the derived
properties of substances to be acquainted with the essential
nature of those substances (as in mathematics it is useful
for the understanding of the property of the equality of the
20 interior angles of a triangle to two right angles to know the
essential nature of the straight and the curved or of the line
and the plane) but also conversely, for the knowledge of the
essential nature of a substance is largely promoted by an
acquaintance with its properties: for, when we are able to

---

[1] i.e. as presupposing the various sorts instead of being presupposed
by them.

[2] The text has ' e.g. the objects of sense or thought before the corresponding faculties or parts ', but this seems a slip of the author's ; the
order suggested is object—function or operation—faculty or part.

give an account conformable to experience of all or most of the properties of a substance, we shall be in the most favourable position to say something worth saying about the essential nature of that subject; in all demonstration a 25 definition of the essence is required as a starting-point, so that definitions which do not enable us to discover the derived properties, or which fail to facilitate even a conjecture about 403^a them, must obviously, one and all, be dialectical and futile.

A further problem presented by the affections of soul is this: are they all affections of the complex of body and soul, or is there any one among them peculiar to the soul by itself? To determine this is indispensable but difficult. If we consider the majority of them, there seems to be no 5 case in which the soul can act or be acted upon without involving the body; e.g. anger, courage, appetite, and sensation generally. Thinking seems the most probable exception; but if this too proves to be a form of imagination or to be impossible without imagination, it too requires a body as a condition of its existence. If there is any way 10 of acting or being acted upon proper to soul, soul will be capable of separate existence; if there is none, its separate existence is impossible. In the latter case, it will be like what is straight, which has many properties arising from the straightness in it, e.g. that of touching a bronze sphere at a point, though straightness divorced from the other constituents of the straight thing cannot touch it in this way; it cannot be so divorced at all, since it is always found in a body. 15 It therefore [1] seems that all the affections of soul involve a body—passion, gentleness, fear, pity, courage, joy, loving, and hating; in all these there is a concurrent affection of the body. In support of this we may point to the fact that, while sometimes on the occasion of violent and striking occurrences there is no excitement or fear felt, on others faint 20 and feeble stimulations produce these emotions, viz. when the body is already in a state of tension resembling its condition when we are angry. Here is a still clearer case: in the absence of any external cause of terror we find ourselves experiencing the feelings of a man in terror. From all this it

[1] Reading δή in l. 16.

is obvious that the affections of soul are enmattered formulable essences.

25   Consequently their definitions ought to correspond, e g.
anger should be defined as a certain mode of movement of
such and such a body (or part or faculty of a body) by
this or that cause and for this or that end.   That is precisely
why the study of the soul must fall within the science of
Nature, at least so far as in its affections it manifests this
double character.   Hence a physicist would define an
30 affection of soul differently from a dialectician; the latter
would define e.g. anger as the appetite for returning
pain for pain, or something like that, while the former would
define it as a boiling of the blood or warm substance sur-
403ᵇ rounding the heart.   The latter assigns the material conditions, the former the form or formulable essence; for what
he states[1] is the formulable essence of the fact, though for its
actual existence there must be embodiment of it in a material
such as is described by the other.   Thus the essence of a
house is assigned in such a formula as 'a shelter against
5 destruction by wind, rain, and heat'; the physicist would
describe it as 'stones, bricks, and timbers'; but there is a
third possible description which would say that it was that
form in that material with that purpose or end.   Which,
then, among these is entitled to be regarded as the genuine
physicist?   The one who confines himself to the material, or
the one who restricts himself to the formulable essence alone?
Is it not rather the one who combines both in a single formula?   If this is so, how are we to characterize the other two?
Must we not say that there is no type of thinker who concerns himself with those qualities or attributes of the material
which are in fact inseparable from the material, and without
10 attempting even in thought to separate them?   The physicist
is he who concerns himself with all the properties active and
passive of bodies or materials thus or thus defined; attributes
not considered as being of this character he leaves to others,
in certain cases it may be to a specialist, e.g. a carpenter or

---

[1] The reading here adopted in l. 2 is that of the *editio altera* of Biehl's
text (ed. Apelt) viz. ὅδε, the MS. evidence for which is much superior to
that for εἶδος.

a physician, in others (*a*) where they are inseparable in fact,
but are separable from any particular kind of body by an
effort of abstraction, to the mathematician, (*b*) where they 15
are separate both in fact and in thought from body altogether, to the First Philosopher or metaphysician. But
we must return from this digression, and repeat that the
affections of soul are inseparable ¹ from the material substratum of animal life, to which we have seen that such
affections, e. g. passion and fear, attach, and have not the
same mode of being as a line or a plane.

2   For our study of soul it is necessary, while formulating 20
the problems of which in our further advance we are to find
the solutions, to call into council the views of those of our
predecessors who have declared any opinion on this subject,
in order that we may profit by whatever is sound in their
suggestions and avoid their errors.

The starting-point of our inquiry is an exposition of
those characteristics which have chiefly been held to belong
to soul in its very nature. Two characteristic marks have 25
above all others been recognized as distinguishing that
which has soul in it from that which has not—movement
and sensation. It may be said that these two are what our
predecessors have fixed upon as characteristic of soul.

Some say that what originates movement is both pre-
eminently and primarily soul; believing that what is not
itself moved cannot originate movement in another, they 30
arrived at the view that soul belongs to the class of things
in movement. This is what led Democritus to say that soul
is a sort of fire or hot substance ; his 'forms' or atoms are 404^a
infinite in number ; those which are spherical he calls fire
and soul, and compares them to the motes in the air
which we see in shafts of light coming through windows ;
the mixture of seeds of all sorts he calls the elements of the
whole of Nature (Leucippus gives a similar account) ; the 5
spherical atoms are identified with soul because atoms of
that shape are most adapted to permeate everywhere, and
to set all the others moving by being themselves in move-

<hr>

¹ Reading in l. 17, with most MSS., τῆς ψυχῆς ἀχώριστα.

ment. This implies the view that soul is identical with what produces movement in animals. That is why, further, they 10 regard respiration as the characteristic mark of life ; as the environment compresses the bodies of animals, and tends to extrude those atoms which impart movement to them, because they themselves are never at rest, there must be a reinforcement of these by similar atoms coming in from without in the act of respiration ; for they prevent the extrusion of those which are already within by counteracting the compressing and consolidating force of the environment; 15 and animals continue to live only so long as they are able to maintain this resistance.

The doctrine of the Pythagoreans seems to rest upon the same ideas ; some of them declared the motes in air, others what moved them, to be soul. These motes were referred to because they are seen always in movement, even in a complete calm.

20 The same tendency is shown by those who define soul as that which moves itself; all seem to hold the view that movement is what is closest to the nature of soul, and that while all else is moved by soul, it alone moves itself. This belief arises from their never seeing anything originating movement which is not first itself moved.

25 Similarly also Anaxagoras (and whoever agrees with him in saying that mind set the whole in movement) declares the moving cause of things to be soul. His position must, however, be distinguished from that of Democritus. Democritus roundly identifies soul and mind, for he identifies what appears with what is true—that is why he commends Homer for the phrase ' Hector lay with thought 30 distraught '[1]; he does not employ mind as a special faculty **404^b** dealing with truth, but identifies soul and mind. What Anaxagoras says about them is more obscure; in many places he tells us that the cause of beauty and order is mind, elsewhere that it is soul ; it is found, he says, in all 5 animals, great and small, high and low, but mind (in the sense of intelligence) appears not to belong alike to all animals, and indeed not even to all human beings.

[1] *Il.* xxiii. 698.

All those, then, who had special regard to the fact that
what has soul in it is moved, adopted the view that soul
is to be identified with what is eminently originative of
movement. All, on the other hand, who looked to the fact
that what has soul in it knows or perceives what is, identify soul with the principle or principles of Nature, accord- 10
ing as they admit several such principles or one only. Thus
Empedocles declares that it is formed out of all his elements, each of them also being soul; his words are:

> For 'tis by Earth we see Earth, by Water Water,
> By Ether Ether divine, by Fire destructive Fire,
> By Love Love, and Hate by cruel Hate.[1]   15

In the same way Plato in the *Timaeus*[2] fashions the soul
out of his elements; for like, he holds, is known by like,
and things are formed out of the principles or elements, so
that soul must be so too. Similarly also in his lectures ' On
Philosophy' it was set forth that the Animal-itself is   20
compounded of the Idea itself of the One together with the
primary length, breadth, and depth, everything else, the
objects of its perception, being similarly constituted. Again
he puts his view in yet other terms: Mind is the monad,
science or knowledge the dyad (because[3] it goes undeviat-
ingly from one point to another), opinion the number of
the plane,[4] sensation the number of the solid[5]; the numbers are by him expressly identified with the Forms themselves or principles, and are formed out of the elements;
now things are apprehended either by mind or science or   25
opinion or sensation, and these same numbers are the
Forms of things.

Some thinkers, accepting both premisses, viz. that the
soul is both originative of movement and cognitive, have
compounded it of both and declared the soul to be a self-
moving number.

As to the nature and number of the first principles   30
opinions differ. The difference is greatest between those who
regard them as corporeal and those who regard them as

---

[1] Fr. 109 Diels.   [2] 35 A ff.
[3] Like the straight line, whose number is the dyad.
[4] The triad.   [5] The tetrad.

405ᵃ incorporeal, and from both dissent those who make a blend and draw their principles from both sources. The number of principles is also in dispute; some admit one only, others assert several. There is a consequent diversity in their several accounts of soul; they assume, naturally enough, that what is in its own nature originative of
5 movement must be among what is primordial. That has led some to regard it as fire, for fire is the subtlest of the elements and nearest to incorporeality; further, in the most primary sense, fire both is moved and originates movement in all the others.

Democritus has expressed himself more ingeniously than the rest on the grounds for ascribing each of these two characters to soul; soul and mind are, he says, one and
10 the same thing, and this thing must be one of the primary and indivisible bodies, and its power of originating movement must be due to its fineness of grain and the shape of its atoms; he says that of all the shapes the spherical is the most mobile, and that this is the shape of the particles of both fire and mind.

Anaxagoras, as we said above,[1] seems to distinguish between soul and mind, but in practice he treats them as
15 a single substance, except that it is mind that he specially posits as the principle of all things; at any rate what he says is that mind alone of all that is is simple, unmixed, and pure. He assigns both characteristics, knowing and origination of movement, to the same principle, when he says that it was mind that set the whole in movement.

Thales, too, to judge from what is recorded about him,
20 seems to have held soul to be a motive force, since he said that the magnet has a soul in it because it moves the iron.

Diogenes (and others) held the soul to be air because he believed air to be finest in grain and a first principle; therein lay the grounds of the soul's powers of knowing and originating movement. As the primordial principle from which all other things are derived, it is cognitive; as finest in grain, it has the power to originate movement.
25   Heraclitus too says that the first principle—the 'warm

---
[1] 40ᵇ1–6

exhalation' of which, according to him, everything else is
composed—is soul; further, that this exhalation is most
incorporeal and in ceaseless flux; that what is in movement
requires that what knows it should be in movement; and
that all that is has its being essentially in movement
(herein agreeing with the majority).

Alcmaeon also seems to have held a similar view about
soul; he says that it is immortal because it resembles 'the 30
immortals', and that this immortality belongs to it in
virtue of its ceaseless movement; for all the 'things divine',
moon, sun, the planets, and the whole heavens, are in
perpetual movement.

Of more superficial writers, some, e. g. Hippo, have pro- 405^b
nounced it to be water; they seem to have argued from the
fact that the seed of all animals is fluid, for Hippo tries to
refute those who say that the soul is blood, on the ground
that the seed, which is the primordial soul, is not blood.

Another group (Critias, for example) did hold it to be 5
blood; they take perception to be the most characteristic
attribute of soul, and hold that perceptiveness is due to
the nature of blood.

Each of the elements has thus found its partisan, except
earth—earth has found no supporter unless we count as
such those who have declared soul to be, or to be com- 10
pounded of, *all* the elements. All, then, it may be said,
characterize the soul by three marks, Movement. Sensation,
Incorporeality, and each of these is traced back to the first
principles. That is why (with one exception) all those
who define the soul by its power of knowing make it either
an element or constructed out of the elements. The
language they all use is similar; like, they say, is known 15
by like; as the soul knows everything, they construct it
out of all the principles. Hence all those who admit but
one cause or element, make the soul also one (e. g. fire
or air), while those who admit a multiplicity of principles
make the soul also multiple. The exception is Anaxagoras; he alone says that mind is impassible and has 20
nothing in common with anything else.[1] But, if this is so,

[1] Fr. 12.

how or in virtue of what cause can it know? That Anaxagoras has not explained, nor can any answer be inferred from his words. All who acknowledge pairs of opposites among their principles, construct the soul also out of these contraries, while those who admit as principles only one con-
25 trary of each pair, e. g. either hot or cold, likewise make the soul some one of these. That is why, also, they allow themselves to be guided by the names ; those who identify soul with the hot argue that ζῆν (to live) is derived from ζεῖν (to boil), while those who identify it with the cold say that soul (ψυχή) is so called from the process of respiration and refrigeration (κατάψυξις).

30 Such are the traditional opinions concerning soul, together with the grounds on which they are maintained.

We must begin our examination with movement; for, **3** doubtless, not only is it false that the essence of soul is cor-
406ᵃ rectly described by those who say that it is what moves (or is capable of moving) itself, but it is an impossibility that movement should be even an attribute of it.

We have already[1] pointed out that there is no necessity that what originates movement should itself be moved. There are two senses in which anything may be moved—either (a) indirectly, owing to something other than itself,
5 or (b) directly, owing to itself. Things are 'indirectly moved' which are moved as being contained in something which is moved, e. g. sailors in a ship, for they are moved in a different sense from that in which the ship is moved ; the ship is 'directly moved', they are 'indirectly moved', because they are in a moving vessel. This is clear if we consider their limbs ; the movement proper to the legs (and so to man) is walking, and in this case the sailors are not
10 walking. Recognizing the double sense of ' being moved ', what we have to consider now is whether the soul is 'directly moved' and participates in such direct movement.

There are four species of movement—locomotion, alteration, diminution, growth ; consequently if the soul is moved, it must be moved with one or several or all of

---

[1] *Phys.* viii. 5, esp. 257ᵃ 31–258ᵇ 9.

these species of movement. Now if its movement is not incidental, there must be a movement natural to it, and, 15 if so, as all the species enumerated involve place, place must be natural to it. But if the essence of soul be to move itself, its being moved cannot be incidental to it, as it is to what is white or three cubits long; they too can be moved, but only incidentally—what is moved is that of which 'white' and 'three cubits long' are the attributes, the body in which they inhere; hence *they* have no place: but 20 if the soul naturally partakes in movement, it follows that it must have a place.

Further, if there be a movement natural to the soul, there must be a counter-movement unnatural to it, and conversely. The same applies to rest as well as to movement; for the *terminus ad quem* of a thing's natural movement is the place of its natural rest, and similarly the 25 *terminus ad quem* of its enforced movement is the place of its enforced rest. But what meaning can be attached to enforced movements or rests of the soul, it is difficult even to imagine.

Further, if the natural movement of the soul be upward, the soul must be fire; if downward, it must be earth; for upward and downward movements are the definitory characteristics of these bodies. The same reasoning applies to the intermediate movements, *termini*, and bodies. Further, since the soul is observed to originate movement 30 in the body, it is reasonable to suppose that it transmits to the body the movements by which it itself is moved, and so, reversing the order, we may infer from the movements of the body back to similar movements of the soul. Now the 406ᵇ body is moved from place to place with movements of locomotion. Hence it would follow that the soul too must in accordance with the body change either its place as a whole or the relative places of its parts. This carries with it the possibility that the soul might even quit its body and re-enter it, and with this would be involved the possibility of a resurrection of animals from the dead. But. it may be contended, the 5 soul can be moved indirectly by something else; for an animal can be pushed out of its course. Yes, but that to whose *essence* belongs the power of being moved by itself, cannot be moved by something else except incidentally,[1] just as what is good by or in itself cannot owe its goodness to something external to it or to some end to which it is a means.

10   If the soul *is* moved, the most probable view is that what moves it is sensible things.[2]

We must note also that, if the soul moves itself, it must be the mover itself that is moved, so that it follows that if movement is in every case a displacement of that which is in movement, in that respect in which it is said to be moved, the movement of the soul must be a departure from its essential nature, at least if its self-movement is essential to it, not incidental.

15   Some go so far as to hold that the movements which the soul imparts to the body in which it is are the same in kind as those with which it itself is moved. An example of this is Democritus, who uses language like that of the comic dramatist Philippus, who accounts for the movements that Daedalus imparted to his wooden Aphrodite by saying that he poured quicksilver into it ; similarly Demo-
20 critus says that the spherical atoms which according to him constitute soul, owing to their own ceaseless movements draw the whole body after them and so produce its movements. We must urge the question whether it is these very same atoms which produce rest also—how they could do so, it is difficult and even impossible to say. And, in general, we may object that it is not in this way that the
25 soul appears to originate movement in animals—it is through intention or process of thinking.

It is in the same fashion that the *Timaeus*[3] also tries to give a physical account of how the soul moves its body; the soul, it is there said, is in movement, and so owing to their mutual implication moves the body also. After compounding the soul-substance out of the elements and

---

[1] i.e. so that what is moved is not it but something which 'goes along with it', e.g. a vehicle in which it is contained.

[2] Sc. in which case the movement can only be 'incidental'; for, as we shall see later, it is really the bodily organ of sensation that then is 'moved'.

[3] 35 A ff.

dividing it in accordance with the harmonic numbers, in order that it may possess a connate sensibility for ' harmony ' 30 and that the whole may move in movements well attuned, the Demiurge bent the straight line into a circle; this single circle he divided into two circles united at two common points ; one of these he subdivided into seven circles. All this 407ᵃ implies that the movements of the soul are identified with the local movements of the heavens.

Now, in the first place, it is a mistake to say that the soul is a spatial magnitude. It is evident that Plato means the soul of the whole to be like the sort of soul which is called mind—not like the sensitive or the desiderative 5 soul, for the movements of neither of these are circular. Now mind is one and continuous in the sense in which the process of thinking is so, and thinking is identical with the thoughts which are its parts ; these have a serial unity like that of number, not a unity like that of a spatial magnitude. Hence mind cannot have that kind of unity either ; mind is either without parts or is continuous in some other way than that which characterizes a spatial magnitude. How, indeed, if it were a spatial magnitude, could mind 10 possibly think ? Will it think with any one indifferently of its parts ? In this case, the ' part ' must be understood either in the sense of a spatial magnitude or in the sense of a point (if a point *can* be called a part of a spatial magnitude). If we accept the latter alternative, the points being infinite in number, obviously the mind can never exhaustively traverse them ; if the former, the mind must think the same thing over and over again, indeed an infinite number of times (whereas it is manifestly possible to think a thing once only). 15 If contact of any part whatsoever of itself with the object is all that is required, why need mind move in a circle, or indeed possess magnitude at all? On the other hand, if contact with the whole circle is necessary, what meaning can be given to the contact of the parts? Further, how could what has no parts think what has parts, or what has parts think what has none? [1] We must identify the circle referred to with mind ; for it is mind whose movement is thinking, 20

[1] Sc. but mind in fact thinks or cognizes both.

and it is the circle whose movement is revolution, so that if thinking is a movement of revolution, the circle which has this characteristic movement must be mind.[1]

If the circular movement is eternal, there must be something which mind is always thinking—what *can* this be? For all practical processes of thinking have limits—they all go on for the sake of something outside the process, and all theoretical processes come to a close in the same way as the phrases in speech which express processes and results of
25 thinking. Every such linguistic phrase is either definitory or demonstrative. Demonstration has both a starting-point and may be said to end in a conclusion or inferred result ; even if the process never reaches final completion, at any rate it never returns upon itself again to its starting-point, it goes on assuming a fresh middle term or a fresh extreme, and moves straight forward, but circular movement returns to
30 its starting-point. Definitions, too, are closed groups of terms.

Further, if the same revolution is repeated, mind must repeatedly think the same object.

Further, thinking has more resemblance to a coming to rest or arrest than to a movement; the same may be said of inferring.

It might also be urged that what is difficult and enforced
407ᵇ is incompatible with blessedness; if the movement of the soul is not of its essence, movement of the soul must be contrary to its nature.[2] It must also be painful for the soul to be inextricably bound up with the body; nay more, if, as is frequently said and widely accepted, it is better for mind not to be embodied, the union must be for it undesirable.

5   Further, the cause of the revolution of the heavens is left obscure. It is not the essence of soul which is the cause of this circular movement—that movement is only incidental to soul—nor is, *a fortiori*, the body its cause. Again, it is not even asserted that it is better that soul should be so moved ; and yet the reason for which God caused the soul

---

[1] Omitting νόησις in l. 22, with Sophonias and Torstrik.
[2] Sc. ' and so a hindrance to its bliss '.

to move in a circle can only have been that movement was 10
better for it than rest, and movement of this kind better
than any other. But since this sort of consideration is more
appropriate to another field of speculation, let us dismiss it
for the present.

The view we have just been examining, in company with
most theories about the soul, involves the following absurdity: they all join the soul to a body, or place it in a body, 15
without adding any specification of the reason of their
union, or of the bodily conditions required for it. Yet such
explanation can scarcely be omitted; for some community
of nature is presupposed by the fact that the one acts and
the other is acted upon, the one moves and the other is
moved; interaction always implies a *special* nature in the
two interagents. All, however, that these thinkers do is to 20
describe the specific characteristics of the soul; they do not
try to determine anything about the body which is to contain it, as if it were possible, as in the Pythagorean myths,
that any soul could be clothed upon with any body—an
absurd view, for each body seems to have a form and shape
of its own. It is as absurd as to say that the art of carpentry
could embody itself in flutes; each art must use its tools, 25
each soul its body.

4   There is yet another theory about soul, which has
commended itself to many as no less probable than any
of those we have hitherto mentioned, and has rendered
public account of itself in the court of popular discussion. 30
Its supporters say that the soul is a kind of harmony, for
(*a*) harmony is a blend or composition of contraries, and
(*b*) the body is compounded out of contraries. Harmony,
however, is a certain proportion or composition of the
constituents blended, and soul can be neither the one nor
the other of these. Further, the power of originating
movement cannot belong to a harmony, while almost all
concur in regarding this as a principal attribute of soul.
It is more appropriate to call health (or generally one of 408^a
the good states of the body) a harmony than to predicate
it of the soul. The absurdity becomes most apparent

when we try to attribute the active and passive affections
of the soul to a harmony; the necessary readjustment of
5 their conceptions is difficult.   Further, in using the word
'harmony' we have one or other of two cases in our mind;
the most proper sense is in relation to spatial magnitudes
which have motion and position, where harmony means
the disposition and cohesion of their parts in such a
manner as to prevent the introduction into the whole of
anything homogeneous with it, and the secondary sense,
derived from the former, is that in which it means the
ratio between the constituents so blended; in neither of
10 these senses is it plausible to predicate it of soul.   That
soul is a harmony in the sense of the mode of composition
of the parts of the body is a view easily refutable; for there
are many composite parts and those variously compounded;
of what bodily part is mind or the sensitive or the appetitive
faculty the mode of composition?   And what *is* the mode
of composition which constitutes each of them?   It is
equally absurd to identify the soul with the ratio of the
15 mixture; for the mixture which makes flesh has a different
ratio between the elements from that which makes bone.
The consequence of this view will therefore be that distributed throughout the whole body there will be many
souls, since every one of the bodily parts is a different mixture of the elements, and the ratio of mixture is in each
case a harmony, i. e. a soul.

From Empedocles at any rate we might demand an
answer to the following question—for he says that each of
the parts of the body is what it is in virtue of a ratio
20 between the elements : is the soul identical with this ratio,
or is it not rather something over and above this which is
formed in the parts?   Is love the cause of any and every
mixture, or only of those that are in the right ratio?   Is
love this ratio itself, or is love something over and above
this?   Such are the problems raised by this account.   But,
on the other hand, if the soul is different from the mixture,
25 why does it disappear at one and the same moment with
that relation between the elements which constitutes flesh or
the other parts of the animal body?   Further, if the soul

is not identical with the ratio of mixture, and it is consequently not the case that each of the parts has a soul, what
is that which perishes when the soul quits the body?

That the soul cannot either be a harmony, or be moved
in a circle, is clear from what we have said. Yet that it 30
can be moved incidentally is, as we said above,[1] possible,
and even that in a sense it can move itself, i. e. in the sense
that *the vehicle* in which it is can be moved, and moved by
it; in no other sense can the soul be moved in space.

More legitimate doubts might remain as to its movement
in view of the following facts. We speak of the soul as being 408ᵇ
pained or pleased, being bold or fearful, being angry,
perceiving, thinking. All these are regarded as modes of
movement, and hence it might be inferred that the soul
is moved. This, however, does not necessarily follow.
We may admit to the full that being pained or pleased, or 5
thinking, are movements (each of them a 'being moved'),
and that the movement is originated by the soul. For
example we may regard anger or fear as such and such
movements of the heart, and thinking as such and such
another movement of that organ, or of some other; these
modifications may arise either from changes of place in
certain parts or from qualitative alterations (the special nature 10
of the parts and the special modes of their changes being
for our present purpose irrelevant). Yet to say[2] that it is
the soul which is angry is as inexact as it would be to say
that it is the soul that weaves webs or builds houses. It
is doubtless better to avoid saying that the soul pities or
learns or thinks, and rather to say that it is the man who
does this with his soul. What we mean is not that the 15
movement is in the soul, but that sometimes it terminates
in the soul and sometimes starts from it, sensation e. g.
coming from without inwards, and reminiscence starting
from the soul and terminating with the movements, actual
or residual, in the sense organs.

The case of mind is different; it seems to be an independent substance implanted within the soul and to be

[1] 406ᵃ 30 ff., ᵇ5–8.
[2] Reading in l. 11 τὸ δὲ λέγειν, with most MSS. and Philoponus.

incapable of being destroyed. If it could be destroyed at all, it would be under the blunting influence of old age. 20 What really happens in respect of mind in old age is, however, exactly parallel to what happens in the case of the sense organs; if the old man could recover the proper kind of eye, he would see just as well as the young man. The incapacity of old age is due to an affection not of the soul but of its vehicle, as occurs in drunkenness or disease. Thus it is that in old age the activity of mind or intellectual apprehension declines only through the decay of some other 25 inward part; mind itself is impassible. Thinking, loving, and hating are affections not of mind, but of that which has mind, so far as it has it. That is why, when this vehicle decays, memory and love cease; they were activities not of mind, but of the composite which has perished; mind is, no doubt, something more divine and 30 impassible. That the soul cannot be moved is therefore clear from what we have said, and if it cannot be moved at all, manifestly it cannot be moved by itself.

Of all the opinions we have enumerated, by far the most unreasonable is that which declares the soul to be a self-moving number; it involves in the first place all the impossibilities which follow from regarding the soul as moved, and in the second special absurdities which follow 409ᵃ from calling it a number. How are we to imagine a unit being moved? By what agency? What sort of movement can be attributed to what is without parts or internal differences? If the unit is both originative of movement and itself capable of being moved, it must contain difference.[1]

Further, since they say a moving line generates a surface 5 and a moving point a line, the movements of the psychic units must be lines (for a point is a unit having position, and the number of the soul is, of course, somewhere and has position).

Again, if from a number a number or a unit is subtracted, the remainder is another number; but plants and many animals when divided continue to live, and each segment is thought to retain the same kind of soul.

[1] Sc. 'and so, be no unit'.

It must be all the same whether we speak of units or 10
corpuscles ; for if the spherical atoms of Democritus became
points, nothing being retained but their being a quantum,
there must remain in each a moving and a moved part, just
as there is in what is continuous ; what happens has nothing
to do with the size of the atoms, it depends solely upon
their being a quantum.   That is why there must be some- 15
thing to originate movement in the units.   If in the animal
what originates movement is the soul, so also must it be in
the case of the number, so that not the mover and the
moved together, but the mover only, will be the soul.
But how is it possible for one of the units to fulfil this
function of originating movement?   There must be *some*
difference between such a unit and all the other units, and what 20
difference can there be between one placed unit and another
except a difference of position?   If then, on the other hand,
these psychic units within the body are different from the
points *of* the body, there will be two sets of units both occupying the same place ; for each unit will occupy a point.   And
yet, if there can be two, why cannot there be an infinite
number ?   For if things can occupy an indivisible place,
they must themselves be indivisible.   If, on the other hand, 25
the points of the body are identical with the units whose
number is the soul, or if the number of the points in the
body is the soul, why have not all bodies souls?   For
all bodies contain points or an infinity of points.

Further, how is it possible for these points to be isolated
or separated from their bodies, seeing that lines cannot be 30
resolved into points ?

5   The result is, as we have said,[1] that this view, while on
the one side identical with that of those who maintain that
soul is a subtle kind of body,[2] is on the other entangled in
the absurdity peculiar to Democritus' way of describing
the manner in which movement is originated by soul. 409ᵇ
For if the soul is present throughout the whole percipient
body, there must, if the soul be a kind of body, be two
bodies in the same place ; and for those who call it a

[1] 408ᵇ 33 ff.   [2] e.g. Heraclitus, and Diogenes of Apollonia.

5 number, there must be many points at one point, or every
body must have a soul, unless the soul be a different sort of
number—other, that is, than the sum of the points existing
in a body. Another consequence that follows is that the
animal must be moved by its number precisely in the way
that Democritus explained its being moved by his spherical
psychic atoms. What difference does it make whether we
speak of small spheres or of large [1] units, or, quite simply, of
10 units in movement? One way or another, the movements of
the animal must be due to their movements. Hence those
who combine movement and number in the same subject
lay themselves open to these and many other similar absurdities. It is impossible not only that these characters should
give the definition of soul—it is impossible that they should
even be attributes of it. The point is clear if the attempt
15 be made to start from this as the account of soul and explain from it the affections and actions of the soul, e. g. reasoning, sensation, pleasure, pain, &c. For, to repeat what
we have said earlier,[2] movement and number do not facilitate even conjecture about the derivative properties of soul.

Such are the three ways in which soul has traditionally
been defined; one group of thinkers declared it to be that
20 which is most originative of movement because it moves
itself, another group to be the subtlest and most nearly incorporeal of all kinds of body. We have now sufficiently
set forth the difficulties and inconsistencies to which these
theories are exposed. It remains now to examine the
doctrine that soul is composed of the elements.

The reason assigned for this doctrine is that thus the
soul may perceive or come to know everything that is, but
25 the theory necessarily involves itself in many impossibilities.
Its upholders assume that like is known only by like, and
imagine that by declaring the soul to be composed of the
elements they succeed in identifying the soul with all the
things it is capable of apprehending. But the elements are
not the only things it knows; there are many others, or, more
exactly, an infinite number of others, formed out of the
30 elements. Let us admit that the soul knows or perceives the

---

[1] i.e. extended.   [2] 402[b] 25–403[a] 2.

elements out of which each of these composites is made up; but by what means will it know or perceive the composite whole, e. g. what God, man, flesh, bone (or any other compound) is? For each *is*, not merely the elements of which 410^a it is composed, but those elements combined in a determinate mode or ratio, as Empedocles himself says of bone,

> The kindly Earth in its broad-bosomed moulds[1]
> Won of clear Water two parts out of eight   5
> And four of Fire; and so white bones were formed.

Nothing, therefore, will be gained by the presence of the elements in the soul, unless there be also present there the various formulae of proportion and the various compositions in accordance with them. Each element will indeed know its fellow outside, but there will be no knowledge of bone or man, unless they too are present in the constitution of the soul. The impossibility of this needs no 10 pointing out; for who would suggest that stone or man could enter into the constitution of the soul? The same applies to 'the good' and 'the not-good', and so on.

Further, the word 'is' has many meanings: it may be used of a 'this' or substance, or of a quantum, or of a quale, or of any other of the kinds of predicates we have distinguished. Does the soul consist of all of these or not? 15 It does not appear that all have common elements. Is the soul formed out of those elements alone which enter into substances? If so, how will it be able to know each of the other kinds of thing? Will it be said that each kind of thing has elements or principles of its own, and that the soul is formed out of the whole of these? In that case, 20 the soul must be a quantum *and* a quale *and* a substance. But all that can be made out of the elements of a quantum is a quantum, not a substance. These (and others like them) are the consequences of the view that the soul is composed of all the elements.

It is absurd, also, to say both (*a*) that like is not capable of being affected by like, and (*b*) that like is perceived or known by like, for perceiving, and also both thinking and 25

---

[1] Burnet 'broad funnels', fr. 96 Diels.

knowing, are, on their own assumption, ways of being affected or moved.

There are many puzzles and difficulties raised by saying, as Empedocles does, that each set of things is known by means of its corporeal elements and by reference to something in soul which is like them, and additional testimony
30 is furnished by this new consideration ; for all the parts of the animal body which consist wholly of earth such as
410ᵇ bones, sinews, and hair seem to be wholly insensitive and consequently not perceptive even of objects earthy like themselves, as they ought to have been.

Further, each of the principles will have far more ignorance than knowledge, for though each of them will know one thing. there will be many of which it will be ignorant. Empedocles at any rate must conclude that his God is the
5 least intelligent of all beings, for of him alone is it true that there is one thing, Strife, which he does not know, while there is nothing which mortal beings do not know, for there is nothing which does not enter into their composition.

In general, we may ask, Why has not everything a soul, since everything either is an element, or is formed out of one or several or all of the elements ? Each must certainly know one or several or all.
10 The problem might also be raised, What is that which unifies the elements into a soul? The elements correspond, it would appear, to the matter ; what unites them, whatever it is, is the supremely important factor. But it is impossible that there should be something superior to, and dominant over, the soul (and *a fortiori* over the mind) ; it is reasonable to hold that mind is by nature most primordial
15 and dominant, while their statement is that it is the elements which are first of all that is.

All, both those who assert that the soul, because of its knowledge or perception of what is, is compounded out of the elements, and those who assert that it is of all things the most originative of movement, fail to take into consideration all kinds of soul. In fact (1) not all beings that perceive can originate movement; there appear to be
20 certain animals which are stationary, and yet local move-

ment is the only one, so it seems, which the soul originates in animals. And (2) the same objection holds against all those who construct mind and the perceptive faculty out of the elements; for it appears that plants live, and yet are not endowed with locomotion or perception, while a large number of animals are without discourse of reason. Even if these points were waived and mind admitted to be a part of the soul (and so too the perceptive faculty), still, 25 even so, there would be kinds and parts of soul of which they had failed to give any account.

The same objection lies against the view expressed in the 'Orphic' poems: there it is said that the soul comes in from the whole when breathing takes place, being borne in upon the winds.[1] Now this cannot take place in the case 30 of plants. nor indeed in the case of certain classes of animal, for not all classes of animal breathe. This fact has escaped 411^a the notice of the holders of this view.

If we must construct the soul out of the elements, there is no necessity to suppose that *all* the elements enter into its construction; one element in each pair of contraries will suffice to enable it to know both that element itself and its contrary. By means of the straight line we know 5 both itself and the curved—the carpenter's rule enables us to test both—but what is curved does not enable us to distinguish either itself or the straight.

Certain thinkers say that soul is intermingled in the whole universe, and it is perhaps for that reason that Thales came to the opinion that all things are full of gods. This presents some difficulties: Why does the soul when it resides in air or fire not form an animal, while it does so 10 when it resides in mixtures of the elements, and that although it is held to be of higher quality when contained in the former? (One might add the question, why the soul in air is maintained to be higher and more immortal than that in animals.) Both possible ways of replying to the former question lead to absurdity or paradox; for it is beyond paradox to say that fire or air is an animal, and 15 it is absurd to refuse the name of animal to what has soul

---

[1] Orpheus, fr. 11 Diels.

in it. The opinion that the elements have soul in them
seems to have arisen from the doctrine that a whole must
be homogeneous with its parts. If it is true that animals
become animate by drawing into themselves a portion of
what surrounds them, the partisans of this view are bound
to say that the soul of the Whole too is homogeneous with
20 all its parts. If the air sucked in is homogeneous, but soul
heterogeneous, clearly while some part of soul will exist in
the inbreathed air, some other part will not. The soul
must either be homogeneous, or such that there are some
parts of the Whole in which it is not to be found.

From what has been said it is now clear that knowing as
an attribute of soul cannot be explained by soul's being
25 composed of the elements, and that it is neither sound nor
true to speak of soul as moved. But since (a) knowing,
perceiving, opining, and further (b) desiring, wishing, and
generally all other modes of appetition, belong to soul,
30 and (c) the local movements of animals, and (d) growth,
maturity, and decay are produced by the soul, we must
ask whether each of these is an attribute of the soul as
411ᵇ a whole, i. e. whether it is with the whole soul we think,
perceive, move ourselves, act or are acted upon, or whether
each of them requires a different part of the soul? So
too with regard to life. Does it depend on one of the
parts of soul? Or is it dependent on more than one? Or
on all? Or has it some quite other cause?

5   Some hold that the soul is divisible, and that one part
thinks, another desires. If, then, its nature admits of its
being divided, what can it be that holds the parts together? Surely not the body; on the contrary it seems
rather to be the soul that holds the body together; at any
rate when the soul departs the body disintegrates and
decays. If, then, there is something else which makes the
soul one, this unifying agency would have the best right
10 to the name of soul, and we shall have to repeat for it the
question: Is *it* one or multipartite? If it is one, why not at
once admit that 'the soul' is one? If it has parts, once
more the question must be put: What holds *its* parts
together, and so *ad infinitum*?

The question might also be raised about the parts of the
soul: What is the separate rôle of each in relation to the
body? For, if the whole soul holds together the whole 15
body, we should expect each part of the soul to hold
together a part of the body. But this seems an impossibility; it is difficult even to imagine what sort of bodily
part mind will hold together, or how it will do this.

It is a fact of observation that plants and certain insects
go on living when divided into segments; this means that 20
each of the segments has a soul in it identical in species,
though not numerically identical in the different segments,
for both of the segments for a time possess the power of
sensation and local movement. That this does not last is
not surprising, for they no longer possess the organs necessary for self-maintenance. But, all the same, in each of the
bodily parts there are present all the parts of soul, and the 25
souls so present are homogeneous with one another and
with the whole; this means that the several parts of the
soul are indisseverable from one another, although the
whole soul is[1] divisible. It seems also that the principle
found in plants is also a kind of soul; for this is the only
principle which is common to both animals and plants;
and this exists in isolation from the principle of sensation,
though there is nothing which has the latter without the 30
former.

[1] Sc. 'in a sense, i.e. so as to preserve its homogeneity in even its
smallest part'.

BOOK II

412^a LET the foregoing suffice as our account of the views 1
concerning the soul which have been handed on by our
predecessors; let us now dismiss them and make as it were
a completely fresh start, endeavouring to give a precise
5 answer to the question, What is soul? i. e. to formulate the
most general possible definition of it.

We are in the habit of recognizing, as one determinate
kind of what is, substance, and that in several senses, (a) in
the sense of matter or that which in itself is not 'a this',
and (b) in the sense of form or essence, which is that
precisely in virtue of which a thing is called 'a this', and
thirdly (c) in the sense of that which is compounded of both
10 (a) and (b). Now matter is potentiality, form actuality;
of the latter there are two grades related to one another as
e. g. knowledge to the exercise of knowledge.

Among substances are by general consent reckoned
bodies and especially natural bodies; for they are the
principles of all other bodies. Of natural bodies some have
life in them, others not; by life we mean self-nutrition
15 and growth (with its correlative decay). It follows that
every natural body which has life in it is a substance in
the sense of a composite.[1]

But since it is also a *body* of such and such a kind, viz.
having life, the *body* cannot be soul; the body is the
subject or matter, not what is attributed to it. Hence the
20 soul must be a substance in the sense of the form of a
natural body having life potentially within it. But
substance[2] is actuality, and thus soul is the actuality of
a body as above characterized. Now the word actuality
has two senses corresponding respectively to the possession
of knowledge and the actual exercise of knowledge. It
is obvious that the soul is actuality in the first sense,
viz. that of knowledge as possessed, for both sleeping
25 and waking presuppose the existence of soul, and of these
waking corresponds to actual knowing, sleeping to know-

---

[1] i.e. (c) supra.   [2] Sc. in the sense of form.

ledge possessed but not employed, and, in the history
of the individual, knowledge comes before its employment
or exercise.

That is why the soul is the first grade of actuality of a
natural body having life potentially in it. The body so
described is a body which is organized. The parts of plants 412^b
in spite of their extreme simplicity are 'organs'; e.g. the
leaf serves to shelter the pericarp, the pericarp to shelter
the fruit, while the roots of plants are analogous to the
mouth of animals, both serving for the absorption of food.
If, then, we have to give a general formula applicable to all
kinds of soul, we must describe it as the first grade of 5
actuality of a natural organized body. That is why we
can wholly dismiss as unnecessary the question whether the
soul and the body are one: it is as meaningless as to ask
whether the wax and the shape given to it by the stamp
are one, or generally the matter of a thing and that of
which it is the matter. Unity has many senses (as many
as 'is' has), but the most proper and fundamental sense of
both is the relation of an actuality to that of which it is
the actuality.

We have now given an answer to the question, What is 10
soul?—an answer which applies to it in its full extent. It
is substance in the sense which corresponds to the definitive formula of a thing's essence. That means that it
is 'the essential whatness' of a body of the character just
assigned.[1] Suppose that what is literally an ' organ ',[2] like
an axe, were a *natural* body, its 'essential whatness', would
have been its essence, and so its soul; if this disappeared
from it, it would have ceased to be an axe, except in name.
As it is,[3] it is just an axe; it wants the character which is 15
required to make its whatness or formulable essence a
soul; for that, it would have had to be a *natural* body
of a particular kind, viz. one having *in itself* the power
of setting itself in movement and arresting itself. Next,
apply this doctrine in the case of the 'parts' of the living
body. Suppose that the eye were an animal—sight would

---

[1] Viz. organized, or possessed potentially of life.
[2] i.e instrument.   [3] Being an artificial, not a natural, body.

have been its soul, for sight is the substance or essence of
20 the eye which corresponds to the formula,[1] the eye being merely
the matter of seeing ;[2] when seeing is removed the eye is
no longer an eye, except in name—it is no more a real eye
than the eye of a statue or of a painted figure. We must
now extend our consideration from the ' parts ' to the
whole living body; for what the departmental sense is to
the bodily part which is its organ, that the whole faculty
of sense is to the whole sensitive body as such.

25 We must not understand by that which is ' potentially
capable of living ' what has lost the soul it had, but only
what still retains it ; but seeds and fruits are bodies which
possess the qualification.[3] Consequently, while waking is
actuality in a sense corresponding to the cutting and the
413ᵃ seeing,[4] the soul is actuality in the sense corresponding to
the power of sight and the power in the tool ;[5] the body
corresponds to what exists in potentiality ; as the pupil
plus the power of sight constitutes the eye, so the soul *plus*
the body constitutes the animal.

From this it indubitably follows that the soul is inseparable from its body, or at any rate that certain parts of it are
5 (if it has parts)—for the actuality of some of them is nothing
but the actualities of their bodily parts. Yet some may be
separable because they are not the actualities of any body
at all. Further, we have no light on the problem whether
the soul may not be the actuality of its body in the sense
in which the sailor is the actuality [6] of the ship.

This must suffice as our sketch or outline determination
10 of the nature of soul.

Since what is clear or logically more evident emerges from ₂
what in itself is confused but more observable by us, we
must reconsider our results from this point of view. For it
is not enough for a definitive formula to express as most
15 now do the mere fact; it must include and exhibit the ground

---

[1] i.e. which states what it is to be an eye.
[2] Punctuating in l. 20 λόγον (ὁ δ' . . . ὄψεως), ἧς, with Bywater.
[3] Though only potentially, i.e. they are at a further remove from
actuality than the fully formed and organized body.
[4] i.e. to the second grade of actuality.
[5] i.e. to the first grade of actuality.　　　　　　[6] i.e. actuator.

also. At present definitions are given in a form analogous to the conclusion of a syllogism ; e. g. What is squaring ? The construction of an equilateral rectangle equal to a given oblong rectangle. Such a definition is in form equivalent to a conclusion.[1] One that tells us that squaring is the discovery of a line which is a mean proportional between the two unequal sides of the given rectangle discloses the ground of what is defined.

We resume our inquiry from a fresh starting-point by 20 calling attention to the fact that what has soul in it differs from what has not in that the former displays life Now this word has more than one sense, and provided any one alone of these is found in a thing we say that thing is living. Living, that is, may mean thinking or perception or local movement and rest, or movement in the sense of nutrition, decay and growth. Hence we think of plants also as living, 25 for they are observed to possess in themselves an originative power through which they increase or decrease in all spatial directions ; they grow up *and* down, and everything that grows increases its bulk alike in both directions or indeed in all, and continues to live so long as it can absorb nutri- 30 ment.

This power of self-nutrition can be isolated from the other powers mentioned, but not they from it—in mortal beings at least. The fact is obvious in plants ; for it is the only psychic power they possess.

This is the originative power the possession of which leads 413ᵇ us to speak of things as *living* at all, but it is the possession of sensation that leads us for the first time to speak of living things as animals ; for even those beings which possess no power of local movement but do possess the power of sensation we call animals and not merely living things.

The primary form of sense is touch, which belongs to all animals. Just as the power of self-nutrition can be isolated 5 from touch and sensation generally, so touch can be iso- lated from all other forms of sense. (By the power of self- nutrition we mean that departmental power of the soul which is common to plants and animals : all animals

---

[1] i. e. it has nothing in it corresponding to a middle term.

whatsoever are observed to have the sense of touch.) What
10 the explanation of these two facts is, we must discuss later.[1]
At present we must confine ourselves to saying that soul is
the source of these phenomena and is characterized by them,
viz. by the powers of self-nutrition, sensation, thinking,
and motivity.

Is each of these a soul or a part of a soul? And if a part,
a part in what sense? A part merely distinguishable by
15 definition or a part distinct in local situation as well? In the
case of certain of these powers, the answers to these questions are easy, in the case of others we are puzzled what to
say. Just as in the case of plants which when divided are
observed to continue to live though removed to a distance
from one another (thus showing that in *their* case the soul
of each individual plant before division was actually one,
potentially many), so we notice a similar result in other
20 varieties of soul, i.e. in insects which have been cut in two;
each of the segments possesses both sensation and local
movement; and if sensation, necessarily also imagination
and appetition; for, where there is sensation, there is also
pleasure and pain, and, where these, necessarily also
desire.

We have no evidence as yet about mind or the power to
25 think; it seems to be a widely different kind of soul, differing as what is eternal from what is perishable; it alone is
capable of existence in isolation from all other psychic
powers. All the other parts of soul, it is evident from what
we have said, are, in spite of certain statements to the contrary, incapable of separate existence though, of course,
distinguishable by definition. If opining is distinct from per-
30 ceiving, to be capable of opining and to be capable of perceiving must be distinct, and so with all the other forms of
living above enumerated. Further, some animals possess all
these parts of soul, some certain of them only, others one only
(this is what enables us to classify animals); the cause must
414^a be considered later.[2] A similar arrangement is found also within the field of the senses; some classes of animals have all

---

[1] iii. 12, esp. 434^a 22-30, ^b10 ff.   [2] iii. 12, 13.

the senses, some only certain of them, others only one, the most indispensable, touch.

Since the expression 'that whereby we live and perceive' has two meanings, just like the expression 'that whereby we 5 know'—that may mean either (a) knowledge or (b) the soul, for we can speak of knowing *by* or *with* either, and similarly that whereby we are in health may be either[1] (a) health or (b) the body or some part of the body ; and since of the two terms thus contrasted knowledge or health is the name of a form, essence, or ratio, or if we so express it an actuality of a recipient matter—knowledge of what is 10 capable of knowing, health of what is capable of being made healthy[2] (for the operation of that which is capable of originating change terminates and has its seat in what is changed or altered) ; further, since it is the soul by or with which primarily we live, perceive, and think:—it follows that the soul must be a ratio or formulable essence, not a matter or subject. For, as we said,[3] the word substance has three meanings—form, matter, and the complex of both—and of 15 these three what is called matter is potentiality, what is called form actuality. Since then the complex here is the living thing, the body cannot be the actuality of the soul; it is the soul which is the actuality of a certain kind of body. Hence the rightness of the view that the soul cannot be without a body, while it cannot *be* a body ; it is not a body but 20 something relative to a body. That is why it is *in* a body, and a body of a definite kind. It was a mistake, therefore, to do as former thinkers did, merely to fit it into a body without adding a definite specification of the kind or character of that body. Reflection confirms the observed fact ; the actuality of 25 any given thing can only be realized in what is already potentially that thing, i. e. in a matter of its own appropriate to it. From all this it follows that soul is an actuality or formulable essence of something that possesses a potentiality of being besouled.

---

[1] Omitting ᾧ in l. 7, with Bywater.
[2] The reading ὑγιαστοῦ (in l. 10) is better than ὑγιαστικοῦ. As between the two forms the MS. evidence is of little if any value.
[3] 412ᵃ 7.

Of the psychic powers above enumerated [1] some kinds of 3
living things, as we have said,[2] possess all, some less than all,
30 others one only. Those we have mentioned are the nutritive, the appetitive, the sensory, the locomotive, and the
power of thinking. Plants have none but the first, the
nutritive, while another order of living things has this *plus*
414ᵇ the sensory. If any order of living things has the
sensory, it must also have the appetitive; for appetite is
the genus of which desire, passion, and wish are the
species; now all animals have one sense at least, viz.
touch, and whatever has a sense has the capacity for
pleasure and pain and therefore has pleasant and painful
objects present to it, and wherever these are present, there
5 is desire, for desire is just appetition of what is pleasant.
Further, all animals have the sense for food (for touch is
the sense for food); the food of all living things consists
of what is dry, moist, hot, cold, and these are the qualities
apprehended by touch; all other sensible qualities are
10 apprehended by touch only indirectly. Sounds, colours,
and odours contribute nothing to nutriment; flavours fall
within the field of tangible qualities. Hunger and thirst are
forms of desire, hunger a desire for what is dry and hot,
thirst a desire for what is cold and moist; flavour is a
sort of seasoning added to both. We must later [3] clear up
15 these points, but at present it may be enough to say that all
animals that possess the sense of touch have also appetition. The case of imagination is obscure; we must examine
it later.[4] Certain kinds of animals possess in addition the
power of locomotion, and still another order of animate
beings, i.e. man and possibly another order like man or
20 superior to him, the power of thinking, i.e. mind. It is
now evident that a single definition can be given of
soul only in the same sense as one can be given of figure.
For, as in that case there is no figure distinguishable and
apart from triangle, &c., so here there is no soul apart from
the forms of soul just enumerated. It is true that a highly
general definition can be given for figure which will fit all

---

[1] 413ᵃ 23–5, ᵇ11–13, 21–4.   [2] 413ᵇ 32–414ᵃ 1.
[3] c. II. iii. 12. 434ᵇ 18–21, *De Sensu* 4.   [4] iii. 3, 11. 433ᵇ 31–434ᵃ 7.

figures without expressing the peculiar nature of any
figure. So here in the case of soul and its specific forms.
Hence it is absurd in this and similar cases to demand an 25
absolutely general definition which will fail to express the
peculiar nature of anything that *is*, or again, omitting this,
to look for separate definitions corresponding to each
infima species. The cases of figure and soul are exactly
parallel; for the particulars subsumed under the common name in both cases—figures and living beings
—constitute a series, each successive term of which 30
potentially contains its predecessor, e. g. the square the
triangle, the sensory power the self-nutritive. Hence we
must ask in the case of each order of living things, What is
its soul, i e. What is the soul of plant, animal, man? Why
the terms are related in this serial way must form the sub-
ject of later examination.[1] But the facts are that the power 415^a
of perception is never found apart from the power of self-
nutrition, while—in plants—the latter is found isolated from
the former. Again, no sense is found apart from that of
touch, while touch *is* found by itself; many animals have 5
neither sight, hearing, nor smell. Again, among living
things that possess sense some have the power of locomotion, some not. Lastly, certain living beings—a small
minority—possess calculation and thought, for (among
mortal beings) those which possess calculation have all the
other powers above mentioned, while the converse does not 10
hold—indeed some live by imagination alone, while others
have not even imagination. The mind that knows with
immediate intuition presents a different problem.[2]

It is evident that the way to give the most adequate
definition of soul is to seek in the case of *each* of its forms for
the most appropriate definition.

4   It is necessary for the student of these forms of soul first
to find a definition of each, expressive of what it is, and 15
then to investigate its derivative properties, &c. But if we
are to express what each is, viz. what the thinking power
is, or the perceptive, or the nutritive, we must go farther

[1] iii. 12, 13.   [2] Cf. iii. 4-8.

back and first give an account of thinking or perceiving, for in the order of investigation the question of what an agent does precedes the question, what enables it to do what 20 it does. If this is correct, we must on the same ground go yet another step farther back and have some clear view of the objects of each ; thus we must *start* with these objects, e. g. with food, with what is perceptible, or with what is intelligible.

It follows that first of all we must treat of nutrition and reproduction,[1] for the nutritive soul is found along with all the others and is the most primitive and widely distributed power of soul, being indeed that one in virtue of which all 25 are said to have life. The acts in which it manifests itself are reproduction and the use of food—reproduction, I say, because for any living thing that has reached its normal development and which is unmutilated, and whose mode of generation is not spontaneous, the most natural act is the production of another like itself, an animal producing an animal, a plant a plant, in order that, as far as its nature allows, it **415ᵇ** may partake in the eternal and divine. That is the goal towards which all things strive, that for the sake of which they do whatsoever their nature renders possible. The phrase ' for the sake of which ' is ambiguous ; it may mean either (*a*) the end to achieve which, or (*b*) the being in whose interest, the act is done. Since then no living thing is able to partake in what is eternal and divine by uninterrupted continuance (for nothing perishable can for ever remain one 5 and the same), it tries to achieve that end in the only way possible to it, and success is possible in varying degrees ; so it remains not indeed as the self-same individual but continues its existence in something *like* itself—not numerically but specifically one.[2]

The soul is the cause or source of the living body. The terms cause and source have many senses. But the soul is the cause of its body alike in all three senses which 10 we explicitly recognize. It is (*a*) the source or origin of

---

[1] Sc. ' which we shall see to be inseparable from nutrition '.

[2] There is an unbroken current of the same specific life flowing through a discontinuous series of individual beings of the same species united by descent.

movement, it is (*b*) the end, it is (*c*) the essence of the whole living body.

That it is the last, is clear; for in everything the essence is identical with the ground of its being, and here, in the case of living things, their being is to live, and of their being and their living the soul in them is the cause or source. Further, the actuality of whatever is potential is identical with its formulable essence.

It is manifest that the soul is also the final cause of its body. For Nature, like mind, always does whatever it does for the sake of something, which something is its end. To that something corresponds in the case of animals the soul and in this it follows the order of nature; all natural bodies are organs of the soul. This is true of those that enter into the constitution of plants as well as of those which enter into that of animals. This shows that that for the sake of which they are is soul. We must here recall the two senses of 'that for the sake of which',viz. (*a*) the end to achieve which, and (*b*) the being in whose interest, anything is or is done.

We must maintain, further, that the soul is also the cause of the living body as the original source of local movement. The power of locomotion is not found, however, in all living things. But change of quality and change of quantity are also due to the soul. Sensation is held to be a qualitative alteration, and nothing except what has soul in it is capable of sensation. The same holds of the quantitative changes which constitute growth and decay; nothing grows or decays naturally[1] except what feeds itself, and nothing feeds itself except what has a share of soul in it.

Empedocles is wrong in adding that growth in plants is to be explained, the downward rooting by the natural tendency of earth to travel downwards, and the upward branching by the similar natural tendency of fire to travel upwards. For he misinterprets up and down; up and down are not for all things what they are for the whole Cosmos: if we are to distinguish and identify organs according to their *functions*, the roots of plants are analogous to the head in

[1] i.e. of itself.

animals. Further, we must ask what is the force that holds
together the earth and the fire which tend to travel in
contrary directions ; if there is no counteracting force, they
will be torn asunder ; if there is, this must be the soul and
the cause of nutrition and growth. By some the element
of fire is held to be *the* cause of nutrition and growth,
10 for it alone of the primary bodies or elements is observed
to feed and increase *itself*. Hence the suggestion that in
both plants and animals it is it which is the operative force.
A concurrent cause in a sense it certainly is, but not the
15 principal cause ; that is rather the soul ; for while the
growth of fire goes on without limit so long as there is
a supply of fuel, in the case of all complex wholes formed in
the course of nature there is a limit or ratio which determines their size and increase, and limit and ratio are marks
of soul but not of fire, and belong to the side of formulable
essence rather than that of matter.

Nutrition and reproduction are due to one and the same
psychic power. It is necessary first to give precision to our
20 account of food, for it is by this function of absorbing food
that this psychic power is distinguished from all the others.
The current view is that what serves as food to a living
thing is what is contrary to it—not that in every pair of
contraries each is food to the other : to be food a contrary
must not only be transformable into the other and vice versa,
it must also in so doing increase the bulk of the other.
Many a contrary is transformed into its other and vice versa,
where neither is even a quantum and so cannot increase in
25 bulk, e. g. an invalid into a healthy subject. It is clear that
not even those contraries which satisfy both the conditions
mentioned above are food to one another in precisely the
same sense ; water may be said to feed fire, but not fire
water. Where the members of the pair are elementary bodies
only one of the contraries, it would appear, can be said to
feed the other. But there is a difficulty here. One set of
30 thinkers assert that like is fed, as well as increased in
amount, by like. Another set, as we have said, maintain
the very reverse, viz. that what feeds and what is fed are
contrary to one another ; like, they argue, is incapable of

being affected by like; but food is changed in the process
of digestion, and change is always *to* what is opposite or to
what is intermediate. Further, food is acted upon by 35
what is nourished by it, not the other way round, as timber **416**^b
is worked by a carpenter and not conversely; there is a
change in the carpenter but it is merely a change from not-
working to working. In answering this problem it makes
all the difference whether we mean by 'the food' the 'finished'
or the 'raw' product. If we use the word food of both, viz.
of the completely undigested and the completely digested
matter, we can justify both the rival accounts of it; taking 5
food in the sense of undigested matter, it is the contrary of
what is fed by it, taking it as digested it is like what is fed
by it. Consequently it is clear that in a certain sense we may
say that both parties are right, both wrong.

Since nothing except what is alive can be fed, what is
fed is the besouled body and just because it has soul in it.
Hence food is essentially related to what has soul in it. 10
Food has a power which is other than the power to increase
the bulk of what is fed by it; so far forth as what has soul
in it is a quantum, food may increase its quantity, but it is
only so far as what has soul in it is a 'this-somewhat' or
substance that food acts *as* food; in that case it maintains
the being of what is fed, and that continues to be what it is
so long as the process of nutrition continues. Further, it is 15
the agent in generation, i.e. not the generation of the individual fed but the reproduction of another like it; the
substance of the individual fed is already in existence;
the existence of no substance is a self-generation but only
a self-maintenance.

Hence the psychic power which we are now studying
may be described as that which tends to maintain whatever
has this power in it of continuing such as it was, and food
helps it to do its work. That is why, if deprived of food,
it must cease to be.

The process of nutrition involves three factors, (*a*) what 20
is fed, (*b*) that wherewith it is fed, (*c*) what does the feeding;
of these (*c*) is the first soul,[1] (*a*) the body which has that

---

[1] i.e. the earliest and most indispensable kind of soul.

soul in it, (*b*) the food. But since it is right to call things after the ends they realize, and the end of this soul is to generate another being like that in which it is, the first soul 25 ought to be named the reproductive soul. The expression (*b*) 'wherewith it is fed' is ambiguous just as is the expression 'wherewith the ship is steered'; that may mean either (i) the hand or (ii) the rudder, i.e. either (i) what is moved and sets in movement, or (ii) what is merely moved. We can apply this analogy here if we recall that all food must be capable of being digested, and that what produces digestion is warmth; that is why everything that has soul in it possesses warmth.

30 We have now given an outline account of the nature of food; further details must be given in the appropriate place.[1]

Having made these distinctions let us now speak of 5 sensation in the widest sense. Sensation depends, as we have said,[2] on a process of movement or affection from without, for it is held to be some sort of change of quality. 35 Now some thinkers assert that like is affected only by like; 417ᵃ in what sense this is possible and in what sense impossible, we have explained in our general discussion of acting and being acted upon.[3]

Here arises a problem: why do we not perceive the senses themselves [4] as well as the external objects of sense, or why without the stimulation of external objects do they not produce sensation, seeing that they contain in themselves 5 fire, earth, and all the other elements, which are the direct or indirect objects of sense? It is clear that what is sensitive is so only potentially, not actually. The power of sense is parallel to what is combustible, for that never ignites itself spontaneously, but requires an agent which has the power of starting ignition; otherwise it could have set itself on fire, and would not have needed actual fire to set it ablaze.

---

[1] In a lost (or never written) work *On Nutrition* or *On Increase and Nutrition*; cf. Bonitz, *Index* 104ᵇ 16-28.
[2] 415ᵇ 24, cf. 410ᵃ 25.   [3] *De Gen. et Corr.* 323ᵇ 18 ff.
[4] This probably means the *sensoria*.

In reply we must recall that we use the word 'perceive' in two ways, for we say (a) that what has the power to 10 hear or see, 'sees' or 'hears', even though it is at the moment asleep, and also (b) that what is actually seeing or hearing, 'sees' or 'hears'. Hence 'sense' too must have two meanings, sense potential, and sense actual. Similarly ' to be a sentient ' means either (a) to have a certain power or (b) to manifest a certain activity. To begin with, for a time, let us speak as if there were no difference between (i) being 15 moved or affected, and (ii) being active, for movement is a kind of activity—an imperfect kind, as has elsewhere been explained.¹ Everything that is acted upon or moved is acted upon by an agent which is actually at work. Hence it is that in one sense, as has already been stated,² what acts and what is acted upon are like, in another unlike, i. e. prior to and 20 during the change the two factors are unlike, after it like.

But we must now distinguish not only *between* what is potential and what is actual but also different senses in which things can be said to be potential or actual; up to now we have been speaking as if each of these phrases had only one sense. We can speak of something as ' a knower ' either (a) as when we say that man is a knower, meaning that man falls within the class of beings that know or have knowledge, or (b) as when we are speaking of a man who 25 possesses a knowledge of grammar ; each of these is so called as having in him a certain potentiality, but there is a difference between their respective potentialities, the one (a) being a potential knower, because his kind or matter is such and such, the other (b), because he can in the absence of any external counteracting cause realize his knowledge in actual knowing at will. This implies a third meaning of ' a knower ' (c), one who is already realizing his knowledge— he is a knower in actuality and in the most proper sense is knowing, e. g. this A.³ Both the former are potential 30 knowers, who realize their respective potentialities, the one (a) by change of quality, i. e. repeated transitions from one

¹ *Phys.* 201ᵇ 31, 257ᵇ 8.   ² 416ᵃ 29–ᵇ9.
³ i.e. this individual item of grammatical knowledge, e. g. that the 1st person singular of the perfect indicative active of λύω ends in -a.

417ᵇ

state to its opposite[1] under instruction, the other (b) by the transition from the inactive possession of sense or grammar to their active exercise. The two kinds of transition are distinct.

Also the expression 'to be acted upon' has more than one meaning; it may mean either (a) the extinction of one of two contraries by the other, or (b) the maintenance of what is potential by the agency of what is actual and already like what is acted upon, with such likeness as is compatible 5 with one's being actual and the other potential. For what possesses knowledge becomes an actual knower by a transition which is either not an alteration of it at all (being in reality a development into its true self or actuality) or at least an alteration in a quite different sense from the usual meaning.

Hence it is wrong to speak of a wise man as being 'altered' when he uses his wisdom, just as it would be absurd to speak of a builder as being altered when he is using his skill in building a house.

10　What in the case of knowing or understanding leads from potentiality to actuality ought not to be called teaching[2] but something else. That which starting with the power to know learns or acquires knowledge through the agency of one who actually knows and has the power of teaching either (a) ought not to be said 'to be acted upon' at all *or* 15 (b) we must recognize two senses of alteration, viz. (i) the substitution of one quality for another, the first being the contrary of the second, or (ii) the development of an existent quality from potentiality in the direction of fixity or nature.

In the case of what is to possess sense, the first transition is due to the action of the male parent and takes place before birth so that at birth the living thing is, in respect of sensation, at the stage which corresponds to the *possession* of knowledge. Actual sensation corresponds to the stage of the exercise of knowledge. But between the two cases 20 compared there is a difference; the objects that excite the sensory powers to activity, the seen, the heard, &c., are out-

---

[1] viz. from ignorance or error to knowledge or truth.
[2] It would have been clearer had he said 'learning'.

side. The ground of this difference is that what actual
sensation apprehends is individuals, while what knowledge
apprehends is universals, and these are in a sense within
the soul. That is why a man can exercise his knowledge
when he wishes, but his sensation does not depend upon
himself—a sensible object must be there. A similar 25
statement must be made about our *knowledge* of what is
sensible—on the same ground, viz. that the sensible objects
are individual and external.

A later more appropriate occasion may be found[1]
thoroughly to clear up all this. At present it must be 30
enough to recognize the distinctions already drawn; a thing
may be said to be potential in either of two senses, (a) in
the sense in which we might say of a boy that he may
become a general or (b) in the sense in which we might say
the same of an adult, and there are two corresponding senses
of the term 'a potential sentient'. There are no separate 418^a
names for the two stages of potentiality; we have pointed out
that they are different and how they are different. We cannot help using the incorrect terms 'being acted upon or
altered' of the two transitions involved. As we have said,[2]
what has the power of sensation is potentially like what
the perceived object is actually; that is, while at the beginning
of the process of its being acted upon the two interacting
factors are dissimilar, at the end the one acted upon is 5
assimilated to the other and is identical in quality with it.

6 In dealing with each of the senses we shall have first to
speak of the objects which are perceptible by each. The
term 'object of sense' covers three kinds of objects, two
kinds of which are, in our language, directly perceptible,
while the remaining one is only incidentally perceptible. Of
the first two kinds one (a) consists of what is perceptible
by a single sense, the other (b) of what is perceptible by any 10
and all of the senses.[3] I call by the name of special
object of this or that sense that which cannot be perceived
by any other sense than that one and in respect of which no

---

[1] iii. 4, 5.   [2] 417^a 12–20.
[3] Really, it is enough if it is perceptible by more than one sense.

error is possible; in this sense colour is the special object of sight, sound of hearing, flavour of taste. Touch, indeed, discriminates more than one set of different qualities.
15 Each sense has one kind of object which it discerns, and never errs in reporting that what is before it is colour or sound (though it may err as to what it is that is coloured or where that is, or what it is that is sounding or where that is). Such objects are what we propose to call the special objects of this or that sense.

'Common sensibles' are movement, rest, number, figure, magnitude; these are not peculiar to any one sense, but are common to all. There are at any rate certain kinds of movement which are perceptible both by touch and by sight.

20   We speak of an incidental object of sense where e. g. the white object which we see is the son of Diares; here because 'being the son of Diares' is incidental to the directly visible white patch we speak of the son of Diares as being (incidentally) perceived or seen by us. Because this is only incidentally an object of sense, it in no way as such affects the senses. Of the two former kinds, both of which are in their own nature perceptible by sense, the first kind— that of special objects of the several senses—constitute
25 *the* objects of sense in the strictest sense of the term and it is to them that in the nature of things the structure of each several sense is adapted.

The object of sight is the visible, and what is visible is 7 (*a*) colour and (*b*) a certain kind of object which can be described in words but which has no single name; what we mean by (*b*) will be abundantly clear as we proceed. Whatever is visible is colour and colour is what lies upon
30 what is in its own nature visible; 'in its own nature' here means not that visibility is involved in the definition of what thus underlies colour, but that that substratum contains in itself the cause of visibility. Every colour has in it the power to set in movement what is actually trans-
418ᵇ parent; that power constitutes its very nature. That is why it is not visible except with the help of light; it

is only in light that the colour of a thing is seen.   Hence
our first task is to explain what light is.

Now there clearly is something which is transparent,
and by 'transparent' I mean what is visible, and yet not 5
visible in itself, but rather owing its visibility to the colour
of something else; of this character are air, water, and
many solid bodies.   Neither air nor water is transparent
because it is air or water ; they are transparent because
each of them has contained in it a certain substance which is
the same in both and is also found in the eternal body
which constitutes the uppermost shell of the physical
Cosmos.   Of this substance light is the activity—the
activity of what is transparent so far forth as it has in it
the determinate power of becoming transparent ; where 10
this power is present, there is also the potentiality of the
contrary, viz. darkness.   Light is as it were the proper
colour of what is transparent, and exists whenever the
potentially transparent is excited to actuality by the
influence of fire or something resembling ' the uppermost
body' ; for fire too contains something which is one and
the same with the substance in question.

We have now explained what the transparent is and
what light is; light is neither fire nor any kind whatsoever
of body nor an efflux from any kind of body (if it were, it 15
would again itself be a kind of body)—it is the presence of
fire or something resembling fire in what is transparent.
It is certainly not a body, for two bodies cannot be present
in the same place.   The opposite of light is darkness ;
darkness is the absence from what is transparent of the
corresponding positive state above characterized ; clearly
therefore, light is just the presence of that.

Empedocles (and with him all others who used the same 20
forms of expression) was wrong in speaking of light as
' travelling' or being at a given moment between the earth
and its envelope, its movement being unobservable by us ;
that view is contrary both to the clear evidence of argument
and to the observed facts ; if the distance traversed were
short, the movement might have been unobservable, but where 25
the distance is from extreme East to extreme West, the
draught upon our powers of belief is too great.

What is capable of taking on colour is what in itself is colourless, as what can take on sound is what is soundless; what is colourless includes (*a*) what is transparent and (*b*) what is invisible or scarcely visible, i. e. what is 'dark'. 30 The latter (*b*) is the same as what is transparent, when it is potentially, not of course when it is actually transparent; it is the same substance which is now darkness, now light.

419^a Not everything that is visible depends upon light for its visibility. This is only true of the 'proper' colour of things. Some objects of sight which in light are invisible, in darkness stimulate the sense; that is, things that appear fiery or shining. This class of objects has no simple 5 common name, but instances of it are fungi, flesh,[1] heads, scales, and eyes of fish. In none of these is what is seen their own 'proper' colour. Why we see these at all is another question. At present what is obvious is that what is seen in light is always colour. That is why without the help of light colour remains invisible. Its being colour at all 10 means precisely its having in it the power to set in movement what is already actually transparent, and, as we have seen, the actuality of what is transparent is just light.

The following experiment makes the necessity of a medium clear. If what has colour is placed in immediate contact with the eye, it cannot be seen. Colour sets in movement not the sense organ but what is transparent, e. g. the air, and that, extending continuously from the 15 object of the organ, sets the latter in movement. Democritus misrepresents the facts when he expresses the opinion that if the interspace were empty one could distinctly see an ant on the vault of the sky; that is an impossibility. Seeing is due to an affection or change of what has the perceptive faculty, and it cannot be affected by the seen colour itself; it remains that it must be affected by what comes between. Hence it is indispensable that there be 20 *something* in between—if there were nothing, so far from

---

[1] Reading κρέας in l. 5 with Chandler. In fact flesh is, and horn is not, an instance of the class.

seeing with greater distinctness, we should see nothing at
all.

We have now explained the cause why colour cannot be
seen otherwise than in light. Fire on the other hand is seen
both in darkness and in light; this double possibility
follows necessarily from our theory, for it is just fire
that makes what is potentially transparent actually transparent.

The same account holds also of sound and smell; if 25
the object of either of these senses is in immediate contact
with the organ no sensation is produced. In both cases
the object sets in movement only what lies between, and
this in turn sets the organ in movement: if what sounds or
smells is brought into immediate contact with the organ,
no sensation will be produced. The same, in spite of all 30
appearances, applies also to touch and taste; why there is
this apparent difference will be clear later.[1] What comes
between in the case of sounds is air; the corresponding
medium in the case of smell has no name. But, corresponding to what is transparent in the case of colour, there
is a quality found both in air and water, which serves as
a medium for what has smell—I say ' in water ' because 35
animals that live in water as well as those that live on land
seem to possess the sense of smell, and ' in air ' because 419ᵇ
man and all other land animals that breathe, perceive smells
only when they breathe air in. The explanation of this
too will be given later.[2]

8   Now let us, to begin with, make certain distinctions about
sound and hearing.

Sound may mean either of two things—(a) actual, and 5
(b) potential, sound. There are certain things which, as
we say, ' have no sound ', e. g. sponges or wool, others which
have, e. g. bronze and in general all things which are smooth
and solid—the latter are said to have a sound because they
can make a sound, i. e. can generate actual sound between
themselves and the organ of hearing.

Actual sound requires for its occurrence (i, ii) two such

[1] 422ᵇ 34 ff.   [2] 421ᵇ 13–422ᵃ 6.

10 bodies and (iii) a space between them; for it is generated by an impact. Hence it is impossible for one body only to generate a sound—there must be a body impinging and a body impinged upon; what sounds does so by striking against something else, and this is impossible without a movement from place to place.

As we have said, not all bodies can by impact on one another produce sound; impact on wool makes no sound, 15 while the impact on bronze or any body which is smooth and hollow does. Bronze gives out a sound when struck because it is smooth; bodies which are hollow owing to reflection repeat the original impact over and over again, the body originally set in movement being unable to escape from the concavity.

Further, we must remark that sound is heard both in air and in water, though less distinctly in the latter. Yet neither air nor water is the principal cause of sound. 20 What is required for the production of sound is an impact of two solids against one another and against the air. The latter condition is satisfied when the air impinged upon does not retreat before the blow, i. e. is not dissipated by it.

That is why it must be struck with a sudden sharp blow, if it is to sound—the movement of the whip must outrun the dispersion of the air, just as one might get in a stroke at a heap or whirl of sand as it was travelling rapidly past. 25 An echo occurs, when, a mass of air having been unified, bounded, and prevented from dissipation by the containing walls of a vessel, the air originally struck by the impinging body and set in movement by it rebounds from this mass of air like a ball from a wall. It is probable that in all generation of sound echo takes place, though it is frequently only indistinctly heard. What happens here must be analogous to what happens in the case of light; light is 30 *always* reflected—otherwise it would not be diffused and outside what was directly illuminated by the sun there would be blank darkness; but this reflected light is not always strong enough, as it *is* when it is reflected from water, bronze, and other smooth bodies, to cast a shadow, which is the distinguishing mark by which we recognize light.

It is rightly said that an empty space plays the chief part in the production of hearing, for what people mean by 'the vacuum' is the air, which is what causes hearing, when that air is set in movement as one continuous mass ; but owing to its friability it emits no sound, being dissipated 35 by impinging upon any surface which is not smooth.   When **420**^a the surface on which it impinges is quite smooth, what is produced by the original impact is a united mass, a result due to the smoothness of the surface with which the air is in contact at the other end.

What has the power of producing sound is what has the power of setting in movement a single mass of air which is continuous from the impinging body up to the organ of hearing.   The organ of hearing is physically united with air,[1] and because it is *in* air, the air inside is moved con- currently with the air outside.   Hence animals do not hear 5 with all parts of their bodies, nor do all parts admit of the entrance of air ; for even the part which can be moved and can sound has not air everywhere in it.[2] Air in itself is, owing to its friability, quite soundless ; only when its dissipation is prevented is its movement sound.   The air in the ear is built into a chamber just to prevent this dissipating movement, in order that the animal may accurately appre- 10 hend all varieties of the movements of the air outside. That is why we hear also in water, viz. because the water cannot get into the air chamber or even, owing to the spirals, into the outer ear. If this does happen, hearing ceases, as it also does if the tympanic membrane is damaged, just as sight ceases if the membrane covering the pupil is damaged.   It is also a test of deafness whether the ear does 15 or does not reverberate like a horn; the air inside the ear has always a movement of its own, but the sound we hear is always the sounding of something else, not of the organ itself.   That is why we say that we hear with what is empty and echoes, viz. because what we hear with is a chamber which contains a bounded mass of air.

---

[1] i.e. it has air incorporated in its structure.
[2] Reading ἔμψοφον in l. 7 : the required air is localized not only in the body but in the ear.

Which is it that ' sounds ', the striking body or the struck ?
20 Is not the answer ' it is both, but each in a different way '?
Sound is a movement of what can rebound from a smooth
surface when struck against it.　As we have explained [1] not
everything sounds when it strikes or is struck, e.g. if one
needle is struck against another, neither emits any sound.
25 In order, therefore, that sound may be generated, what is
struck must be smooth, to enable the air to rebound and be
shaken off from it in one piece.

The distinctions between different sounding bodies show
themselves only in actual sound ; [2] as without the help of
light colours remain invisible, so without the help of actual
sound the distinctions between acute and grave sounds
remain inaudible.　Acute and grave are here metaphors,
transferred from their proper sphere, viz. that of touch,
30 where they mean respectively (*a*) what moves the sense
much in a short time, (*b*) what moves the sense little in a
long time.　Not that what is sharp really moves fast, and
what is grave, slowly, but that the difference in the qualities
of the one and the other movement is due to their respective
420ᵇ speeds.　There seems to be a sort of parallelism between
what is acute or grave to hearing and what is sharp or
blunt to touch ; what is sharp as it were stabs, while what
is blunt pushes, the one producing its effect in a short, the
other in a long time, so that the one is quick, the other
slow.

5　Let the foregoing suffice as an analysis of sound.　Voice
is a kind of sound characteristic of what has soul in it ;
nothing that is without soul utters voice, it being only by
a metaphor that we speak of the voice of the flute or the lyre
or generally of what (being without soul) possesses the
power of producing a succession of notes which differ in
length and pitch and timbre.　The metaphor is based on
the fact that all these differences are found also in voice.
Many animals are voiceless, e.g. all non-sanguineous animals
10 and among sanguineous animals fish.　This is just what we
should expect, since voice is a certain movement of air.

---

[1] 419ᵇ 6, 13.
[2] i.e. when these bodies, e.g. the strings of a lyre, are actually sounding.

The fish, like those in the Achelous, which are said to have
voice, really make the sounds with their gills or some
similar organ. Voice is the sound made by an animal, and
that with a special organ. As we saw, everything that
makes a sound does so by the impact of something (*a*) against
something else, (*b*) across a space, (*c*) filled with air ; hence 15
it is only to be expected that no animals utter voice except
those which take in air. Once air is inbreathed, Nature
uses it for two different purposes, as the tongue is used both
for tasting and for articulating; in that case of the two
functions tasting is necessary for the animal's existence
(hence it is found more widely distributed), while articulate
speech is a luxury subserving its possessor's well-being;
similarly in the former case Nature employs the breath 20
both as an indispensable means to the regulation of the
inner temperature of the living body and also as the matter
of articulate voice, in the interests of its possessor's well-
being. Why its former use is indispensable must be
discussed elsewhere.[1]

The organ of respiration is the windpipe, and the organ
to which this is related as means to end is the lungs. The
latter is the part of the body by which the temperature of
land animals is raised above that of all others. But what 25
primarily requires the air drawn in by respiration is not
only this but the region surrounding the heart. That is
why when animals breathe the air must penetrate inwards.

Voice then is the impact of the inbreathed air against
the ' windpipe ', and the agent that produces the impact is
the soul resident in these parts of the body. Not every
sound, as we said, made by an animal is voice (even with 30
the tongue we may merely make a sound which is not
voice, or without the tongue as in coughing) ; what produces
the impact must have soul in it and must be accompanied
by an act of imagination, for voice is a sound *with a
meaning*, and is not *merely* the result of any impact of the
breath as in coughing ; in voice the breath in the windpipe
is used as an instrument to knock with against the walls of
the windpipe. This is confirmed by our inability to speak 421^a

[1] *De Resp.* 478^a 28; *P.A.* 642^a 31-^b4.

when we are breathing either out or in—we can only do so
by holding our breath; we make the movements with the
breath so checked.   It is clear also why fish are voiceless;
they have no windpipe.   And they have no windpipe
5 because they do not breathe or take in air.   Why they do
not is a question belonging to another inquiry.[1]

    Smell and its object are much less easy to determine 9
than what we have hitherto discussed; the distinguishing
characteristic of the object of smell is less obvious than
those of sound or colour.   The ground of this is that our
power of smell is less discriminating and in general inferior
10 to that of many species of animals; men have a poor sense
of smell and our apprehension of its proper objects is inse-
parably bound up with and so confused by pleasure and
pain, which shows that in us the organ is inaccurate.   It is
probable that there is a parallel failure in the perception
of colour by animals that have hard eyes: probably they
discriminate differences of colour only by the presence or
15 absence of what excites fear, and that it is thus that human
beings distinguish smells.   It seems that there is an analogy
between smell and taste, and that the species of tastes
run parallel to those of smells—the only difference being
that our sense of taste is more discriminating than our sense
of smell, because the former is a modification of touch,
which reaches in man the maximum of discriminative
20 accuracy.   While in respect of all the other senses we fall
below many species of animals, in respect of touch we far
excel all other species in exactness of discrimination.   That
is why man is the most intelligent of all animals.   This is
confirmed by the fact that it is to differences in the organ
of touch and to nothing else that the differences between
man and man in respect of natural endowment are due;
25 men whose flesh is hard are ill-endowed by nature, men whose
flesh is soft, well-endowed.

    As flavours may be divided into (*a*) sweet, (*b*) bitter, so
with smells.   In some things the flavour and the smell have
the same quality, i.e. both are sweet or both bitter, in others

[1] Cf. *De Resp.* 474ᵇ 25–9, 476ᵃ 6–15; *P. A.* 669ᵃ 2–5.

they diverge. Similarly a smell, like a flavour, may be pungent, astringent, acid, or succulent. But, as we said, 30 because smells are much less easy to discriminate than flavours, the names of these varieties are applied to smells only metaphorically ; for example ' sweet ' is extended from 421^b the taste to the smell of saffron or honey, ' pungent ' to that of thyme, and so on.[1]

In the same sense in which hearing has for its object both the audible and the inaudible, sight both the visible 5 and the invisible, smell has for its object both the odorous and the inodorous. ' Inodorous ' may be either (*a*) what has no smell at all, or (*b*) what has a small or feeble smell. The same ambiguity lurks in the word ' tasteless '.

Smelling, like the operation of the senses previously examined, takes place through a medium, i.e. through air or water—I add water, because water-animals too (both 10 sanguineous and non-sanguineous) seem to smell just as much as land-animals ; at any rate some of them make directly for their food from a distance if it has any scent. That is why the following facts constitute a problem for us. All animals smell in the same way, but man smells only when he inhales ; if he exhales or holds his breath, he ceases to smell, no difference being made whether the odorous 15 object is distant or near, or even placed inside the nose and actually on the wall of the nostril ; it is a disability common to all the senses not to perceive what is in immediate contact with the organ of sense, but our failure to apprehend what is odorous without the help of inhalation is peculiar (the fact is obvious on making the experiment). Now since bloodless animals do not breathe, they must, it might be 20 argued, have some novel sense not reckoned among the usual five. Our reply must be that this is impossible, since it is scent that is perceived ; a sense that apprehends what is odorous and what has a good or bad odour cannot be anything but smell. Further, they are observed to be deleteriously effected by the same strong odours as man is, e.g. bitumen, sulphur, and the like. These animals must 25

---

[1] Because of the felt likeness.between the respective smells and the really sweet or pungent tastes of the same herbs, &c.

be able to smell without being able to breathe. The probable explanation is that in man the organ of smell has a
certain superiority over that in all other animals just as his
eyes have over those of hard-eyed animals. Man's eyes have
in the eyelids a kind of shelter or envelope, which must be
30 shifted or drawn back in order that we may see, while hard-
eyed animals have nothing of the kind, but at once see
whatever presents itself in the transparent medium. Similarly in certain species of animals the organ of smell is like
422ᵃ the eye of hard-eyed animals, uncurtained, while in others
which take in air it probably has a curtain over it, which
is drawn back in inhalation, owing to the dilating of the
veins or pores. That explains also why such animals cannot
5 smell under water ; to smell they must first inhale, and that
they cannot do under water.

Smells come from what is dry as flavours from what is
moist. Consequently the organ of smell is potentially dry.

What can be tasted is always something that can be 10
touched, and just for that reason it cannot be perceived
through an interposed foreign body, for touch means the
10 absence of any intervening body. Further, the flavoured
and tasteable body is suspended in a liquid matter, and this
is tangible. Hence, if we lived in water, we should perceive
a sweet object introduced into the water, but the water
would not be the medium *through* which we perceived ;
our perception would be due to the solution of the sweet
substance in what we imbibed, just as if it were mixed with
some drink. There is no parallel here to the perception of
colour, which is due neither to any blending of anything
with anything, nor to any efflux of anything from anything.
15 In the case of taste, there is nothing corresponding to the
medium in the case of the senses previously discussed ;
but as the object of sight is colour, so the object of taste
is flavour. But nothing excites a perception of flavour
without the help of liquid ; what acts upon the sense of
taste must be either actually or potentially liquid like what
is saline ; it must be both (*a*) itself easily dissolved, and (*b*)
20 capable of dissolving along with itself the tongue. Taste

apprehends both (*a*) what has taste and (*b*) what has no taste, if we mean by (*b*) what has only a slight or feeble flavour or what tends to destroy the sense of taste. In this it is exactly parallel to sight, which apprehends both what is visible and what is invisible (for darkness is invisible and yet is discriminated by sight; so is, in a different way, what is over-brilliant), and to hearing, which apprehends both sound and silence, of which the one is audible and the other inaudible, and also over loud sound. This corresponds in the case of hearing to over-bright light in the case of sight. As a faint sound is 'inaudible', so in a sense is a loud or violent sound. The word 'invisible' and similar privative terms cover not only (*a*) what is simply without some power, but also (*b*) what is adapted by nature to have it but has not it or has it only in a very low degree, as when we say that a species of swallow is 'footless' or that a variety of fruit is 'stoneless'.[1] So too taste has as its object both what can be tasted and the tasteless—the latter in the sense of what has little flavour or a bad flavour or one destructive of taste. The difference between what is tasteless and what is not seems to rest ultimately on that between what is drinkable and what is undrinkable—both are tasteable, but the latter is bad and tends to destroy taste, while the former is the normal stimulus of taste. What is drinkable is the common object of both touch and taste.

Since what can be tasted is liquid, the organ for its perception cannot be either (*a*) actually liquid or (*b*) incapable of becoming liquid. Tasting means a being affected by [2] what can be tasted as such; hence the organ of taste must be liquefied, and so to start with must be non-liquid but capable of liquefaction without loss of its distinctive nature. This is confirmed by the fact that the tongue cannot taste either when it is too dry or when it is too moist; in the latter case what occurs is due to a contact with the pre-existent moisture in the tongue itself, when after a foretaste of some strong flavour we try to taste another flavour; it is in this way that sick persons find everything they taste

---

[1] Cf. *Hist. An.* 487ᵇ 24-29 and *Frag.* 267 R.
[2] Sc. 'and so, as we have seen, a being assimilated to'.

bitter, viz. because, when they taste, their tongues are over-
flowing with bitter moisture.

10   The species of flavour are, as in the case of colour, (*a*)
simple, i.e. the two contraries, the sweet and the bitter, (*b*)
secondary, viz. (i) on the side of the sweet, the succulent,
(ii) on the side of the bitter, the saline, (iii) between
these come the pungent, the harsh, the astringent, and the
acid; these pretty well exhaust the varieties of flavour.
15 It follows that what has the power of tasting is what is
potentially of that kind, and that what is tasteable is what
has the power of making it actually what it itself already is.

Whatever can be said of what is tangible, can be said of 11
touch, and vice versa; if touch is not a single sense but a
group of senses, there must be several kinds of what is
tangible.   It is a problem whether touch is a single sense
20 or a group of senses.   It is also a problem, what is the
organ of touch; is it or is it not the flesh (including what
in certain animals is homologous with flesh)?   On the
second view, flesh is 'the medium' of touch, the real organ
being situated farther inward.   The problem arises because
the field of each sense is according to the accepted view
determined as the range between a single pair of contraries,
white and black for sight, acute and grave for hearing,
25 bitter and sweet for taste; but in the field of what is
tangible we find several such pairs, hot cold, dry moist,
hard soft, &c.   This problem finds a partial solution, when it
is recalled that in the case of the other senses more than one
pair of contraries are to be met with, e. g. in sound not only
30 acute and grave but loud and soft, smooth and rough,
&c.; there are similar contrasts in the field of colour.   Nevertheless we are unable clearly to detect in the case of touch
what the single subject is which underlies the contrasted
qualities and corresponds to sound in the case of hearing.
To the question whether the organ of touch lies inward
or not (i.e. whether we need look any farther than the flesh),
423^a no indication in favour of the second answer can be drawn
from the fact that if the object comes into contact with the
flesh it is at once perceived.   For even under present

conditions if the experiment is made of making a web and
stretching it tight over the flesh, as soon as this web is
touched the sensation is reported in the same manner as
before, yet it is clear that the organ is not in this membrane.
If the membrane could be *grown* on to the flesh, the report 5
would travel still quicker. The flesh plays in touch very
much the same part as would be played in the other
senses by an air-envelope growing round our body; had we
such an envelope attached to us we should have supposed
that it was by a single organ that we perceived sounds,
colours, and smells, and we should have taken sight, hearing,
and smell to be a single sense. But as it is, because that 10
through which the different movements are transmitted is
not naturally attached to our bodies, the difference of the
various sense-organs is too plain to miss. But in the case
of touch the obscurity remains.

There must be such a naturally attached 'medium' as
flesh, for no living body could be constructed of air or
water; it must be something solid. Consequently it must
be composed of earth along with these, which is just what
flesh and its analogue in animals which have no true flesh
tend to be. Hence of necessity the medium through which 15
are transmitted the manifoldly contrasted tactual qualities
must be a body naturally attached to the organism. That
they are manifold is clear when we consider touching with
the tongue; we apprehend at the tongue all tangible qualities as well as flavour. Suppose all the rest of our flesh was,
like the tongue, sensitive to flavour, we should have identified the sense of taste and the sense of touch; what 20
saves us from this identification is the fact that touch and
taste are not always found together in the same part of the
body. The following problem might be raised. Let us
assume that every body has depth, i.e. has three dimensions,
and that if two bodies have a third body between them
they cannot be in contact with one another; let us remember
that what is liquid is a body and must be or contain water, 25
and that if two bodies touch one another under water,
their touching surfaces cannot be dry, but must have water
between, viz. the water which wets their bounding surfaces;

from all this it follows that in water two bodies cannot be
in contact with one another.   The same holds of two bodies
in air—air being to bodies in air precisely what water is to
30 bodies in water—but the facts are not so evident to our
observation, because we live in air, just as animals that live
in water would not notice that the things which touch one
423ᵇ another in water have wet surfaces.   The problem, then, is :
does the perception of all objects of sense take place in the
same way, or does it not, e.g. taste and touch requiring
contact (as they are commonly thought to do), while all
other senses perceive over a distance ?   The distinction
5 is unsound ; we perceive what is hard or soft, as well
as the objects of hearing, sight, and smell, through a
' medium', only that the latter are perceived over a *greater*
distance than the former ; that is why the facts escape our
notice.   For we do perceive everything through a medium ;
but in these cases the fact escapes us.   Yet, to repeat what
we said before, if the medium for touch were a membrane
separating us from the object without our observing its
10 existence, we should be relatively to it in the same condition
as we are now to air or water in which we are immersed ;
in their case we fancy we can touch objects, nothing coming in
between us and them.   But there remains this difference
between what can be touched and what can be seen or can
sound ; in the latter two cases we perceive because the
medium produces a certain effect upon us, whereas in the
perception of objects of touch we are affected not *by* but
15 *along with* the medium ; it is as if a man were struck through
his shield, where the shock is not first given to the shield
and passed on to the man, but the concussion of both is
simultaneous.[1]

In general, flesh and the tongue are related to the real
organs of touch and taste, as air and water are to those of
20 sight, hearing, and smell.   Hence in neither the one case nor

---

[1] As, according to Aristotle, transmission *through a medium* may be
timeless, the fact that there is no interval of time between the shock
to the shield and that to the body behind it, would not show that the
medium in touch was in any way different from that of any of the other
senses. (V. Baeumker, *Problem der Materie*, pp. 5 ;, 56.) The difference
is that in touch what is affected is in effect a *single* continuous body.

the other can there be any perception of an object if it is
placed immediately upon the organ, e.g. if a white object is
placed on the surface of the eye. This again shows that what
has the p 'wer of perceiving the tangible is seated inside.
Only so would there be a complete analogy with all the other
senses. In their case if you place the object on the *organ*
it is not perceived, here if you place it on the flesh it *is* 25
perceived ; therefore flesh is not the organ but the *medium*
of touch.

What can be touched are distinctive qualities of body *as*
body ; by such differences I mean those which characterize
the elements, viz. hot cold, dry moist, of which we have
spoken earlier in our treatise on the elements.¹ The organ 30
for the perception of these is that of touch—that part of
the body in which primarily the sense of touch resides.
This is that part which is potentially such as its object is
actually : for all sense-perception is a process of being so
affected; so that that which makes something such as it itself 424ᵃ
actually is makes the other such because the other is already
potentially such. That is why when an object of touch is
equally hot and cold or hard and soft we cannot perceive ;
what we perceive must have a degree of the sensible quality
lying beyond the neutral point. This implies that the sense
itself is a 'mean' ² between any two opposite qualities which
determine the field of that sense. It is to this that it owes its 5
power of discerning the objects in that field. What is 'in the
middle' is fitted to discern; relatively to either extreme it
can put itself in the place of the other. As what is to
perceive *both* white and black must, to begin with, be actually
neither but potentially either (and so with all the other
sense-organs), so the organ of touch must be neither hot
nor cold.

Further, as in a sense sight had ³ for its object both 10

---

¹ *De Gen. et Corr.* ii. 2, 3.
² 'The Mean' is what possesses any two contrasting qualities in
equipoise ; what is so placed may be so related to more than one pair
of contraries. In general, each pair determines the range or field of
one sense, at the extremities of which they lie while 'the Mean' occupies
the centre, but more than one pair may be found within the same field,
'the Mean' being equally central to all of them.
³ 422ᵃ 20 ff.

what was visible and what was invisible (and there was a parallel truth about all the other senses discussed),[1] so touch has for its object both what is tangible and what is intangible. Here by 'intangible' is meant (a) what like air possesses some quality of tangible things in a very slight degree and (b) what possesses it in an excessive degree, as destructive things do.

15 We have now given an outline account of each of the several senses.

The following results applying to any and every sense 12 may now be formulated.

(A) By a 'sense' is meant what has the power of receiving into itself the sensible forms of things without the matter. This must be conceived of as taking place in the way in which a piece of wax takes on the impress of a signet-ring 20 without the iron or gold; we say that what produces the impression is a signet of bronze or gold, but its particular metallic constitution makes no difference: in a similar way the sense is affected by what is coloured or flavoured or sounding, but it is indifferent what in each case the *substance* is; what alone matters is what *quality* it has, i.e. in what *ratio* its constituents are combined.[2]

(B) By 'an organ of sense' is meant that in which ultimately such a power is seated.

25 The sense and its organ are the same in fact, but their essence is not the same. What perceives is, of course, a spatial magnitude, but we must not admit that either the having the power to perceive or the sense itself is a magnitude; what they are is a certain ratio[3] or power *in a*

421[b] 3–6, 422[a] 29.

[2] In any case of the action of one body X on another Y it is the form of X that acts and the result is the presence in Y of a form identical with that of X, which is therefore taken on by Y without the matter which in X accompanied it. The peculiarity in the case of a sense (not clearly indicated here) is that the form so induced is not present in Y in the same way as it is in a merely physical or inanimate body. This is brought out by St. Thomas in his commentary on the passage.

[3] The word here translated 'ratio' is the word which elsewhere I have rendered 'formulable essence'; it is declared by Aristotle to be synonymous with 'form'. It must not be regarded as identical with the mere numerical proportion between the material ingredients or

magnitude. This enables us to explain why objects of
sense which possess one of two opposite sensible qualities in
a degree largely in excess of the other opposite destroy the
organs of sense; if the movement set up by an object is too 30
strong for the organ, the equipoise of contrary qualities in
the organ, which just *is* its sensory power, is disturbed; it
is precisely as concord and tone are destroyed by too
violently twanging the strings of a ly,re. This explains also
why plants cannot perceive, in spite of their having a portion
of soul in them and obviously being affected by tangible
objects themselves; for undoubtedly their temperature can
be lowered or raised. The explanation is that they have no 424ᵇ
mean of contrary qualities, and so no principle in them capable of taking on the forms of sensible objects without
their matter; in the case of plants the affection is an affection
by form-and-matter together. The problem might be raised:
Can what cannot smell be said to be affected by smells or
what cannot see by colours, and so on? It might be said that 5
a smell is just what can be smelt, and if it produces any
effect it can only be so as to make something smell it, and
it might be argued that what cannot smell cannot be
affected by smells and further that what can smell can be
affected by it only in so far as it has in it the power to smell
(similarly with the proper objects of all the other senses).
Indeed that this *is* so is made quite evident as follows.
Light or darkness, sounds and smells leave *bodies* quite 10
unaffected; what does affect bodies is not these but the
bodies which are their vehicles, e. g. what splits the trunk of
a tree is not the sound of the thunder but the air which accompanies thunder. Yes, but, it may be objected, bodies are
affected by what is tangible and by flavours. If not, by
what are things that are without soul affected, i. e. altered
in quality? Must we not, then, admit that the objects of the
other senses also may affect them? Is not the true account

constituents of the organ: it is at least what the Schoolmen called
forma operans and is here expressly identified with the force or power
incorporated in the organ, which when evoked by the stimulating agency
of the external object manifests itself as the apprehension or discrimination of the objective quality inwardized by the process described.
With Beare, *Greek Theories of Elementary Cognition*, p. 225, n. 2, I
take ἐκείνου to mean the organ, not the object.

this, that all bodies *are* capable of being affected by smells
15 and sounds, but that some on being acted upon, having no
boundaries of their own, disintegrate, as in the instance of air,
which does become odorous, showing that *some* effect is
produced on it by what is odorous? But smelling is more
than such an affection by what is odorous—*what* more? Is
not the answer that, while the air owing to the momentary
duration of the action upon it of what is odorous does
itself become perceptible to the sense of smell, smelling is
an *observing* of the result produced?[1]

[1] Here Aristotle (vainly) endeavours to bridge the gap between the
two senses of ' perceiving ', (*a*) the physical affection of the sense-organ
by the sensigenous object, and (*b*) the psychical activity or reaction
which consists in becoming or being aware of its sensible quality.

1 THAT there is no sixth sense in addition to the five enumerated—sight, hearing, smell, taste, touch—may be established by the following considerations:

If we have actually sensation of everything of which touch can give us sensation (for all the qualities of the tangible *qua* 25 tangible are perceived by us through touch); and if absence of a sense necessarily involves absence of a sense-organ; and if (1) all objects that we perceive by immediate contact with them are perceptible by touch, which sense we actually possess, and (2) all objects that we perceive through media, i.e. without immediate contact, are perceptible by or through 30 the simple elements, e.g. air and water (and this is so arranged that (*a*) if more than one kind of sensible object is perceivable through a single medium, the possessor of a sense-organ homogeneous with that medium has the power of perceiving both kinds of objects; for example, if the sense-organ is made of air, and air is a medium both for sound and for colour; and that (*b*) if more than one medium can transmit the same kind of sensible objects, as e.g. water as well as **425ª** air can transmit colour, both being transparent, then the possessor of either alone will be able to perceive the kind of objects transmissible through both); and if of the simple elements two only, air and water, go to form sense-organs (for the pupil is made of water, the organ of hearing is made of air, and the organ of smell of one or other of these two, while fire is found either in none or in all—warmth being 5 an essential condition of all sensibility—and earth either in none or, if anywhere, specially mingled with the components of the organ of touch; wherefore it would remain that there can be no sense-organ formed of anything except water and air); and if these sense-organs are actually found in certain animals;—then all the possible senses are possessed by those animals that are not imperfect or mutilated (for 10 even the mole is observed to have eyes beneath its skin); so that, if there is no fifth element and no property other than those which belong to the four elements of our world, no sense can be wanting to such animals.

Further, there cannot be a special sense-organ for the
15 common sensibles either, i. e. the objects which we perceive
incidentally through this or that special sense, e.g. movement, rest, figure, magnitude, number, unity; for all these
we perceive by movement, e. g. magnitude by movement,
and therefore also figure (for figure is a species of magnitude),
what is at rest by the absence of movement: number is
perceived by the negation of continuity, and by the special
sensibles; for each sense perceives one class of sensible
20 objects. So that it is clearly impossible that there should
be a special sense for any one of the common sensibles, e g.
movement; for, if that were so, our perception of it would
be exactly parallel to our present perception of what is
sweet by vision. *That* is so because we have a sense for
each of the two qualities, in virtue of which when they
happen to meet in one sensible object we are aware of both
contemporaneously. If it were not like this our perception
25 of the common qualities would always be incidental, i. e. as
is the perception of Cleon's son, where we perceive him not
as Cleon's son but as white, and the white thing which we
really perceive happens to be Cleon's son.

But in the case of the common sensibles there is already
in us a general sensibility which enables us to perceive them
directly; there is therefore no special sense required for
their perception: if there were, our perception of them would
have been exactly like what has been above [1] described.

30 The senses perceive each other's special objects incidentally; not because the percipient sense is this or that special
sense, but because all form a unity: this incidental perception
takes place whenever sense is directed at one and the same
moment to two disparate qualities in one and the same ob-
425^b ject, e. g. to the bitterness and the yellowness of bile; the
assertion of the identity of both cannot be the act of either
of the senses; hence the illusion of sense, e.g. the belief that
if a thing is yellow it is bile.

It might be asked why we have more senses than one.
5 Is it to prevent a failure to apprehend the common sensibles,
e.g. movement, magnitude, and number, which go along with

[1] ll. 24–7.

the special sensibles? Had we no sense but sight, and that
sense¹ no object but white, they would have tended to escape
our notice and everything would have merged for us into an
indistinguishable identity because of the concomitance of
colour and magnitude. As it is, the fact that the common sensibles are given in the objects of more than one sense reveals
their distinction from each and all of the special sensibles. 10

2 Since it is through sense that we are aware that we are
seeing or hearing, it must be either by sight that we are
aware of seeing, or by some sense other than sight. But the
sense that gives us this new sensation must perceive both
sight and its object, viz. colour: so that either (1) there
will be two senses both percipient of the same sensible
object, or (2) the sense must be percipient of itself. Further, 15
even if the sense which perceives sight were different from
sight, we must either fall into an infinite regress, or we must
somewhere assume a sense which is aware of itself. If so,
we ought to do this in the first case.

This presents a difficulty: if to perceive by sight is just
to see, and what is seen is colour (or the coloured), then if
we are to *see* that which sees, that which sees originally
must be coloured. It is clear therefore that 'to perceive by 20
sight' has more than one meaning; for even when we are
not *seeing*, it is by sight that we discriminate darkness from
light, though not in the same way as we distinguish one
colour from another. Further, in a sense even that which sees
is coloured; for in each case the sense-organ is capable of
receiving the sensible object without its matter. That is
why even when the sensible objects are gone the sensings 25
and imaginings continue to exist in the sense-organs.

The activity of the sensible object and that of the percipient sense is one and the same activity, and yet the
distinction between their being remains. Take as illustration actual sound and actual hearing: a man may have
hearing and yet not be hearing, and that which has a sound
is not always sounding. But when that which can hear is
actively hearing and that which can sound is sounding, then 30

¹ Reading in l. 7 αὔτη, with Jackson.

the actual hearing and the actual sound are merged in one
426^1 (these one might call respectively hearkening and sounding).

If it is true that the movement, both the acting and the
being acted upon, is to be found in that which is acted upon,[1]
both the sound and the hearing so far as it is actual must
be found in that which has the faculty of hearing ; for it is
in the passive factor that the actuality of the active or motive
5 factor is realized ; that is why that which causes movement
may be at rest.   Now the actuality of that which can sound
is just sound or sounding, and the actuality of that which can
hear is hearing or hearkening; 'sound' and 'hearing' are
both ambiguous.   The same account applies to the other
senses and their objects.   For as the-acting-and-being-acted-
10 upon is to be found in the passive, not in the active factor, so
also the actuaity of the sensible object and that of the sensitive subject are both realized in the latter.   But while in
some cases each aspect of the total actuality has a distinct
name, e.g. sounding and hearkening, in some one or other is
nameless, e.g. the actuality of sight is called seeing, but the
actuality of colour has no name: the actuality of the
faculty of taste is called tasting, but the actuality of flavour
15 has no name.   Since the actualities of the sensible object and
of the sensitive faculty are *one* actuality in spite of the
difference between their modes of being, actual hearing
and actual sounding appear and disappear from existence
at one and the same moment, and so actual savour and
actual tasting, &c., while as potentialities one of them may
20 exist without the other.   The earlier students of nature
were mistaken in their view that without sight there was
no white or black, without taste no savour.   This statement
of theirs is partly true, partly false: 'sense' and 'the sensible
object' are ambiguous terms, i.e. may denote either poten-
25 tialities or actualities : the statement is true of the latter, false
of the former.   This ambiguity they wholly failed to notice.

If voice always implies a concord,[2] and if the voice and
the hearing of it are in one sense one and the same,[3] and if

---

[1] Cf. *Phys.* iii. 3.
[2] Read in l. 27 ἡ φωνὴ συμφωνία, with Sophonias and Priscianus.
[3] Omitting καὶ . . . αὐτὸ in l. 28, with Torstrik.

concord always implies a ratio, hearing as well as what
is heard must be a ratio. That is why the excess of either 30
the sharp or the flat destroys the hearing. (So also in the
case of savours excess destroys the sense of taste, and in the 426^b
case of colours excessive brightness or darkness destroys the
sight, and in the case of smell excess of strength whether in
the direction of sweetness or bitterness is destructive.) This
shows that the sense is a ratio.

That is also why the objects of sense are (1) pleasant
when the sensible extremes such as acid or sweet or
salt being pure and unmixed are brought into the proper
ratio;[1] then they are pleasant: and in general what is 5
blended is more pleasant[2] than the sharp or the flat alone ;
or, to touch, that which is capable of being either warmed
or chilled : the sense and the ratio are identical : while (2) in
excess the sensible extremes are painful or destructive.

Each sense then is relative to its particular group of
sensible qualities : it is found in a sense-organ as such[3]
and discriminates the differences which exist within that
group ; e.g. sight discriminates white and black, taste sweet 10
and bitter, and so in all cases. Since we also discriminate
white from sweet, and indeed each sensible quality from
every other, with what do we perceive that they are different? It must be by sense; for what is before us is sensible
objects. (Hence it is also obvious that the flesh cannot be 15
the ultimate sense-organ : if it were, the discriminating power
could not do its work without immediate contact with the
object.)

Therefore (1) discrimination between white and sweet
cannot be effected by two agencies which remain separate ;
both the qualities discriminated must be present to something that is one and single. On any other supposition
even if I perceived sweet and you perceived white, the
difference between them would be apparent. What says 20
that two things are different must be one; for sweet is

---

[1] i.e. that which is involved in the structure of the sense-organ.

[2] Omit συμφωνία in l. 6.

[3] The qualification appears to mean that the sense-organ may in other
respects have other qualities. Thus the tongue can touch as well as
taste.

different from white. Therefore what asserts this difference
must be self-identical, and as what asserts, so also what
thinks or perceives. That it is not possible by means of
two agencies which remain separate to discriminate two
objects which are separate. is therefore obvious; and that
(2) it is not possible to do this in separate moments of time
may be seen if we look at it as follows. For as what asserts
the difference between the good and the bad is one and the
25 same, so also the time at which it asserts the one to be
different and the other to be different is not accidental
to the assertion (as it is for instance when I now assert
a difference but do not assert that there is now a
difference); it asserts thus—both now and that the objects
are different now ; the objects therefore must be present
at one and the same moment. Both the discriminating
power and the time of its exercise must be one and
undivided.

But, it may be objected, it is impossible that what is
30 self-identical should be moved at one and the same time
with contrary movements in so far as it is undivided, and
in an undivided moment of time. For if what is sweet be
the quality perceived, it moves the sense or thought in this
427ᵃ determinate way, while what is bitter moves it in a contrary
way, and what is white in a different way. Is it the
case then that what discriminates, though both numerically
one and indivisible, is at the same time divided in its being?
In one sense, it is what is divided that perceives two separate
objects at once, but in another sense it does so *qua* undivided;
for it is divisible in its being, but spatially and numerically
undivided.

5 But is not this impossible? For while it is true that
what is self-identical and undivided may be both contraries
at once *potentially*, it cannot be self-identical in its being—
it must lose its unity by being put into activity. It is not
possible to be at once white and black, and therefore it must
also be impossible for a thing to be affected at one and the
same moment by the forms of both, assuming it to be the
case that sensation and thinking are properly so described.[1]

---

[1] i.e. as the being affected by the forms of sensible qualities.

The answer is that just as what is called a 'point' is, as 10
being at once one and two,[1] properly said to be divisible, so
here, that which discriminates is *qua* undivided one, and
active in a single moment of time, while so far forth as it is
divisible it twice over uses the same [2] dot at one and the
same time. So far forth then as it takes the limit as two,
it discriminates two separate objects with what in a sense is
divided : while so far as it takes it as one, it does so with
what is one [3] and occupies in its activity a single moment
of time.

About the principle in virtue of which we say that animals
are percipient, let this discussion suffice.   15

3   There are two distinctive peculiarities by reference to
which we characterize the soul—(1) local movement and
(2) thinking, discriminating, and perceiving. Thinking both
speculative and practical is regarded as akin to a form of
perceiving ; for in the one as well as the other the soul 20
discriminates and is cognizant of something which *is*. Indeed the ancients go so far as to identify thinking and
perceiving ; e.g. Empedocles says [4] 'For 'tis in respect of
what is present that man's wit is increased', and again [5]
'Whence it befalls them from time to time to think diverse
thoughts', and Homer's phrase [6] 'For suchlike is man's mind' 25
means the same. They all look upon thinking as a bodily
process like perceiving, and hold that like is *known* as well
as *perceived* by like, as I explained at the beginning of our
discussion.[7] Yet they ought at the same time to have
accounted for error also ; for it is more intimately connected 427^b
with animal existence and the soul continues longer in the
state of error than in that of truth. They cannot escape
the dilemma : either (1) whatever seems is true (and there
are some who accept this) or (2) error is contact with the
unlike ; for that is the opposite of the knowing of like
by like.

But it is a received principle that error as well as know- 5
ledge in respect to contraries is one and the same.

---

[1] Read in l. 10 ᾗ μία καὶ δύο (ἡ μία καὶ δύο cod. L).
[2] Read in l. 12 διαιρετὸν ὑπάρχει, δὶς τῷ αὐτῷ, with most MSS. and
Alexander.   [3] Read in l. 14 ἑνί, ἑνί.
[4] Fr. 106.   [5] Fr. 108.   [6] *Od.* xviii. 136.   [7] 404^b 8–18.

That perceiving and practical thinking are not identical
is therefore obvious; for the former is universal in the
animal world, the latter is found in only a small division of
it. Further, speculative thinking is also distinct from perceiving—I mean that in which we find rightness and wrong-
10 ness—rightness in prudence, knowledge, true opinion, wrong-
ness in their opposites; for perception of the special objects
of sense is always free from error, and is found in all animals,
while it is possible to think falsely as well as truly, and
thought is found only where there is discourse of reason
as well as sensibility. For imagination is different from
15 either perceiving or discursive thinking, though it is not
found without sensation, or judgement without it. That
this activity is not the same kind of thinking as judgement is obvious. For imagining lies within our own
power whenever we wish (e.g. we can call up a picture, as in
the practice of mnemonics by the use of mental images),
20 but in forming opinions we are not free: we cannot escape
the alternative of falsehood or truth. Further, when we
think something to be fearful or threatening, emotion is
immediately produced, and so too with what is encouraging;
but when we merely imagine we remain as unaffected as
persons who are looking at a painting of some dreadful or
encouraging scene. Again within the field of judgement
25 itself we find varieties—knowledge, opinion, prudence, and
their opposites; of the differences between these I must
speak elsewhere.[1]

Thinking is different from perceiving and is held to be in
part imagination, in part judgement: we must therefore first
mark off the sphere of imagination and then speak of judge-
428^a ment. If then imagination is that in virtue of which an
image arises for us, excluding metaphorical uses of the
term, is it[2] a single faculty or disposition relative to
images, in virtue of which we discriminate and are either
in error or not? The faculties in virtue of which we do
this are sense, opinion, science, intelligence.

5 That imagination is not sense is clear from the following

---

[1] The reference is perhaps to *E. N.* 1139^b 15 ff.
[2] Read in ll. 3-4 ⟨ἄρα⟩ μία . . . ψευδόμεθα;

considerations: Sense is either a faculty or an activity, e.g.
sight or seeing: imagination takes place in the absence of
both, as e.g. in dreams. (2) Again, sense is always present,
imagination not. If actual imagination and actual sensation
were the same, imagination would be found in all the brutes:
this is held not to be the case; e.g. it is not found in ants 10
or bees or grubs. (3) Again, sensations are always true,
imaginations are for the most part false. (4) Once more,
even in ordinary speech, we do not, when sense functions
precisely with regard to its object, say that we imagine it
to be a man, but rather when there is some failure of accuracy in its exercise. And (5), as we were saying before,[1] 15
visions appear to us even when our eyes are shut.
Neither is imagination *any* of the things that are never
in error: e.g. knowledge or intelligence; for imagination
may be false.

It remains therefore to see if it is opinion, for opinion
may be either true or false.

But opinion involves belief (for without belief in what 20
we opine we cannot have an opinion), and in the brutes
though we often find imagination we never find belief.
Further, every opinion is accompanied by belief, belief by
conviction, and conviction by discourse of reason: while
there are some of the brutes in which we find imagination,
without discourse of reason.[2] It is clear then that imagination cannot, again, be (1) opinion *plus* sensation, or (2) 25
opinion mediated by sensation, or (3) a blend of opinion
and sensation;[3] this is impossible both for these reasons
and because[4] the content of the supposed opinion cannot
be different from that of the sensation (I mean that imagination must be the blending of the perception of white with
the opinion that it is white: it could scarcely be a blend of
the opinion that it is good with the perception that it 30
is white): to imagine is therefore (on this view) identical 428ᵇ
with the thinking of exactly the same as what one in the
strictest sense perceives. But what we imagine is sometimes

---

[1] ll. 7-8.　　　　[2] Retaining ἔτι ... οὔ in ll. 22-4.
[3] For these three views cf. Pl. *Tim.* 52 A, *Soph.* 264 A, B, *Phil.* 39 B.
[4] Omit δῆλον in l. 27, with Shorey.

false though our contemporaneous judgement about it is true; e.g. we imagine the sun to be a foot in diameter though we are convinced that it is larger than the inhabited part of the earth, and the following dilemma presents itself. Either (a) while the fact has not changed and the observer has neither
5 forgotten nor lost belief in the true opinion which he had, that opinion has disappeared, or (b) if he retains it then his opinion is at once true and false. A true opinion, however, becomes false only when the fact alters without being noticed.

Imagination is therefore neither any one of the states enumerated, nor compounded out of them.

10 But since when one thing has been set in motion another thing may be moved by it, and imagination is held to be a movement and to be impossible without sensation, i. e. to occur in beings that are percipient and to have for its content what can be perceived, and since movement may be produced by actual sensation and that movement is necessarily similar in character to the sensation itself, this movement must be (1)
15 necessarily (a) incapable of existing apart from sensation, (b) incapable of existing except when we perceive, (2) such that in virtue of its possession that in which it is found may present various phenomena both active and passive, and (3) such that it may be either true or false.

The reason of the last characteristic is as follows. Perception (1) of the special objects of sense is never in error or admits the least possible amount of falsehood. (2) That of the concomitance of the objects concomitant with the sensible
20 qualities [1] comes next: in this case certainly we may be deceived; for while the perception that there is white before us cannot be false, the perception that what is white is this or that may be false. (3) Third comes the perception of the universal attributes which accompany the concomitant objects to which the special sensibles attach (I mean e. g. of movement and magnitude); it is in respect of these that the greatest amount of sense-illusion is possible.

25 The motion which is due to the activity of sense in these three modes of its exercise will differ from the activity of

[1] Transfer ἃ . . . αἰσθητοῖς from l. 24 to l. 20 after ταῦτα, with Bywater.

sense ;[1] (1) the first kind of derived motion is free from error while the sensation is present ; (2) and (3) the others may be erroneous whether it is present or absent, especially when the object of perception is far off.   If then imagination 30 presents no other features than those enumerated and is[2] what we have described, then imagination must be a 429ᵃ movement resulting from an actual exercise of a power of sense.

As sight is the most highly developed sense, the name φαντασία (imagination) has been formed from φάος (light) because it is not possible to see without light.

And because imaginations remain in the organs of sense and resemble sensations, animals in their actions are largely 5 guided by them, some (i. e. the brutes) because of the non-existence in them of mind, others (i. e. men) because of the temporary eclipse in them of mind by feeling or disease or sleep.

About imagination, what it is and why it exists, let so much suffice.

4   Turning now to the part of the soul with which the soul 10 knows and thinks (whether this is separable from the others in definition only, or spatially as well) we have to inquire (1) what differentiates this part, and (2) how thinking can take place.

If thinking is like perceiving, it must be either a process in which the soul is acted upon by what is capable of being thought, or a process different from but analogous to that. The thinking part of the soul must therefore be, while 15 impassible, capable of receiving the form of an object ; that is, must be potentially identical in character with its object without being the object.   Mind must be related to what is thinkable, as sense is to what is sensible.

Therefore, since everything is a possible object of thought, mind in order, as Anaxagoras says,[3] to dominate, that is, to know, must be pure from all admixture ; for the co-presence of 20 what is alien to its nature is a hindrance and a block : it follows

---

[1] Retaining τῆς αἰσθήσεως in l. 26.
[2] Read ἐστί in l. 1, with Bekker.   [3] Fr. 12.

that it too, like the sensitive part, can have no nature of its
own, other than that of having a certain capacity. Thus
that in the soul which is called mind (by mind I mean
that whereby the soul thinks and judges) is, before it
thinks, not actually any real thing. For this reason it
cannot reasonably be regarded as blended with the body :
25 if so, it would acquire some quality, e. g. warmth or cold, or
even have an organ like the sensitive faculty : as it is, it
has none. It was a good idea to call the soul ' the place
of forms ',[1] though (1) this description holds only of the
intellective soul, and (2) even this is the forms only
potentially, not actually.

Observation of the sense-organs and their employment
30 reveals a distinction between the impassibility of the sensitive and that of the intellective faculty. After strong
stimulation of a sense we are less able to exercise it than
429ᵇ before, as e. g. in the case of a loud sound we cannot hear
easily immediately after, or in the case of a bright colour
or a powerful odour we cannot see or smell, but in the case
of mind thought about an object that is highly intelligible
renders it more and not less able afterwards to think
objects that are less intelligible : the reason is that while
the faculty of sensation is dependent upon the body, mind
is separable from it.

5 Once the mind has become each set of its possible
objects, as a man of science has, when this phrase is used of
one who is actually a man of science (this happens when he is
now able to exercise the power on his own initiative),[2] its
condition is still one of potentiality, but in a different sense
from the potentiality which preceded the acquisition of knowledge by learning or discovery : the mind too is then able to
think *itself*.

10 Since we can distinguish between a spatial magnitude
and what it is to be such, and between water and what it is to
be water, and so in many other cases (though not in all ;
for in certain cases the thing and its form are identical),

---

[1] The idea is Platonic, but the actual expression is not found in the
extant works of Plato.
[2] Cf. 417ᵃ 21–ᵇ2.

flesh and what it is to be flesh are discriminated either by different faculties,[1] or by the same faculty in two different states : for flesh necessarily involves matter and is like what is snub-nosed, a *this* in a *this*.[2] Now it is by means of the sensitive faculty that we discriminate the hot and the cold, i. e. the factors which combined in a certain ratio 15 constitute flesh : the essential character of flesh is apprehended by something different either wholly separate from the sensitive faculty or related to it as a bent line to the same line when it has been straightened out.

Again in the case of abstract objects what is straight is analogous to what is snub-nosed ; for it necessarily implies a continuum as its matter : its constitutive essence is different, if we may distinguish between straightness and what is straight: let us take it to be two-ness. It must be 20 apprehended, therefore, by a different power or by the same power in a different state. To sum up, in so far as the realities it knows are capable of being separated from their matter, so it is also with the powers of mind.

The problem might be suggested : if thinking is a passive affection, then if mind is simple and impassible and has nothing in common with anything else, as Anaxagoras says,[3] how can it come to think at all? For interaction between 25 two factors is held to require a precedent community of nature between the factors. Again it might be asked, is mind a possible object of thought to itself? For if mind is thinkable *per se* and what is thinkable is in kind one and the same, then either (*a*) mind will belong to everything, or (*b*) mind will contain some element common to it with all other realities which makes them all thinkable.

(1) Have not we already disposed of the difficulty about interaction involving a common element, when we said[4] 30 that mind is in a sense potentially whatever is thinkable, though actually it is nothing until it has thought? What it thinks must be in it just as characters may be said to be 430[a] on a writing-tablet on which as yet nothing actually stands written: this is exactly what happens with mind.

---

[1] Read in l. 13 σάρκα ἢ ἄλλῳ, with most MSS.
[2] i.e. a particular form in a particular matter.   [3] Fr. 12.   [4] [a]15-24.

(2) Mind is itself thinkable in exactly the same way as its objects are. For (*a*) in the case of objects which involve no matter, what thinks and what is thought are identical; for speculative knowledge and its object are identical.
5 (Why mind is not always thinking we must consider later)[1] (*b*) In the case of those which contain matter each of the objects of thought is only potentially present. It follows that while *they* will not have mind in them (for mind is a potentiality of them only in so far as they are capable of being disengaged from matter) mind may yet be thinkable.

10   Since in every class of things, as in nature as a whole, we 5 find two factors involved, (1) a matter which is potentially all the particulars included in the class, (2) a cause which is productive in the sense that it makes them all (the latter standing to the former, as e. g. an art to its material), these distinct elements must likewise be found within the soul.

And in fact mind as we have described it[2] is what it is by 15 virtue of becoming all things, while there is another which is what it is by virtue of making all things : this is a sort of positive state like light ; for in a sense light makes potential colours into actual colours.

Mind in this sense of it is separable, impassible, unmixed, since it is in its essential nature activity (for always the active is superior to the passive factor, the originating force to the matter which it forms).

20   Actual knowledge is identical with its object: in the individual, potential knowledge is in time prior to actual knowledge, but in the universe as a whole it is not prior even in time.[3] Mind is not at one time knowing and at another not. When mind is set free from its present conditions it appears as just what it is and nothing more : this alone is immortal and eternal (we do not, however, remember its former activity because, while mind in this sense is impassible,
25 mind as passive is destructible),[4] and without it nothing thinks.

---

[1] Ch. 5.   [2] In ch. 4.
[3] Reading in l. 21 οἰδὲ χρόνῳ, with most MSS. and Themistius.
[4] οὐ . . . φθαρτός in ll. 23–5 is probably parenthetical.

6 The thinking then of the simple objects of thought is
found in those cases where falsehood is impossible :
where the alternative of true or false applies, there we
always find a putting together of objects of thought in a
quasi-unity. As Empedocles said that ' where heads of
many a creature sprouted without necks '[1] they afterwards by
Love's power were combined, so here too objects of thought 30
which were given separate are combined, e. g. ' incommen-
surate ' and ' diagonal ' : if the combination be of objects
past or future the combination of thought includes in its
content the date. For falsehood always involves a syn- 430ᵇ
thesis ; for even if you assert that what is white is not white
you have included not-white in a synthesis. It is possible
also to call all these cases division as well as combination.
However that may be, there is not only the true or false
assertion that Cleon is white but also the true or false assertion that he *was* or *will be* white. In each and every case that 5
which unifies is mind.

Since the word ' simple ' has two senses, i. e. may mean
either (*a*) ' not capable of being divided ' or (*b*) ' not actually
divided', there is nothing to prevent mind from knowing what
is undivided, e. g. when it apprehends a length (which is
actually undivided) and that in an undivided time ; for
the time is divided or undivided in the same manner as the
line. It is not possible, then, to tell what part of the line it 10
was apprehending[2] in each half of the time : the object
has no actual parts until it has been divided : if in thought
you think each half separately, then by the same act you
divide the time also, the half-lines becoming as it were new
wholes of length. But if you think it as a whole consisting
of these two possible parts, then also you think it in a
time which corresponds to both parts together. (But what
is not quantitatively but qualitatively simple is thought in 15
a simple time and by a simple act of the soul.)[3]

But that which [4] mind thinks and the time in which it

---

[1] Fr. 57.   [2] Reading ἐνόει in l. 10, with cod. L.
[3] ll. 14–15 τὸ . . . ψυχῆς, dealing not, like the rest of ll 6–20, with the
quantitatively divisible though undivided but with the qualitatively
simple, should either be treated as a parenthesis, or placed, as Bywater
places it, after μήκει in l. 20.
[4] Read in l. 16 ὃ νοεῖ, with Vicomercatus and Bywater.

thinks are in this case divisible only incidentally and not as
such. For in them too there is something indivisible (though,
it may be, not isolable) which gives unity to the time and the
whole of length ; and this is found equally in every continuum whether temporal or spatial.

20   Points and similar instances of things that divide, themselves being indivisible, are realized in consciousness in the
same manner as privations.

A similar account may be given of all other cases, e. g.
how evil or black is cognized ; they are cognized, in a sense,
by means of their contraries. That which cognizes must
have an element of potentiality in its being, and one of the
contraries must be in it.[1] But if there is anything that has
25 no contrary, then it knows itself and is actually and possesses
independent existence.

Assertion is the saying of something concerning something,
e. g. affirmation, and is in every case either true or false :
this is not always the case with mind : the thinking of the
definition in the sense of the constitutive essence is never in
error nor is it the assertion of something concerning something, but, just as while the seeing of the special object of
sight can never be in error, the belief that the white object
30 seen is a man may be mistaken, so too in the case of objects
which are without matter.

431^a   Actual knowledge is identical with its object : potential 7
knowledge in the individual is in time prior to actual knowledge but in the universe it has no priority even in time ; for all
things that come into being arise from what actually is.   In
the case of sense clearly the sensitive faculty already was
5 potentially what the object makes it to be actually ; the
faculty is not affected or altered. This must therefore be a
different kind from movement ; for movement is, as we saw,[2]
an activity of what is imperfect, activity in the unqualified
sense, i. e. that of what has been perfected, is different from
movement.

---

[1] i.e. it must be characterized actually by one and potentially by the
other of the contraries. Omit τῶν αἰτίων in l. 25 and read τῶν ἐναντίων
(so cod. S in l. 25) ἐν αὐτῷ after ἐν εἶναι in l. 24.
[2] Cf. 417^b 2-16.

To perceive then is like bare asserting or knowing ; but
when the object is pleasant or painful, the soul makes a
quasi-affirmation or negation, and pursues or avoids the
object. To feel pleasure or pain is to act with the sensitive 10
mean towards what is good or bad as such. Both avoidance
and appetite when actual are identical with this : the faculty
of appetite and avoidance are not different, either from one
another or from the faculty of sense-perception ; but their
being *is* different.

To the thinking soul images serve as if they were contents of perception (and when it asserts or denies them to 15
be good or bad it avoids or pursues them). That is why the
soul never thinks without an image. The process is like that
in which the air modifies the pupil in this or that way and
the pupil transmits the modification to some third thing
(and similarly in hearing), while the ultimate point of
arrival is one, a single mean, with different manners of
being.

With what part of itself the soul discriminates sweet 20
from hot[1] I have explained before [2] and must now describe
again as follows : That with which it does so is a sort of
unity, but in the way just mentioned,[3] i. e. as a connecting
term. And the two faculties it connects,[4] being one by analogy
and numerically,[5] are each [6] to each as the qualities discerned
are to one another (for what difference does it make whether
we raise the problem of discrimination between disparates or
between contraries, e. g. white and black ?). Let then *C* be 25
to *D* as *A* is to *B* :[7] it follows *alternando* that *C* : *A* :: *D* : *B*.
If then *C* and *D* belong to one subject, the case will be the
same with them as with *A* and *B* ; *A* and *B* form a single

---

[1] i.e. the sweetness and the heat in a sweet-hot object.
[2] 426ᵇ 12-427ᵃ 14.   [3] i.e. as one thing with two aspects; cf. l. 19.
[4] i. e. the faculty by which we discern sweet and that by which we
discern hot.
[5] i.e. (1) by standing in an analogical relation to their objects (cf. ll.
25-7) and (2) by belonging to the one ἔσχατον αἰσθητήριον (cf. ll. 27-9).
[6] Reading in l. 23 ἔχει ⟨ἑκάτερον⟩.
[7] i.e. let the faculty that discerns sweet be to that which discerns
hot as sweet is to hot. Omit τὸ λευκὸν and τὸ μέλαν in ll. 25-6; the
point seems to be that the power of discerning sweet and the power of
discerning hot belongs to the same subject (the ἔσχατον αἰσθητήριον) as
sweetness and heat may belong to the same object.

identity with different modes of being ; so too will the former
431^b pair. The same reasoning holds if *A* be sweet and *B* white.

The faculty of thinking then thinks the forms in the images, and as in the former case [1] what is to be pursued or avoided is marked out for it, so where there is no sensation and it is engaged upon the images it is moved 5 to pursuit or avoidance. E.g. perceiving by sense that the beacon is fire, it recognizes in virtue of the general faculty of sense that it signifies an enemy, because it sees it moving ; but sometimes by means of the images or thoughts which are within the soul, just as if it were seeing, it calculates and deliberates what is to come by reference to what is present ; and when it makes a pronouncement, as in the case of sensation it pronounces the object to be pleasant or painful, in this case it avoids or pursues; and so generally in cases of action.

10 That too which involves no action, i.e. that which is true or false, is in the same province with what is good or bad : yet they differ in this, that the one set imply and the other do not a reference to a particular person.

The so-called abstract objects the mind thinks just as, if one had thought of the snub-nosed not as snub-nosed but as hollow, one would have thought of an actuality without 15 the flesh in which it is embodied :[2] it is thus that the mind when it is thinking the objects of Mathematics thinks as separate elements which do not exist separate. In every case the mind which is actively thinking is the objects which it thinks. Whether it is possible for it while not existing separate from spatial conditions to think anything that is separate, or not, we must consider later.[3]

20 Let us now summarize our results about soul, and repeat 8 that the soul is in a way all existing things ; for existing things are either [4] sensible or thinkable, and knowledge is in

---

[1] i.e. that of sense-data.

[2] Reading in ll. 13–15 (after Bywater, in the main) εἰ ⟨τις⟩ τὸ σιμόν, ἢ μὲν σιμὸν οὔ [κεχωρισμένως], ἢ δὲ κοῖλον [εἴ τις] ἐνόει, ἐνεργειαν ἄνευ τῆς σαρκὸς ἂν ἐνό-ι ἐν ᾗ [τὸ κοῖλον].

[3] This promise does not seem to have been fulfilled.

[4] Reading in l. 21 ἐστι πάντα· ἢ γὰρ, with most MSS., Them., Phil., and the *Vetus Translatio*.

a way what is knowable, and sensation is in a way what is sensible : in *what* way we must inquire.

Knowledge and sensation are divided to correspond with the realities, potential knowledge and sensation 25 answering to potentialities, actual knowledge and sensation to actualities. Within the soul the faculties of knowledge and sensation are *potentially* these objects, the one what is knowable, the other what is sensible.[1] They must be either the things themselves or their forms. The former alternative is of course impossible : it is not the stone which is present in the soul but its form.

It follows that the soul is analogous to the hand ; for 432^a as the hand is a tool of tools,[2] so the mind is the form of forms and sense the form of sensible things.

Since according to common agreement there is nothing outside and separate in existence from sensible spatial magnitudes, the objects of thought are in the sensible forms, viz. both the abstract objects and all the states 5 and affections of sensible things. Hence (1) no one can learn or understand anything in the absence of sense, and (2) when the mind is actively aware of anything it is necessarily aware of it along with an image ; for images are like sensuous contents except in that they contain no matter.

Imagination is different from assertion and denial ; for what is true or false involves a synthesis of concepts. In 10 what will the primary concepts differ from images ? Must we not say that neither these nor even our other concepts are images, though they necessarily involve them ?

9   The soul of animals is characterized by two faculties, (*a*) 15 the faculty of discrimination which is the work of thought and sense, and (*b*) the faculty of originating local movement. Sense and mind we have now sufficiently examined. Let us next consider what it is in the soul which originates movement. Is it a single part of the soul separate either

[1] Reading in l. 27 ταῦτα with E², Sophonias, and the *Vetus Trans-latio*.

[2] i.e. a tool for using tools.

20 spatially or in definition? Or is it the soul as a whole? If it is a part, is that part different from those usually distinguished or already mentioned by us, or is it one of them? The problem at once presents itself, in what sense we are to speak of parts of the soul, or how many we should distinguish. For in a sense there is an infinity of parts: 25 it is not enough to distinguish, with some thinkers,[1] the calculative, the passionate, and the desiderative, or with others [2] the rational and the irrational; for if we take the dividing lines followed by these thinkers we shall find parts far more distinctly separated from one another than these, namely those we have just mentioned: (1) the nutritive, which belongs both 30 to plants and to all animals, and (2) the sensitive, which cannot easily be classed as either irrational or rational; further (3) 432ᵇ the imaginative, which is, in its being, different from all, while it is very hard to say with which of the others it is the same or not the same, supposing we determine to posit *separate* parts in the soul; and lastly (4) the appetitive, which would seem to be distinct both in definition and in power from all hitherto enumerated.

5 It is absurd to break up the last-mentioned faculty: as these thinkers do, for wish is found in the calculative part and desire and passion in the irrational;[3] and if the soul is tripartite appetite will be found in all three parts. Turning our attention to the present object of discussion, let us ask what that is which originates local movement of the animal.

The movement of growth and decay, being found in all 10 living things, must be attributed to the faculty of reproduction and nutrition, which is common to all: inspiration and expiration, sleep and waking, we must consider later:[4] these too present much difficulty: at present we must consider local movement, asking what it is that originates forward movement in the animal.

15 That it is not the nutritive faculty is obvious; for this kind of movement is always for an end and is accompanied

---

[1] Pl. *Rep.* 435–41.   [2] A popular view, cf. *E.N.* 1102ᵃ 26–8.
[3] All three being forms of appetite.
[4] Cf. *De Respiratione, De Somno.*

either by imagination or by appetite; for no animal moves
except by compulsion unless it has an impulse towards or
away from an object. Further, if it were the nutritive faculty,
even plants would have been capable of originating such
movement and would have possessed the organs necessary
to carry it out. Similarly it cannot be the sensitive
faculty either; for there are many animals which have
sensibility but remain fast and immovable throughout their
lives.   10

If then Nature never makes anything without a purpose
and never leaves out what is necessary (except in the case
of mutilated or imperfect growths; and that here we have
neither mutilation nor imperfection may be argued from
the facts that such animals (*a*) can reproduce their species
and (*b*) rise to completeness of nature and decay to an end),
it follows that, had they been capable of originating forward 25
movement, they would have possessed the organs necessary
for that purpose. Further, neither can the calculative faculty
or what is called 'mind' be the cause of such movement;
for mind as speculative never thinks what is practicable, it
never says anything about an object to be avoided or
pursued, while this movement is always in something which
is avoiding or pursuing an object. No, not even when it is
aware of such an object does it at once enjoin pursuit or 30
avoidance of it; e.g. the mind often thinks of something
terrifying or pleasant without enjoining the emotion of
fear. It is the heart that is moved (or in the case of a
pleasant object some other part). Further, even when the 433^a
mind does command and thought bids us pursue or avoid
something, sometimes no movement is produced; we act in
accordance with desire, as in the case of moral weakness.
And, generally, we observe that the possessor of medical
knowledge is not necessarily healing, which shows that something else is required to produce action in accordance with
knowledge; the knowledge alone is not the cause. Lastly, 5
appetite too is incompetent to account fully for movement;
for those who successfully resist temptation have appetite
and desire and yet follow mind and refuse to enact that
for which they have appetite.

These two at all events appear to be sources of movement: 10
appetite and mind (if one may venture to regard imagina-
10 tion as a kind of thinking; for many men[1] follow their
imaginations contrary to knowledge, and in all animals
other than man there is no thinking or calculation but
only imagination).

Both of these then are capable of originating local movement, mind and appetite: (1) mind, that is, which calculates means to an end, i. e. mind practical (it differs from
15 mind speculative in the character of its end); while (2)
appetite is in every form of it relative to an end: for that
which is the object of appetite is the stimulant of mind
practical; and that which is last in the process of thinking
is the beginning of the action. It follows that there is a
justification for regarding these two as the sources of movement, i. e appetite and practical thought; for the object
of appetite starts a movement and as a result of that
thought gives rise to movement, the object of appetite
20 being to it a source of stimulation. So too when imagination originates movement, it necessarily involves appetite.

That which moves therefore is a single faculty and the
faculty of appetite; for if there had been two sources of
movement—mind and appetite—they would have produced
movement in virtue of some common character. As it is,
mind is never found producing movement without appetite
(for wish is a form of appetite; and when movement is
produced according to calculation it is also according to
25 wish), but appetite can originate movement contrary to
calculation, for desire is a form of appetite. Now mind is
always right, but appetite and imagination may be either
right or wrong. That is why, though in any case it is the
object of appetite which originates movement, this object
may be either the real or the apparent good. To produce
movement the object must be more than this: it must be
good that can be brought into being by action; and only
30 what can be otherwise than as it is can thus be brought into
being. That then such a power in the soul as has been
described, i. e. that called appetite, originates movement is

---

[1] Reading in l. 10 πολλοί, with Bywater.

clear. Those who distinguish parts in the soul, if they **433**[b]
distinguish and divide in accordance with differences of
power, find themselves with a very large number of parts,
a nutritive, a sensitive, an intellective, a deliberative, and now
an appetitive part; for these are more different from one
another than the faculties of desire and passion.

Since appetites run counter to one another, which happens [5]
when a principle of reason and a desire are contrary and
is possible only in beings with a sense of time (for while
mind bids us hold back because of what is future, desire is
influenced by what is just at hand: a pleasant object which
is just at hand presents itself as both pleasant and good,
without condition in either case, because of want of foresight
into what is farther away in time), it follows that while that [10]
which originates movement must be specifically one, viz.
the faculty of appetite as such (or rather farthest back of all
the object of that faculty; for it is it that itself remaining
unmoved originates the movement by being apprehended
in thought or imagination), the things that originate
movement are numerically many.

All movement involves three factors, (1) that which
originates the movement, (2) that by means of which it
originates it, and (3) that which is moved. The expression
'that which originates the movement' is ambiguous: it
may mean either (a) something which itself is unmoved or
(b) that which at once moves and is moved. Here that [15]
which moves without itself being moved is the realizable
good, that which at once moves and is moved is the faculty
of appetite (for that which is influenced by appetite so far
as it is actually so influenced is set in movement, and
appetite in the sense of actual appetite *is* a kind of movement), while that which is in motion is the animal. The
instrument which appetite employs to produce movement
is no longer psychical but bodily: hence the examination [20]
of it falls within the province of the functions common to
body and soul.[1] To state the matter summarily at present,
that which is the instrument in the production of movement
is to be found where a beginning and an end coincide as

[1] Cf. *De Motu An.* 702ª 21–703ª 22.

e. g. in a ball and socket joint; for there the convex and
the concave sides are respectively an end and a beginning
(that is why while the one remains at rest, the other is
moved): they are separate in definition but not separable
25 spatially. For everything is moved by pushing and pulling.
Hence just as in the case of a wheel, so here there must be
a point which remains at rest, and from that point the
movement must originate.

To sum up, then, and repeat what I have said, inasmuch
as an animal is capable of appetite it is capable of self-
movement; it is not capable of appetite without possessing
imagination; and all imagination is either (1) calculative or
30 (2) sensitive. In the latter all animals, and not only man,
partake.

We must consider also in the case of imperfect animals, II
sc. those which have no sense but touch, what it is that in
434^a them originates movement. Can they have imagination or
not? or desire? Clearly they have feelings of pleasure and
pain, and if they have these they must have desire. But
how can they have imagination? Must not we say that, as
their movements are indefinite, they have imagination and
desire, but indefinitely?

5 Sensitive imagination, as we have said,[1] is found in all
animals, deliberative imagination only in those that are calculative: for whether this or that shall be enacted is
already a task requiring calculation; and there must be a
single standard to measure by, for that is pursued which is
greater. It follows that what acts in this way must be able
to make a unity out of several images.

10 This is the reason why imagination is held not to involve
opinion, in that it does not involve opinion based on
inference, though opinion involves imagination. Hence
appetite contains no deliberative element. Sometimes it
overpowers wish and sets it in movement: at times wish acts
thus upon appetite, like one sphere imparting its movement to another, or appetite[2] acts thus upon appetite,
i. e. in the condition of moral weakness (though by *nature*

---

[1] 433^b 29.   [2] Reading in l. 14 ἢ ἡ ὄρεξις, with Chandler.

the higher faculty is *always* more authoritative and gives rise to movement). Thus *three* modes of movement are possible.   15

The faculty of knowing is never moved but remains at rest. Since the one premiss or judgement is universal and the other deals with the particular (for the first tells us that such and such a kind of man should do such and such a kind of act, and the second that *this* is an act of the kind meant, and I a person of the type intended), it is the latter opinion that really originates movement, not the universal; or rather it 20 is both, but the one does so while it remains in a state more like rest, while the other partakes in movement.

12   The nutritive soul then must be possessed by everything that is alive, and every such thing is endowed with soul from its birth to its death. For what has been born must grow, reach maturity, and decay—all of which are impossible without nutrition. Therefore the nutritive faculty must be 25 found in everything that grows and decays.

But sensation need not be found in all things that live. For it is impossible for touch to belong either (1) to those whose body is uncompounded or (2) to those which are incapable of taking in the forms without their matter.

But animals must be endowed with sensation, since 30 Nature does nothing in vain. For all things that exist by Nature are means to an end, or will be concomitants of means to an end. Every body capable of forward movement would, if unendowed with sensation, perish and fail to reach its end, which is the aim of Nature; for how could it 434^b obtain nutriment? Stationary living things, it is true, have as their nutriment that from which they have arisen; but it is not possible that a body which is not stationary but produced by generation should have a soul and a discerning mind without also having sensation. (Nor yet even if it were not produced by generation.[1] Why should it not have sensation? Because it were better so either for the 5 body or for the soul? But clearly it would not be better

---

[1] Reading γεννητὸν δέ. (ἀλλὰ μὴν οὐδὲ ἀγέννητον· διὰ τί γὰρ οὐχ ἕξει; ... ἐκεῖνο) in ll. 4–7, with Platt.

for either: the absence of sensation will not enable the one to think better or the other to exist better.) Therefore no body which is not stationary has soul without sensation.

But if a body *has* sensation, it must be either simple or
10 compound. And simple it cannot be ; for then it could not have touch, which is indispensable. This is clear from what follows. An animal is a body with soul in it: every body is tangible, i. e. perceptible by touch ; hence necessarily, if an animal is to survive, its body must have tac-
15 tual sensation. All the other senses, e. g. smell, sight, hearing, apprehend through media ; but where there is immediate contact the animal, if it has no sensation, will be unable to avoid some things and take others, and so will find it impossible to survive. That is why taste also is a sort of touch ; it is relative to nutriment, which is just tangible body; whereas sound, colour, and odour are innutri-
20 tious, and further neither grow nor decay. Hence it is that taste also must be a sort of touch, because it is the sense for what is tangible and nutritious.

Both these senses, then, are indispensable to the animal, and it is clear that without touch it is impossible for an animal to be. All the other senses subserve well-being and for that very reason belong not to any and every kind
25 of animal, but only to some, e. g. those capable of forward movement must have them ; for, if they are to survive, they must perceive not only by immediate contact but also at a distance from the object. This will be possible if they can perceive through a medium, the medium being affected and moved by the perceptible object, and the animal by
30 the medium. Just as that which produces local movement causes a change extending to a certain point, and that which gave an impulse causes another to produce a new impulse so that the movement traverses a medium—the first mover impelling without being impelled, the last moved being impelled without impelling, while the medium (or media, for
435[a] there are many) is both—so is it also in the case of alteration, except that the agent produces it without the patient's changing its place. Thus if an object is dipped into wax,

the movement goes on until submersion has taken place, and in stone it goes no distance at all, while in water the disturbance goes far beyond the object dipped : in air the disturbance is propagated farthest of all, the air acting and being acted upon, so long as it maintains an unbroken unity. That is why in the case of reflection it is better, instead of 5 saying that the sight issues from the eye and is reflected, to say that the air, so long as it remains one, is affected by the shape and colour. On a smooth surface the air possesses unity; hence it is that it in turn sets the sight in motion, just as if the impression on the wax were transmitted as far as the wax extends.   10

13 It is clear that the body of an animal cannot be simple, i. e. consist of one element such as fire or air. For without touch it is impossible to have any other sense; for every body that has soul in it must, as we have said,[1] be capable of touch. All the other elements with the exception of earth can constitute organs of sense, but all of 15 them bring about perception only through something else, viz. through the media. Touch takes place by direct contact with its objects, whence also its name. All the other organs of sense, no doubt, perceive by contact, only the contact is mediate : touch alone perceives by immediate contact. Consequently no animal body can consist of these other elements.

Nor can it consist solely of earth. For touch is as it 20 were a mean between all tangible qualities, and its organ is capable of receiving not only all the specific qualities which characterize earth, but also the hot and the cold and all other tangible qualities whatsoever. That is why we have no sensation by means of bones, hair, &c., because they 25 consist of earth. So too plants, because they consist of 435ᵇ earth, have no sensation. Without touch there can be no other sense, and the organ of touch cannot consist of earth or of any other single element.

It is evident, therefore, that the loss of this one sense alone must bring about the death of an animal. For as 5

[1] 434ᵇ 10–24.

on the one hand nothing which is not an animal can have this sense, so on the other it is the only one which is indispensably necessary to what is an animal. This explains, further, the following difference between the other senses and touch. In the case of all the others excess of intensity in the qualities which they apprehend, i. e. excess of intensity in colour, sound, and smell, destroys not the animal 10 but only the organs of the sense (except incidentally, as when the sound is accompanied by an impact or shock, or where through the objects of sight or of smell certain other things are set in motion, which destroy by contact); flavour also destroys only in so far as it is at the same time tangible.[1] But excess of intensity in tangible qualities, e. g. 15 heat, cold, or hardness, destroys the animal itself. As in the case of every sensible quality excess destroys the organ, so here what is tangible destroys touch, which is the essential mark of life; for it has been shown that without touch it is impossible for an animal to be. That is why excess in intensity of tangible qualities destroys not merely the organ, but the animal itself, because this is the only sense which it must have.

All the other senses are necessary to animals, as we have 20 said,[2] not for their being, but for their well-being. Such, e. g., is sight, which, since it lives in air or water, or generally in what is pellucid, it must have in order to see, and taste because of what is pleasant or painful to it, in order that it may perceive these qualities in its nutriment and so may desire to be set in motion, and hearing that it may 25 have communication made to it, and a tongue that it may communicate with its fellows.

---

[1] Reading in l. 13 ἁπτόν.   [2] 434^b 24.

INDEX

INDEX

THE
PARVA NATURALIA

DE SENSU ET SENSIBILI
DE MEMORIA ET REMINISCENTIA
DE SOMNO   DE SOMNIIS
DE DIVINATIONE PER SOMNUM

BY

J. I. BEARE, M.A.

FELLOW OF TRINITY COLLEGE, DUBLIN ; REGIUS PROFESSOR OF GREEK
(SOMETIME PROFESSOR OF MORAL PHILOSOPHY) IN THE
UNIVERSITY OF DUBLIN

DE LONGITUDINE ET BREVITATE VITAE
DE IUVENTUTE ET SENECTUTE
DE VITA ET MORTE   DE RESPIRATIONE

BY

G. R. T. ROSS, M.A., D.PHIL.

LECTURER ON PHILOSOPHY AND EDUCATION IN THE
HARTLEY UNIVERSITY COLLEGE, SOUTHAMPTON

OXFORD
AT THE CLARENDON PRESS

Oxford University Press, Ely House, London W.1

GLASGOW NEW YORK TORONTO MELBOURNE WELLINGTON
CAPE TOWN SALISBURY IBADAN NAIROBI LUSAKA ADDIS ABABA
BOMBAY CALCUTTA MADRAS KARACHI LAHORE DACCA
KUALA LUMPUR HONG KONG TOKYO

FIRST EDITION 1908
REPRINTED LITHOGRAPHICALLY IN GREAT BRITAIN
AT THE UNIVERSITY PRESS, OXFORD
FROM SHEETS OF THE FIRST EDITION
1947, 1954, 1963, 1968

ARISTOTLE

DE SENSU

CHAPTER I

HAVING now definitely considered the soul, by itself, and **436 a**
its several faculties, we must next make a survey of animals
and all living things, in order to ascertain what functions
are peculiar, and what functions are common, to them. What
has been already determined respecting the soul [sc. by itself]
must be assumed throughout. The remaining parts [sc. the
attributes of soul and body conjointly] of our subject must be
now dealt with, and we may begin with those that come first.

The most important attributes of animals, whether common
to all or peculiar to some, are, manifestly, attributes of soul
and body in conjunction, e.g., *sensation, memory, passion,
appetite* and *desire* in general, and, in addition, *pleasure* and
pain. For these[1] may, in fact, be said to belong to all animals. 10
But there are, besides these, certain other attributes, of which
some are common to all living things, while others are peculiar
to certain species of animals. The most important of these
may be summed up in four pairs, viz. *waking* and *sleeping,
youth* and *old age, inhalation* and *exhalation, life* and *death.*
We must endeavour to arrive at a scientific conception of 15
these, determining their respective natures, and the causes of
their occurrence.

But it behoves the Physical Philosopher to obtain also
a clear view of the first principles of *health* and *disease,* inasmuch as neither health nor disease can exist in lifeless things.
Indeed we may say of most physical inquirers, and of those 20
physicians who study their art philosophically, that while the
former complete their works with a disquisition on medicine,
the latter usually base their medical theories on principles **436 b**
derived from Physics.

---

[1] ᵃ 10 ταῦτα, like τούτοις ᵃ 11, refers to *all* the things enumerated. καὶ
γάρ (= *etenim, namque*) confirms all from ᵃ 6 to ᵃ 11, not merely the
superaddition of ἡδονή and λύπη. ['For these also'—sc. pleasure and
pain. Edd.]

That all the attributes above enumerated belong to soul and body in conjunction, is obvious; for they all either imply sensation as [a concomitant, or have it as their medium.
5 Some are either affections or states of sensation, others, means of defending and safe-guarding it, while others, again, involve its destruction or negation. Now it is clear, alike by reasoning and observation, that sensation is generated in the soul through the medium of the body.

We have already, in our treatise *de Anima*, explained the nature of sensation and the act of perceiving by sense, and 10 the reason why this affection belongs to animals. Sensation must, indeed, be attributed to all animals as such, for by its presence or absence we distinguish essentially between what is and what is not an animal.

But coming now to the special senses severally, we may say that touch and taste necessarily appertain to all animals, touch, for the reason given in the *de Anima*,[1] and taste, 15 because of nutrition. It is by taste that one distinguishes in food the pleasant from the unpleasant, so as to flee from the latter and pursue the former : and savour in general is an affection of nutrient matter.

The senses which operate through external media, viz. *smelling, hearing, seeing*, are found in all animals which possess the faculty of locomotion. To all that possess them they are 20 a means of preservation; their final cause being that such creatures may, guided by *antecedent* perception, both pursue their food, and shun things that are bad or destructive. But 437 a in animals which have also intelligence they serve for the attainment of a higher perfection. They bring in tidings of many distinctive qualities of things, from which the knowledge of truth, speculative and practical, is generated in the soul.

Of the two last mentioned, seeing, regarded as a supply for the primary wants of life, and in its direct effects, is the 5 superior sense ; but for developing intelligence, and in its indirect consequences, hearing takes the precedence. The faculty of seeing, thanks to the fact that all bodies are coloured, brings tidings of multitudes of distinctive qualities of all sorts ; whence it is through this sense especially that

[1] Cf. *de An.* 434[b] 10-24.

we perceive the common sensibles, viz. *figure, magnitude, motion, number*: while hearing announces only the distinctive qualities of sound, and, to some few animals, those also of 10 voice. Indirectly, however, it is hearing that contributes most to the growth of intelligence. For rational discourse is a cause of instruction in virtue of its being audible, which[1] it is, not directly, but indirectly ; since it is composed of words, and each word is a thought-symbol. Accordingly, of persons 15 destitute from birth of either sense, the blind are more intelligent than the deaf and dumb.

CHAPTER II

Of the distinctive potency of each of the faculties of sense enough has been said already.

But as to the nature of the sensory organs, or parts of the body in which each of the senses is naturally implanted, inquirers now usually take as their guide the fundamental 20 elements of bodies. Not, however, finding it easy to co-ordinate five senses with four elements, they are at a loss respecting the fifth sense. But they hold the organ of sight to consist of fire, being prompted to this view by a certain sensory affection of whose true cause they are ignorant. This is that, when the eye is pressed or[2] moved, fire appears to flash from it. This naturally takes place in darkness, or when 25 the eyelids are closed, for then, too, darkness is produced.

This theory, however, solves one question only to raise another ; for, unless on the hypothesis that a person who is in his full senses can see an object of vision without being aware of it,[3] the eye must on this theory see itself. But then why does the above affection not occur also when the eye is at rest ? The true explanation of this affection, which will con- 30 tain the answer to our question, and account for the current notion that the eye consists of fire, must be determined in the following way :—

[1] Plato, *Theaet.* 203^b, had laid down this proposition. The comma should precede ἀκουστός in ^{a} 13.
[2] The phenomenon occurs even *without* pressure, when the eye is rolled voluntarily from side to side in darkness. ['And.' Edd.]
[3] For αἰσθανόμενος here cf. 448^a 26-30. Thucyd. v. 26 αἰσθανόμενος = ' in full possession of one's faculties '.

Things which are smooth have the natural property of
shining in darkness, without, however, producing light. Now,
437 b the part of the eye called 'the black', i. e. its central part,
is manifestly smooth. The phenomenon of the flash occurs
only when the eye is moved, because only then could it
possibly occur that the same one object should become as it
were two. The rapidity of the movement has the effect of
making that which sees and that which is seen seem different
5 from one another. Hence the phenomenon does not occur
unless the motion is rapid and takes place in darkness. For
it is in the dark that that which is smooth, e. g. the heads of
certain fishes, and the sepia of the cuttle-fish, naturally shines,
and, when the movement of the eye is slow, it is impossible
that that which sees and that which is seen should appear to
be simultaneously two and one. But, in fact, the eye sees
10 itself in the above phenomenon merely as it does so in
ordinary optical reflexion.

If the visual organ proper really were fire, which is the
doctrine of Empedocles, a doctrine taught also in the *Timaeus*,[1]
and if vision were the result of light issuing from the eye as
from a lantern, why should the eye not have had the power
of seeing even in the dark? It is totally idle to say, as the
15 *Timaeus* does, that the visual ray coming forth in the darkness is quenched. What is the meaning of this 'quenching' of
light? That which, like a fire of coals or an ordinary flame,
is hot and dry is, indeed, quenched by the moist or cold; but
heat and dryness are evidently not attributes of light. Or if
they are attributes of it, but belong to it in a degree so slight
20 as to be imperceptible to us, we should have expected that in
the daytime[2] the light of the sun should be quenched when
rain falls, and that darkness should prevail in frosty weather.
Flame, for example, and ignited bodies are subject to such
extinction, but experience shows that nothing of this sort
happens to the sunlight.

Empedocles at times seems to hold that vision is to be
explained as above stated by light issuing forth from the eye,
25 e. g., in the following passage :—

---

[1] Cf. *Tim.* 45 D.
[2] Probably for τε we should read γε. μεθ' ἡμέραν is emphatic.

'As when one who purposes going abroad prepares
a lantern,
A gleam of fire blazing through the stormy night,
Adjusting thereto, to screen it from all sorts of winds,
transparent sides,
Which scatter the breath of the winds as they blow,
While, out through them leaping, the fire, i. e. all the 30
more subtle part of this,
Shines along his threshold with incessant beams:
So [Divine love] embedded the round "lens", [viz.] the 438 a
primaeval fire fenced within the membranes,
In [its own] delicate tissues ;
And these fended off the deep surrounding flood,
While leaping forth [1] the fire, i. e. all its more subtle part—.'

Sometimes he accounts for vision thus, but at other times
he explains it by emanations from the visible objects.

Democritus, on the other hand, is right in his opinion that 5
the eye is of water ; not, however, when he goes on to explain
seeing as mere mirroring. The mirroring that takes place
in an eye is due to the fact that the eye is smooth, and
it really has its seat not in the eye which *is seen*, but in that
which *sees*. For the case is merely one of reflexion. But it
would seem that even in his time there was no scientific
knowledge of the general subject of the formation of images 10
and the phenomena of reflexion. It is strange too, that it
never occurred to him to ask why, if his theory be true, the
eye alone sees, while none of the other things in which images
are reflected do so.

True, then, the visual organ proper is composed of water,
yet vision appertains to it not because it is so composed, but
because it is translucent—a property common alike to water
and to air. But water is more easily confined and more easily 15
condensed [2] than air ; wherefore it is that the pupil, i. e. the
eye proper, consists of water. That it does so is proved by

---

[1] Diels reads διίεσκον, 'allowed to pass through' (subject αἱ, sc. ὀθόναι).

[2] Εὐπιλητότερον 438ª 15 is wrong. The rendering 'magis spissa',
'denser', slurs the εὐ- to save the sense. We should probably read
ἐναπολητότερον, for which cf. 213ª 27 ἐναπολαμβάνοντες [τὸν ἀέρα] ἐν ταῖς
κλεψύδραις. Cf. also 914ᵇ 11. It is false (cf. 386ᵇ 8-10) to say that water
is εὐπιλητότερον τοῦ ἀέρος, but it is more easily secluded in a capsule.
Thurot after Alexander suggests εὐαπολητότερον, in opposition to δυσ-
απόληπτος.

facts of actual experience. The substance which flows from eyes when decomposing is seen to be water, and this in undeveloped embryos is remarkably cold and glistening. In
20 sanguineous animals the white of the eye is fat and oily, in order that the moisture of the eye may be proof against freezing. Wherefore the eye is of all parts of the body the least sensitive to cold : no one ever feels cold in the part sheltered by the eyelids. The eyes of bloodless animals are covered with a hard scale which gives them similar protection.
25   It is, to state the matter generally, an irrational notion that the eye should see in virtue of something issuing from it ; that the visual ray should extend itself all the way to the stars, or else go out merely to a certain point, and there coalesce, as some say, with rays which proceed from the object. It would be better to suppose this coalescence [1] to take place in the fundament of the eye itself. But even this would be mere trifling. For what is meant by the
30 'coalescence' of light with light? Or how is it possible? Coalescence does not occur between any two things taken at random. And how could the light within the eye coalesce
438 b with that outside it? For the environing membrane comes between them.

That without light vision is impossible has been stated elsewhere ; [2] but, whether the medium between the eye and its objects is air or light, vision is caused by a process through this medium.

5   Accordingly, that the inner part of the eye consists of water is easily intelligible, water being translucent.

Now, as vision outwardly is impossible without [extra-organic] light, so also it is impossible inwardly [without light within the organ]. There must, therefore, be some translucent medium within the eye, and, as this is not air, it must be water. The soul or its perceptive part is not situated at the external surface of the eye, but obviously somewhere within :
10 whence the necessity of the interior of the eye being translucent, i. e. capable of admitting light. And that it is so is

---

[1] Σύμφυσις=*organic* fusion : a *growing* of things into one. The nearest term for this is 'coalescence' in its strict or Latin sense.
[2] Cf. *de An.* 418^b 1 seqq.

plain from actual occurrences. It is matter of experience that soldiers wounded in battle by a sword slash on the temple, so inflicted as to sever [1] the passages of [i. e. inward from] the eye, feel a sudden onset of darkness, as if a lamp had gone out ; because what is called the pupil, i. e. the translucent, which is a sort of inner lamp, is then cut off [from its connexion 15 with the soul].

Hence, if the facts be at all as here stated, it is clear that— if one should explain the nature of the sensory organs in this way, i. e., by correlating each of them with one of the four elements,—we must conceive that the part of the eye immediately concerned in vision consists of water, that the part immediately concerned in the perception of sound consists 20 of air, and that the sense [2] of smell consists of fire. ⟨I say the *sense* of smell, not the *organ*.⟩ For the organ of smell is only potentially that which the sense of smell, as realized, is actually ; since the object of sense is what causes the actualization of each sense, so that it (the sense) must ⟨at the instant of actualization⟩ be ⟨actually⟩ that which before ⟨the moment of actualization⟩ it was potentially. Now, odour is a smoke-like evaporation, and smoke-like evaporation arises from fire. This also helps us to understand why the olfactory organ has 25 its proper seat in the environment of the brain, for cold matter is potentially hot. In the same way must the genesis of the eye be explained. Its structure is an offshoot from the brain, because the latter is the moistest and coldest of all the bodily parts.

The organ of touch proper consists of earth, and the 30 faculty of taste is a particular form of touch. This explains 439 a why the sensory organ of both touch and taste is closely related to the heart. For the heart, as being the hottest of all the bodily parts, is the counterpoise of the brain.

This then is the way in which the characteristics of the bodily organs of sense must be determined. 5

---

[1] [Read perhaps (after Bywater, *J. P.* 28. 242) ὥστε τμηθῆναι, ' so that the passages are cut.' Edd.]

[2] The organs of the other senses are regarded here as being actually ὕδατος, &c., but the organ of smell as being only potentially πυρός (the ὄσφρησις being actually so). Like the brain, near which it is situated, it is actually cold, and only potentially hot.

CHAPTER III

Of the sensibles corresponding to each sensory organ, viz. colour, sound, odour, savour, touch, we have treated in the *de Anima*[1] in general terms, having there determined what their function is, and what is implied in their becoming actualized
10 in relation to their respective organs. We must next consider what account we are to give of any one of them ; what, for example, we should say *colour* is, or *sound*, or *odour*, or *savour* ; and so also respecting [the object of] *touch*. We begin with *colour*.

Now, each of them may be spoken of from two points of view, i. e., either as actual or as potential. We have in the *de Anima*[2] explained in what sense the colour, or sound, regarded as actualized [for sensation], is the same as, and in
15 what sense it is different from, the correlative sensation, the actual seeing or hearing. The point of our present discussion is, therefore, to determine what each sensible object must be in itself, in order to be perceived as it is in actual consciousness.

We have[3] already in the *de Anima* stated of Light that it is the colour of the Translucent, [being so related to it] incidentally ; for whenever a fiery element is in a translucent
20 medium its presence there is Light ; while the privation of it is Darkness. But the 'Translucent', as we call it, is not something peculiar to air, or water, or any other of the bodies usually called translucent, but is a common 'nature' and power, capable of no separate existence of its own, but residing in these, and subsisting likewise in all other bodies in a greater
25 or less degree. As the bodies in which it subsists must have some extreme bounding surface, so too must this. Here,[4] then, we may say that Light is a 'nature' inhering in the Translucent when the latter is without determinate boundary. But it is manifest that, when the Translucent is in determinate

---

[1] Cf. *de An.* 418ᵃ 26 seqq., 419ᵇ 5 seqq., 421ᵃ 7 seqq., 422ᵃ 8 seqq., 422ʰ 17 seqq., for Aristotle's treatment of these sensibles respectively.

[2] *de An.* 425ᵇ 25-426ʰ 8.

[3] ὥσπερ : the apodosis begins at ἡ μὲν οὖν ᵃ 26. For Light and Colour cf. *de An.* 418ᵃ 26 seqq.

[4] Referring back to protasis ᵃ 18.

bodies, its bounding extreme must be something real ; and that
colour is just this 'something' we are plainly taught by facts
—colour being actually either *at* the external limit, or being 30
itself that limit, in bodies. Hence it was that the Pythagoreans named the superficies of a body its ' hue ', for ' hue ',
indeed, lies *at* the limit of the body ; but the limit of the body
is not a real thing ; [1] rather we must suppose that the same
natural substance which, externally, is the vehicle of colour
exists [as such a possible vehicle] also in the interior of the
body.

Air and water, too [i. e. as well as determinately bounded **439 b**
bodies], are seen to possess colour ; for their brightness is of
the nature of colour. But the colour which air or sea presents,
since the body in which it resides is not determinately bounded,
is not the same when one approaches and views it close by as
it is when one regards it from a distance ; whereas in deter- 5
minate bodies the colour presented is definitely fixed, unless,
indeed, when the atmospheric environment causes it to change.
Hence it is clear that that in them which is susceptible of
colour is in both cases the same. It is therefore the Translucent, according to the degree to which it subsists in bodies
(and it does so in all more or less), that causes them to
partake of colour. But since the colour is at the extremity of 10
the body, it must be at the extremity of the Translucent
in the body. Whence it follows that we may define colour as
the limit of the Translucent in determinately bounded body.
For whether we consider the special class of bodies called
translucent, as water and such others, or determinate bodies,
which appear to possess a fixed colour of their own, it is at the
exterior bounding surface [2] that all alike exhibit their colour.

Now, that which when present in air produces light may be
present also in the Translucent which pervades determinate 15
bodies ; or again, it may not be present, but there may be
a privation of it. Accordingly, as in the case of air the
one condition is light, the other darkness, in the same way

---

[1] Thus it differs from τὸ ἔσχατον τοῦ διαφανοῦς, which *is* a 'real thing' ([a]28).
The limit of body is its geometrical surface, and merely *quantitative*, but
colour is a *quality*. In a real thing, quality and quantity are combined.

[2] In 439[b] 14 the comma should come after ὑπάρχει, not after
ἔσχατον.

the colours White and Black are generated in determinate bodies.

We must now treat of the other colours, reviewing the several hypotheses invented to explain their genesis.

20 1. It is conceivable that the White and the Black should be juxtaposed in quantities so minute that [a particle of] either separately would be invisible, though the joint product [of two particles, a black and a white] would be visible; and that they should thus have the other colours for resultants. Their product could, at all events, appear neither white nor black; and, as it must have some colour, and can have neither 25 of these, this colour must be of a mixed character—in fact, a species of colour different from either. Such, then, is a possible way of conceiving the existence of a plurality of colours besides the White and Black; and we may suppose that [of this 'plurality'] many are the result of a [numerical] ratio; for the blacks and whites may be juxtaposed in the ratio of 3 to 2, or of 3 to 4, or in ratios expressible by other numbers; while some may be juxtaposed according to no 30 numerically expressible ratio, but according to some relation of excess or defect in which the blacks and whites involved would be incommensurable quantities; and, accordingly, we may regard all these colours [viz. all those based on numerical ratios] as analogous to the sounds that enter into music,[1] and suppose that those involving simple numerical ratios, like the concords in music, may be those generally regarded as most agreeable; as, for example, purple, crimson, and some few such colours, their fewness being due to the same causes 440 a which render the concords few. The other compound colours may be those which are not based on numbers. Or it may be that, while all colours whatever [except black and white] are based on numbers, some are regular in this respect, others irregular; and that the latter [though now supposed to be all based on numbers], whenever they are not pure,

---

[1] 'Εκεῖ ᵇ 32 refers to ταῖς συμφωνίαις ᵇ 31, implying a wider meaning for this term there than it has in ᵇ 33, where it = the great concords, distinctively called by musical writers αἱ συμφωνίαι (viz. the octave, fourth, and fifth), which have simple ratios. We must remember that musical sounds (though all involve λόγος) are not all concords. These musical sounds in general are those referred to as πολλάς ᵇ 27. The concords are comparatively few (440ᵃ 2).

owe this character to a corresponding impurity[1] in ⌊the arrangement of⌋ their numerical ratios. This then is one conceivable hypothesis to explain the genesis of intermediate colours.

2. Another[2] is that the Black and White appear the one through the medium of the other, giving an effect like that sometimes produced by painters overlaying a less vivid upon a more vivid colour, as when they desire to represent an object appearing under water or enveloped in a haze, and like that produced by the sun, which in itself appears white, but takes a crimson hue when beheld through a fog or a cloud of smoke. On this hypothesis, too, a variety of colours may be conceived to arise in the same way as that already described ; for between those at the surface and those underneath a definite ratio might sometimes exist ; in other cases they might stand in no determinate ratio. To [introduce a theory of colour which would set all these hypotheses aside, and] say with the ancients that colours are emanations, and that the visibility of objects is due to such a cause, is absurd. For they must, in any case, explain sense-perception through Touch ; so that it were better to say at once that visual perception is due to a process set up by the perceived object in the medium between this object and the sensory organ ;

---

[1] By the new hypothesis, all colours are ἐν ἀριθμοῖς, but all need not be τεταγμέναι ἐν ἀριθμοῖς, and only these are καθαραί, i. e. pleasant, or *pure*, colours. Τοιαύτας goes with εἶναι 440ᵃ 6, not with γίγνεσθαι. γίγνεσθαι is here used again as it has been above, 439ᵇ 22, so as to contain the predicate. The colours which are not καθαραί 'arise', owing to their not being such (i. e. not being τεταγμέναι) in their numerical basis. All are ἐν ἀριθμοῖς, but not all τεταγμέναι ἐν ἀριθμοῖς : the same construction as in 440ᵃ 3-4. The αὐτάς ᵃ 5 points the antithesis between the χρόαι on the new and on the old hypothesis. To take τοιαύτας with γίγνεσθαι would involve a contradiction in terms. Hence attempts at correction like Biehl's 'τοῖς αὐτοῖς ante ἀριθ.' Better than this would have been the insertion of τοιούτοις before τοιαύτας. But the construction is quite natural without change, if τοιαύτας be construed with εἶναι and understood as above = τεταγμένας ἐν ἀριθμοῖς. The ἄτακτοι which turn out 'impure' would thus be those in which a single, uniform ratio is not observed throughout all the mixture, but in which the ingredients are some mixed in one ratio, others in another, so that the ratios themselves are mixed, or impure. The τεταγμέναι or καθαραὶ χρόαι are the opposite. So Alexander.

[2] On this second colour-hypothesis we are not dealing with infinitesimally small amounts of black and white : we may now have surfaces of any extent, a black above and a white below, or *vice versa*.

due, that is, to contact [with the medium affected], not to emanations.[1]

20 If we accept the hypothesis of juxtaposition, we must assume not only invisible magnitude, but also imperceptible time, in order that the succession in the arrival of the stimulatory movements may be unperceived, and that the compound colour seen may appear to be one, owing to its successive parts seeming to present themselves at once. On the hypothesis of superposition, however, no such assumption is needful : the stimulatory process produced in the medium by the upper colour, when this is itself unaffected, will be different in kind 25 from that produced by it when affected by the underlying colour. Hence it presents itself as a different colour, i. e. as one which is neither white nor black. So that, if it is impossible to suppose any magnitude to be invisible, and we must assume that there is some distance from which every magnitude is visible, this superposition theory, too [i. e. as well as No. 3 *infra*], might pass as a real theory of colour-mixture. Indeed, in the previous case also there is no reason why, to persons at a distance from the juxtaposed blacks and whites, some one colour should not appear to 30 present itself as a blend of both. [But it would not be so on a nearer view], for it will be shown, in a discussion to be undertaken later on, that there is no magnitude absolutely invisible.[2]

3. [3] There is a mixture of bodies, however, not merely such 440 b as some suppose, i. e. by juxtaposition of their minimal parts, which, owing to [the weakness of our] sense, are imperceptible by us, but a mixture by which they [i. e. the 'matter' of which they consist] are wholly blent together by interpenetration, as we have described it in the treatise on Mixture,[4]

---

[1] We see from 435ᵃ 18 how far Aristotle was prepared to go with the theory which would reduce all sensations to modes of Touch. Alexander's reading (ἡ ἁφῇ καὶ ταῖς) seems to give a simpler sense than that of Biehl, but does not suit the πάντως ('in any case') of ᵃ 17. The insertion of ἥ arose from thinking that Aristotle could in no sense admit ἁφή to a participation in visual activity.

[2] Cf. *de Sensu* vii. 448ᵃ 24–ᵇ 14.

[3] The apodosis to εἰ δ' ἐστί begins with ἀλλὰ ὅτι 440ᵇ 13.

[4] Cf. 328ᵃ 5 seqq. where μῖξις and σύνθεσις are distinguished and severally explained. Cf. Joachim, 'Aristotle's Conception of Chemical Combination,' *Journal of Philology*, xxix. 72 86.

where we dealt with this subject generally in its most comprehensive aspect. For, on the supposition we are criticizing, the only totals capable of being mixed are those which are 5 divisible into minimal parts, [e. g. genera into individuals] as men, horses, or the [various kinds of] seeds. For of mankind as a whole the individual man is such a least part; of horses [as an aggregate], the individual horse. Hence by the juxtaposition of these we obtain a mixed total, consisting [like a troop of cavalry] of both together; but we do not say that by such a process any individual man has been mixed with any individual horse. Not in this way, but by complete 10 interpenetration [of their matter], must we conceive those things to be mixed which are not divisible into minima; and it is in the case of these that natural mixture exhibits itself in its most perfect form. We have explained already in our discourse 'On Mixture' how such mixture is possible. This being the true nature of mixture, it is plain that when bodies are mixed their colours also are necessarily mixed at the same time; and [it is no less plain] that this is the real cause 15 determining the existence of a plurality of colours—not superposition or juxtaposition. For when bodies are thus mixed, their resultant colour presents itself as one and the same at all distances alike; not varying as it is seen nearer or farther away.

Colours will thus, too [as well as on the former hypotheses], be many in number on account of the fact that the ingredients may be combined with one another in a multitude of ratios; 20 some will be based on determinate numerical ratios,[1] while others again will have as their basis a relation of quantitative excess or defect not expressible in integers. And all else that was said in reference to the colours, considered as juxtaposed or superposed, may be said of them likewise when regarded as mixed in the way just described.

Why colours, as well as savours and sounds, consist of species determinate [in themselves] and not infinite [in number] is a question which we shall discuss hereafter.[2]   25

[1] The $\tau \grave{a}$ $\acute{\epsilon}\nu$ $\mathring{a}\rho\iota\theta\mu o\hat{\iota}s$ b 20 includes under it the cases of those merely $\lambda\acute{o}\gamma\varphi$ in some sort of numerical ratio and of those $\acute{\epsilon}\nu$ $\epsilon\mathring{\upsilon}\lambda o\gamma\acute{\iota}\sigma\tau o\iota s$ $\lambda\acute{o}\gamma o\iota s$.
[2] de Sensu, ch. vi. 445[b] 21-29, 446[a] 16-20.

CHAPTER IV

We have now explained what colour is, and the reason why there are many colours ; while before, in our work *de Anima*,[1] we explained the nature of sound and voice. We have next to speak of Odour and Savour, both of which are almost the same physical affection, although they each have their being
30 in different things.[2] Savours, as a class, display their nature more clearly to us than Odours, the cause of which is that the
441 a olfactory sense of man is inferior in acuteness to that of the lower animals, and is, when compared with our other senses, the least perfect of all. Man's sense of Touch, on the contrary, excels that of all other animals in fineness, and Taste is a modification of Touch.

Now the natural substance water *per se* tends to be tasteless. But [since without water tasting is impossible] either (*a*) we must suppose that water contains in itself [uniformly diffused through it] the various kinds of savour, already formed, though
5 in amounts so small as to be imperceptible, which is the doctrine of Empedocles ; or (*b*) the water must be a sort of matter, qualified, as it were, to produce germs of savours of all kinds, so that all kinds of savour are generated from the water, though different kinds from its different parts ; or else (*c*) the water is in itself quite undifferentiated in respect of savour [whether developed or undeveloped], but some agent, such for example as one might conceive Heat or the Sun to be, is the efficient cause of savour.

10 (*a*) Of these three hypotheses, the falsity of that held by Empedocles is only too evident. For we see that when peri-carpal fruits[3] are plucked [from the tree] and exposed in the

---

[1] *de An.* 419^b 5 seqq. (sound), and 420^b 5 seqq. (voice).

[2] i. e. not merely ἐν ἄλλῳ γένει (cf. ch. v. *ad init.*) but also in different physical media and vehicles, ὀσμή being in air and water, χυμός in water. Cf. ch. v. *ad init.* The meaning is clear from Theophr. *De Caus. Pl. VI.* i. 1 χυμὸς μὲν ἡ τοῦ ξηροῦ διὰ τοῦ ὑγροῦ διήθησις ὑπὸ θερμοῦ . . . ὀσμὴ δὲ τοῦ ἐν χυμῷ [*ubi leg.* ἐγχύμου] ξηροῦ ἐν τῷ διαφανεῖ· τοῦτο γὰρ κοινὸν ἀέρος καὶ ὕδατος καὶ σχεδὸν τὸ αὐτὸ πάθος ἐστὶ χυμοῦ τε καὶ ὀσμῆς, οὐκ ἐν τοῖς αὐτοῖς δὲ ἑκάτερον. This book of Theophrastus should be read with the present chapter of Arist. *de Sensu*, and also with ch. v. Cf. *de Sensu* v. *ad init.* 442^b 29, and 443^b 13.

[3] περικαρπίων. Aristotle often (cf. Ideler, *Meteor.* ii. p. 424 'quod περι-κάρπιον hoc et aliis in locis ab Aristotele vocatur, καρπός a Graecis

sun, or subjected to the action of fire, their sapid juices [1] are changed by the heat, which shows that their qualities are not due to their drawing anything from the water in the ground, but to a change which they undergo within the pericarp itself; and we see, moreover, that these juices, when extracted and allowed to lie, instead of sweet become by lapse of time harsh 15 or bitter, or acquire savours of any and every sort; and that, again, by the process of boiling or fermentation [2] they are made to assume almost all kinds of new savours.

(b) It is likewise impossible that water should be a material qualified to generate all kinds of Savour germs [so that different savours should arise out of different parts of the water]; for we see different kinds of taste generated from the same water, having it as their nutriment.

(c) It remains, therefore, to suppose that the water is changed 20 by passively receiving some affection from an external agent. Now, it is manifest that water does not contract the quality of sapidity from the agency of Heat alone. For water is of all liquids the thinnest, thinner even than oil itself, though oil, owing to its viscosity, is more ductile than water, the latter 25 being uncohesive in its particles; whence water is more difficult than oil to hold in the hand without spilling. But since perfectly pure water does not, when subjected to the action of Heat, show any tendency to acquire consistency, we must infer that some other agency than heat is the cause of sapidity. For all savours [i.e. sapid liquors] exhibit a comparative consistency. Heat is, however, a co-agent in the matter.

Now the sapid juices found in pericarpal fruits evidently 441 b exist also in the earth. Hence many of the old natural philo-sophers assert that water has qualities like those of the earth through which it flows, a fact especially manifest in the case of saline springs, for salt is a form of earth. Hence also when

vocatum est') uses περικάρπιον for what ordinary Greeks would have called καρπός, e.g. the grape is for him a περικάρπιον. Cf. Theoph. *De Caus. Pl. I.* 16. 1 καρπὸς δ' ἐστὶ τὸ συγκείμενον σπέρμα μετὰ τοῦ περικαρπίου.

[1] χυμούς in a 12 = χυλούς, but there is no need to adopt this reading.

[2] 'Boiling' would not be adequate as a rendering, and ἕψεσθαι is applied to new wine, or must, 380ᵇ 31-2. Aristotle is here probably thinking of such changes as are undergone by, e.g., the juice of the grape when extracted and left to ferment.

5 liquids are filtered through ashes, a bitter substance, the taste they yield is bitter. There are many wells, too, of which some are bitter, others acid, while others exhibit other tastes of all kinds.

As was to be anticipated, therefore, it is in the vegetable kingdom that tastes occur in richest variety. For, like all things else, the Moist, by nature's law, is affected only by its contrary; and this contrary is the Dry. Thus we see why
10 the Moist is affected by Fire, which, as a natural substance, is dry. Heat is, however, the essential property of Fire, as Dryness is of Earth, according to what has been said in our treatise[1] on the elements. Fire and Earth, therefore, taken absolutely as such, have no natural power to affect, or be affected by, one another; nor have any other pair of sub-
15 stances. Any two things can affect, or be affected by, one another only so far as contrariety to the other resides in either of them.

As, therefore, persons washing Colours or Savours in a liquid cause the water in which they wash to acquire such a quality [as that of the colour or savour], so nature, too, by washing the Dry and Earthy in the Moist, and by filtering the latter, that is, moving it on by the agency of heat through the dry and earthy, imparts to it a certain quality. This affection, wrought
20 by the aforesaid Dry in the Moist, capable of transforming the sense of Taste from potentiality to actuality, is Savour. Savour brings into actual exercise the perceptive faculty which pre-existed only in potency. The activity of sense-perception in general is analogous, not to the process of acquiring knowledge, but to that of exercising knowledge already acquired.

That Savours, either as a quality or as the privation
25 of a quality, belong not to every form of the Dry but to the Nutrient, we shall see by considering that neither the Dry without the Moist, nor the Moist without the Dry, is nutrient. For no single element, but only composite substance, constitutes nutriment for animals. Now, among the perceptible elements of the food which animals assimilate, the tangible are

---

[1] Cf. *de Gen. et Corr.* 328[b] 33 seqq. for the affection of contraries by their contraries, and for what is here said of Fire and Earth.

the efficient causes of growth and decay; it is *qua* hot or cold that the food assimilated causes these; for the heat or cold is 30 the direct cause of growth or decay. It is *qua* gustable, however, that the assimilated food supplies nutrition. For all 442 a organisms are nourished by the Sweet [i. e. the 'gustable' proper], either by itself or in combination with other savours. Of this we must speak with more precise detail in our work on Generation:[1] for the present we need touch upon it only so far as our subject here requires. Heat causes growth, and fits the food-stuff for alimentation; it attracts [into the organic 5 system] that which is light [viz. the sweet], while the salt and bitter it rejects because of their heaviness. In fact, whatever effects external heat produces in external bodies, the same are produced by their internal heat in animal and vegetable organisms. Hence it is [i.e. by the agency of heat as described] that nourishment is effected by the sweet. The other savours are introduced into and blended in food [naturally] on a principle analogous to that on which the saline or the 10 acid is used artificially, i. e. for seasoning. These latter are used because they counteract the[2] tendency of the sweet to be too nutrient, and to float on the stomach.

As the intermediate colours arise from the mixture of white and black, so the intermediate savours arise from the Sweet and Bitter; and these savours, too, severally involve either[3] a definite ratio, or else an indefinite relation of degree, between their components, either having certain integral numbers at the 15 basis of their mixture, and, consequently, of their stimulative effect, or else being mixed in proportions not arithmetically expressible. The tastes which give pleasure in their combination are those which have their components joined in a definite ratio.

[1] *de Gen. An.* 762ᵇ 12 seqq. Cf. also *de Gen. et Corr.* 335ᵃ 10 seqq and *de part. An.* 650ᵃ 3 seqq.

[2] Biehl's ἀντὶ πάντων is not legitimately translatable, though if it could be taken with ταῦτα it might be rendered 'these (viz. the saline and acid) as substitutes for all Nature's variety'. Read ἀντισπᾶν τῷ, without comma before τῷ. For ἀντισπᾶν with dat. cf. 873ᵃ 20.

[3] Thurot's suggestion of δ' ἤ for δή has been adopted. κατὰ λόγον and τῷ μᾶλλον καὶ ἧττον are here as before consistently opposed to one another; they are the alternatives. κατὰ λόγον = 'in determinate ratio.' Cf. 439ᵇ 29-30 κατὰ μὲν λόγον μηδένα, καθ' ὑπεροχὴν δέ τινα καὶ ἔλλειψιν ἀσύμμετρον, the passage to which ᵃ 12 ὥσπερ τὰ χρώματα refers.

The sweet taste alone is Rich, [therefore the latter may be regarded as a variety of the former], while [so far as both imply privation of the Sweet] the Saline is fairly identical with the Bitter. Between the extremes of sweet and bitter come the Harsh, the Pungent, the Astringent, and the Acid. Savours and Colours, it will be observed, contain respectively about the
20 same number of species. For there are seven [1] species of each, if, as is reasonable, we regard Dun [or Grey] as a variety of Black (for the alternative is that Yellow should be classed with White, as Rich with Sweet) ; while [the irreducible colours, viz.] Crimson, Violet, leek-Green, and deep Blue, come between White and Black, and from these all others
25 are derived by mixture.

Again, as Black is a privation of White in the Translucent, so Saline or Bitter is a privation of Sweet in the Nutrient Moist. This explains why the ash of all burnt things is bitter; for the potable [sc. the sweet] moisture has been exuded from them.

30 Democritus [2] and most of the natural philosophers who treat
442 b of sense-perception proceed quite irrationally, for they represent all objects of sense as objects of Touch. Yet, if this is really so, it clearly follows that each of the other senses is a mode of Touch ; but one can see at a glance that this is impossible.

---

[1] a 20-25. We have seven colours if we *either* merge Dun (or Grey) in Black *or* Yellow in White. If we merged both, we should have only six : if we allowed both to stand out, eight. So we have seven savours if we merge Rich in Sweet *or* Saline in Bitter. The clause λείπεται ... γλυκέος should be printed as parenthetical, indicating the other way of obtaining the number seven. The seven colours are thus Crimson, Violet, Green, Blue, Black, White, with *either* Yellow *or* Dun. φαιός is *either* Dun *or* Grey. In spite of Susemihl's computation, ἑπτά is right. Cf. Theophr. *Caus. Pl.* vi. i. 2 τὰ δ' εἴδη τῶν χυμῶν ὡς μὲν εἰς ἀριθμὸν ἀποδοῦναι ῥᾴδιον, οἷον γλυκὺς λιπαρὸς αὐστηρὸς στρυφνὸς δριμὺς ἁλμυρὸς πικρὸς ὀξύς. Here he gives eight species, but in vi. 4. I he writes : αἱ δὲ ἰδέαι τῶν χυμῶν ἑπτὰ δοκοῦσιν εἶναι καθάπερ καὶ τῶν ὀσμῶν καὶ τῶν χρωμάτων, τοῦτο δὲ ἄν τις τὸν ἁλμυρὸν οὐχ ἕτερον τιθῇ τοῦ πικροῦ καθάπερ καὶ τὸ φαιὸν τοῦ μέλανος. ἐὰν δὲ χωρίζῃ συμβαίνει τοῦτον ὄγδοον εἶναι. φαιόν is treated as a shade of black and ἁλμυρόν as a variety of πικρόν, while ξανθόν and λιπαρόν, though closely connected with λευκόν and γλυκύ, are separate qualities and counted in the seven. Cf. βούλεται γὰρ ὁ Πτολεμαῖος ἑπτὰ χρώματα εἶναι τῆς ἴριδος, Olympiod. *in Meteor.* lib. iii. and Ideler, *Meteor.* ii. p. 138.

[2] It is amazing how Thurot can have regarded the following passage as irrelevant. If Democritus' explanation of Taste by the shapes of atoms were correct, Aristotle's theory of it would fall to the ground. Hence he had to grapple with it.

Again, they treat the percepts common to all senses as proper to one. For [the qualities by which they explain 5 taste, viz.] Magnitude and Figure, Roughness and Smoothness, and, moreover, the Sharpness and Bluntness found in solid bodies, are percepts common to all the senses, or if not to all, at least to Sight and Touch. This explains why it is that the senses are liable to err regarding them, while no such error arises respecting their proper sensibles; e. g. the sense of Seeing is not deceived as to Colour, nor is that of Hearing as to Sound.

On the other hand, they reduce the proper to common 10 sensibles, as Democritus does with White and Black; for he asserts that the latter is [a mode of the] rough, and the former [a mode of the] smooth, while he reduces Savours to the atomic figures. Yet surely no one sense, or, if any, the sense of Sight rather than any other, can discern the common sensibles. But if we suppose that the sense of Taste is better able to do so, then—since to discern the smallest objects in each kind is what 15 marks the acutest sense—Taste should have been the sense which best perceived the common sensibles generally, and showed the most perfect power of discerning figures in general.

Again, all the sensibles involve contrariety; e. g. in Colour White is contrary to Black, and in Savours Bitter is contrary to Sweet; but no one figure is reckoned as contrary to any 20 other figure. Else, to which of the possible polygonal figures [to which Democritus reduces Bitter] is the spherical figure [to which he reduces Sweet] contrary?

Again, since figures are infinite in number, savours also should be infinite; [the possible rejoinder—' that they are so, only that some are not perceived '—cannot be sustained] for why should one savour be perceived, and another not?

This completes our discussion of the object of Taste, i. e. Savour; for the other affections of Savours are examined in 25 their proper place in connection with the natural history of Plants.

CHAPTER V

Our conception of the nature of Odours must be analogous to that of Savours ; inasmuch as the Sapid Dry [1] effects [2] in air and water alike, but in a different province of sense, precisely what the Dry effects [3] in the Moist of water only. We custom-
30 arily predicate Translucency of both air and water in common ;
443 a but it is not *qua* translucent that either is a vehicle of odour, but *qua* possessed of a power of washing or rinsing [and so imbibing] the Sapid Dryness.

For the object of Smell exists not in air only : it also exists in water. This is proved by the case of fishes and testacea,
5 which are seen to possess the faculty of smell, although water contains no air (for whenever air is generated within water it rises to the surface), and these creatures do not respire. Hence, if one were to assume that air and water are both moist, it would follow that Odour is the natural substance consisting of the Sapid Dry diffused in the Moist, and whatever is of this kind would be an object of Smell.

That the property of odorousness is based upon the Sapid may be seen by comparing the things which possess with those
10 which do not possess odour. The elements, viz. Fire, Air, Earth, Water, are inodorous, because both the dry and the moist among them are without sapidity, unless some added ingredient produces it. This explains why sea-water possesses odour, for [unlike 'elemental' water] it contains savour and dryness. Salt, too, is more odorous than natron, as the oil
15 which exudes from the former proves, for natron is allied to ['elemental'] earth more nearly than salt. Again, a stone is inodorous, just because it is tasteless, while, on the contrary, wood is odorous, because it is sapid. The kinds of wood, too, which contain more ['elemental'] water are less odorous than others. Moreover, to take the case of metals,[4] gold is inodorous

---

[1] In ᵇ 29 ξηρόν is to be read, not ὑγρόν.
[2] Sc. for the sense of smell.
[3] Sc. for the sense of taste.
[4] To understand Aristotle's point of view as to 'metals' here one should read *Timaeus* 58 D to 59 B, and Theophr. περὶ λίθων, § 1 τῶν ἐν τῇ γῇ συνισταμένων τὰ μέν ἐστιν ὕδατος, τὰ δὲ γῆς· ὕδατος μὲν τὰ μεταλλευόμενα καθάπερ ἄργυρος καὶ χρυσὸς καὶ τἄλλα. Cf. Theophr. *de Caus. Pl.*

because it is without taste, but bronze and iron are odorous; and when the [sapid] moisture [1] has been burnt out of them, their slag is, in all cases, less odorous [than the metals themselves]. Silver and tin are more odorous than the one class of metals, less so than the other, inasmuch as they are watery [2] [to a greater degree than the former, to a less degree 20 than the latter].

Some writers look upon Fumid exhalation, which is a compound of Earth and Air, as the essence of Odour. [Indeed all are inclined to rush to this theory of Odour.[3]] Heraclitus implied his adherence to it when he declared [4] that if all existing things were turned into Smoke, the nose would be the organ to discern them with. All [5] writers incline to refer odour to this cause [sc. exhalation of some sort], but some regard it 25 as aqueous, others as fumid, exhalation; while others, again, hold it to be either. Aqueous exhalation is merely a form of moisture, but fumid exhalation is, as already remarked, composed of Air and Earth. The former when condensed turns into water; the latter, into a particular species of earth. Now, it is unlikely that odour is either of these. For vaporous 30 exhalation consists of mere water [which, being tasteless, is inodorous]; and fumid exhalation cannot occur in water at

vi. 3. 2. Metals belong to what Plato calls τὸ χυτὸν γένος τοῦ ὕδατος; the water (of rivers, &c.) to τὸ ὑγρόν. We must remember that water (the στοιχεῖον) is inodorous and tasteless: that therefore the substance into which it enters is likewise inodorous and tasteless, according to the proportion of such water in it, and so with γῆ. We must carefully distinguish the ὕδωρ and γῆ *as elements* from the common earth and water, which are mixtures. Cf. ἂν μή τι μιγνύμενον ποιῇ 443[a] 11.

[1] τὸ ὑγρόν: sc. τὸ ἔγχυμον: all developed χυμός has τὸ ὑγρόν for its vehicle, but χυμός (i. e. τὸ ἔγχυμον ξηρόν) is the base of ὀσμή: hence the result here mentioned. For when the ὑγρόν is burnt away, the ἔγχυμον ξηρόν has nothing to 'wash' in. Cf. 442[b] 29.

[2] ὑδατώδη is short for τῶν μὲν μᾶλλον τῶν δ' ἧττον ὑδατώδη. They are more odorous than e. g. gold, because they have more common [or less 'elemental'] water in their composition than this, less odorous than bronze and iron, for they contain less common [or more 'elemental'] water.

[3] καὶ ... ὀσμῆς being contradictory of what precedes and follows is rightly bracketed by Biehl after Thurot. The text is still astray, as Christ's ⟨ἐπὶ τοῦτο⟩ [b] 25 gives an unsupported use of ἐπιφέρονται.

[4] The ὅτι is certainly spurious. Cf. the ὅτι of Thucydides iv. 37 (γνοὺς ... ὅτι ... διαφθαρησομένοις) which has lately been given up on the evidence of papyri, and the anacoluthia cured. Cf. Oxyr. Pap. 16 (in Bodleian). For a similar ὡς ... ὅτι cf. 454[a] 15-16.

[5] The apodosis to ἐπεὶ begins with ἀλλ' [a] 29.

all, though, as has been before stated, aquatic creatures also
have the sense of smell.

443 b   Again, the exhalation theory of odour is analogous to the
theory of emanations. If, therefore, the latter is untenable,
so, too, is the former.

It is clearly conceivable that the Moist, whether in air (for
air, too, is essentially moist) or in water, should imbibe the in-
5 fluence of, and have effects wrought in it by, the Sapid Dryness.
Moreover, if the Dry produces in moist media, i.e. water [1] and
air, an effect as of something washed out in them, it is manifest that odours must be something analogous to savours.
Nay, indeed, this analogy is, in some instances, a fact [registered
in language] ; for odours as well as savours are spoken of as
10 *pungent, sweet, harsh, astringent, rich* [=' *savoury* '] ; and one
might regard fetid smells as analogous to bitter tastes ; which
explains why the former are offensive to inhalation as the latter
are to deglutition. It is clear, therefore, that Odour is in both
water and air what Savour is in water alone. This explains
15 why coldness and freezing render Savours dull, and abolish
odours altogether ; for cooling and freezing tend to annul the
kinetic heat which helps to fabricate sapidity.[2]

There are two species of the Odorous. For the statement
of certain writers that the odorous is not divisible into species
is false ; it is so divisible. We must here define the sense in
which these species are to be admitted or denied.

One class of odours, then, is that which runs parallel, as has
20 been observed, to savours : to odours of this class their
pleasantness or unpleasantness belongs incidentally. For
owing to the fact that Savours are qualities of nutrient matter,
the odours connected with these [e. g. those of a certain food]
are agreeable as long as animals have an appetite for the food,
but they are not agreeable to them when sated and no longer
in want of it ; nor are they agreeable, either, to those animals
that do not like the food itself which yields the odours.
25 Hence, as we observed, these odours are pleasant or unpleasant
incidentally, and the same reasoning explains why it is that
they are perceptible to all animals in common.

---

[1] It seems necessary to read (as Thurot suggests) ἐν τῷ ὕδατι after ποιεῖ.
[2] For explanation see above, chap. iv. 441^b 18.

The other class of odours consists of those agreeable[1] in their essential nature, e. g. those of flowers. For these do not in any degree stimulate animals to food, nor do they contribute in any way to appetite; their effect upon it, if any, is rather the opposite. For the verse of Strattis ridiculing 30 Euripides—

> Use not perfumery to flavour soup,

contains a truth.

Those who nowadays introduce such flavours into beverages deforce our sense of pleasure by habituating us to them, 444 a until, from two distinct kinds of sensations combined, pleasure arises as it might from one simple kind.

Of this species of odour man alone is sensible; the other, viz. that correlated with Tastes, is, as has been said before, perceptible also to the lower animals. And odours of the 5 latter sort, since their pleasureableness depends upon taste, are divided into as many species as there are different tastes; but we cannot go on to say this of the former kind of odour, since its nature is agreeable or disagreeable *per se*. The reason why the perception of such odours is peculiar to man is found in the characteristic state of man's brain. For his brain is 10 naturally cold, and the blood which it contains in its vessels is thin and pure but easily cooled (whence it happens that the exhalation arising from food, being cooled by the coldness of this region, produces unhealthy rheums); therefore it is that odours of such a species have been generated for human beings, as a safeguard to health. This is their sole function, 15 and that they perform it is evident. For food, whether dry or moist, though sweet to taste, is often unwholesome; whereas the odour arising from what is fragrant, that odour which is pleasant in its own right, is, so to say, always beneficial to persons in any state of bodily health whatever.

For this reason, too, the perception of odour [in general] is effected through respiration, not in all animals, but in man 20 and certain other sanguineous animals, e. g. quadrupeds, and all that participate freely in the natural substance air; because when odours, on account of the lightness of the heat in them,

---

[1] 443^b 28–30. Aristotle is thinking only of agreeable smells, though he should have thought of disagreeable ones also.

mount to the brain, the health of this region is thereby
promoted. For odour, as a power, is naturally heat-giving.
25 Thus [1] Nature has employed respiration for two purposes:
primarily for the relief thereby brought to the thorax,
secondarily for the inhalation of odour. For while an animal
is inhaling, odour moves in [2] through its nostrils, as it were
'from a side-entrance.'

But the perception of the second class of odours above
described [does not belong to all animals, but] is confined to
30 human beings, because man's brain is, in proportion to his
whole bulk, larger and moister than the brain of any other
animal. This is the reason of the further fact that man
alone, so to speak, among animals perceives and takes pleasure
in the odours of flowers and such things. For the heat and
stimulation set up by these odours are commensurate with the
444 b excess of moisture and coldness in his cerebral region. On all
the other animals which have lungs, Nature has bestowed their
due perception of one of the two kinds of odour [i. e. that connected with nutrition] through [3] the act of respiration, guarding
against the needless creation of two organs of sense ; for in the
fact that they respire the other animals have already sufficient
provision for their perception of the one species of odour
5 only, as human beings have for their perception of both.

But that creatures which do not respire have the olfactory
sense is evident. For fishes, and all insects as a class, have,
thanks to the species of odour correlated with nutrition,
a keen olfactory sense of their proper food from a distance,
10 even when they are very far away from it; such is the case
with bees, and also with the class of small ants, which some
denominate knîpes. Among marine animals, too, the murex
and many other similar animals have an acute perception of
their food by its odour.

It is not equally certain what the organ is whereby they so
15 perceive. This question, of the organ whereby they perceive
odour, may well cause a difficulty, if we assume that smelling

[1] κττακέχρηται ... κίνησιν [b] 25–28 should perhaps come after αἴσθησις 444[b] 7.
[2] The middle entrance to the stage was (says Pollux) reserved for the
principal character. Here odour plays a subordinate part.
[3] Thurot's διὰ τοῦ with ἀποδέδωκεν (for which he might quote 657[a] 7
διὰ γὰρ τῆς ἀναπνοῆς ἡ αἴσθησις τοῖς ἔχουσι μυκτῆρας) has been adopted.

takes place in animals only while respiring (for that this is the
fact is manifest in all the animals which do respire), whereas
none of those just mentioned respires, and yet they have
the sense of smell—unless, indeed, they have some other sense
not included in the ordinary five. This supposition is, however, 20
impossible. For any sense which perceives odour is a sense
of smell, and this they do perceive, though probably not in
the same way as creatures which respire, but when the latter
are respiring the current of breath removes something that is
laid like a lid upon the organ proper (which explains why
they do not perceive odours when not respiring) ; while in
creatures which do not respire this is always off: just as some 25
animals have eyelids on their eyes, and when these are not
raised they cannot see, whereas hard-eyed animals have no
lids, and consequently do not need, besides eyes, an agency to
raise the lids, but see straightway [without intermission]
from the actual moment [1] at which it is first possible for
them to do so [i. e. from the moment when an object first
comes within their field of vision].

Consistently with what has been said above, not one of the
lower animals shows repugnance to the odour of things
which are essentially ill-smelling, unless one of the latter is 30
positively pernicious. They are destroyed, however, by these
things, just as [2] human beings are ; [3] i. e. as human beings get
headaches from, and are often asphyxiated by, the fumes of
charcoal, so the lower animals perish from the strong fumes
of brimstone and bituminous substances ; and it is owing to
experience of such effects that they shun these. For the 445 a
disagreeable odour in itself they care nothing whatever (though
the odours of many plants are essentially disagreeable), unless, indeed, it has some effect upon the taste of their food.

[1] The expression in the Greek of Biehl's text is strange. It might also
be rendered ' In virtue of the mere possession of the faculty of seeing ':
ἐξ αὐτοῦ τοῦ δυνατοῦ ὄντος, sc. ὁρᾶν. But, lids or no lids, this would be so,
and with εὐθύς, as here, it is more natural to make ἐκ refer to the initial
moment of time. δυνατοῦ must *agree with* (not *govern*) ὁρᾶν understood,
the construction being εὐθὺς ἐξ αὐτοῦ τοῦ ⟨ὁρᾶν⟩ δυνατοῦ ὄντος.
[2] ὁμοίως, i. e. not by the odour proper but by the mephitis or gas.
[3] The construction would be improved if καί were transposed to before
καθάπερ [b] 31, and if only a comma were read after πολλάκις [b] 32, οὕτως
answering καθάπερ. Then the καί κτλ. would be explanatory of the ὁμοίως.
So it has here been translated.

5   The senses making up an odd number, and an odd number
having always a middle unit, the *sense* of smell occupies in
itself as it were a middle position between the tactual senses,
i. e. Touch and Taste, and those which perceive through
a medium, i. e. Sight and Hearing. Hence the *object* of smell,
too, is an affection of nutrient substances (which fall within
10 the class of Tangibles), and is also an affection of the audible
and the visible ; whence it is that creatures have the sense
of smell both in air and water. Accordingly, the object of
smell is something common to both of these provinces, i. e. it
appertains both to the tangible on the one hand, and on the
other to the audible and translucent.[1] Hence the propriety
of the figure by which it has been described by us as an
immersion or washing of dryness in the Moist and Fluid. Such
15 then must be our account of the sense in which one is or is
not entitled to speak of the odorous as having *species*.

   The theory held by certain of the Pythagoreans, that some
animals are nourished by odours alone, is unsound. For, in
the first place, we see that food must be composite, since the
bodies nourished by it are not simple. This explains why
waste matter is secreted from food, either within the organisms,
20 or, as in plants, outside them. But since [2] even water by itself
alone, that is, when unmixed, will not suffice for food—for
anything which is to form a consistency must be corporeal—,
it is still much less conceivable that air should be so cor-
porealized [and thus fitted to be food]. But, besides this,
we see that all animals have a receptacle for food, from
which, when it has entered, the body absorbs it. Now, the
25 organ which perceives odour is in the head, and odour enters
with the inhalation of the breath ; so that it goes to the
respiratory region. It is plain, therefore, that odour, *qua*
odour, does not contribute to nutrition ; that, however, it is

---

[1] διαφανεῖ indicates that as above, [a] 9–10, the *objects*, so here the *media*
are referred to. In [a] 12 ἁπτῷ and ἀκουστῷ are virtually the media of Touch
(for there is a sense in which Touch has a medium) and Hearing, as
διαφανεῖ is that of Seeing.

[2] [a] 20. For ἔτι δ᾽ we should read ἐπεὶ δ᾽, the apodosis to which begins ἔτι
πολύ [a] 22. ἐπεὶ οὐδὲ ... ἔτι πολὺ ἧττον frames the *a fortiori* argument.
No new point is introduced at [a] 22, but only the conclusion of the argument
begun by πρῶτον μέν 445[a] 17. To this πρῶτον μέν the πρὸς δὲ τούτοις
[a] 23 corresponds.

serviceable to health is equally plain, as well by immediate
perception as from the arguments above employed; so that
odour is in relation to general health what savour is in the 30
province of nutrition and in relation to the bodies nourished.

This then must conclude our discussion of the several organs **445 b**
of sense-perception.

CHAPTER VI

One might ask : if every body is infinitely divisible, are
its sensible qualities—Colour, Savour, Odour, Sound, Weight, 5
Cold or Heat, [Heaviness or] Lightness, Hardness or Softness
—also infinitely divisible? Or, is this impossible[1] ?

[One might well ask this question], because each of them is
productive of sense-perception, since, in fact, all derive their
name [of 'sensible qualities'] from the very circumstance of
their being *able* to stimulate this. Hence, [if this is so] both
our perception of them should likewise be divisible to infinity,
and every part of a body [however small] should be a perceptible 10
magnitude. For it is impossible, e.g., to see a thing which
is white but not of a certain magnitude.

Since[2] if it were not so, [if its sensible qualities were not
divisible, *pari passu* with body], we might conceive a body
existing but having no colour, or weight, or any such quality ;
accordingly not perceptible at all. For these qualities are the
objects of sense-perception. On this supposition, every perceptible object should be regarded as composed not of
perceptible [but of imperceptible] parts. Yet it must [be really
composed of perceptible parts], since assuredly it does not 15
consist of mathematical [and therefore purely abstract and
non-sensible] quantities. Again, by what faculty should we
discern and cognize these [hypothetical real things without
sensible qualities]? Is it by Reason? But they are not
objects of Reason ; nor does reason apprehend objects in space,

---

[1] Biehl should have printed ἢ ἀδύνατον—the second member of the
ἀπορία—as a question.

[2] b 7. ποιητικὸν γάρ is continued by εἰ γάρ b 11. If (as Alex. 110, 7, W.
thinks) the first part of the argument (ending μὴ ποσὸν δέ) had concluded
for the negative, this second γάρ would be absurd.

except when it acts in conjunction with sense-perception. At the same time, if this be the case [that there are magnitudes, physically real, but without sensible quality], it seems to tell in favour of the atomistic hypothesis; for thus, indeed, [by accepting this hypothesis], the question [with which this chapter begins] might be solved [negatively]. But it is impossible [to 20 accept this hypothesis]. Our views on the subject of atoms are to be found in our treatise on Movement.[1]

The solution of these questions[2] will bring with it also the answer to the question why the species of Colour, Taste, Sound, and other sensible qualities are limited. For in all classes of things lying between extremes the intermediates must be limited. But contraries are extremes, and every object of 25 sense-perception involves contrariety: e.g. in Colour, White ×Black; in Savour, Sweet×Bitter, and in all the other sensibles also the contraries are extremes. Now, that which is continuous is divisible into an infinite number of unequal parts, but into a finite number of equal parts, while that which is not *per se* continuous is divisible into species which are finite in number. Since then, the several sensible qualities of things are to be 30 reckoned as species, while continuity always subsists in these,[3] we must take account of the difference between the Potential and the Actual.[4] It is owing to this difference that we do

---

[1] See *Phys.* vi. 1-2 (231 ᵃ 21-232ᵃ 25).

[2] i. e. the two questions of the ἀπορία. Aristotle in the preceding arguments has only (as Thurot observes) developed the affirmative side of the ἀπορία, leaving the negative (ἢ ἀδύνατον) undeveloped. He has argued *directly* for the affirmative in ᵇ 7-11 (ποιητικὸν . . . δέ), and indirectly in ᵇ 11-20 εἰ γὰρ . . . κινήσεως. There was no need to argue for the negative: for common sense does not require to be convinced that we cannot see or otherwise perceive the infinitesimally small. So we say, but this view now Aristotle takes up and corrects, by his theory that we *can* do so, *potentially*. There is no reason to suppose that Aristotle did argue here for the negative side, and that a portion of the text has been lost.

[3] ᵇ 30. τούτοις, sc. τοῖς πάθεσιν ὡς εἴ'εσιν. All αἰσθητά fall under *either* τὸ συνεχές *or* τὸ μὴ καθ' αὑτὸ συνεχές. The latter is divisible into εἴδη which partake of its continuity (sc. of ἡ, κατὰ συμβεβηκὸς συνέχεια). The πάθη, being εἴδη, also possess this continuity : but, if so, why are not infinitesimal μεγέθη αἰσθητά perceived, their qualities having (in virtue of this continuity ἡ κατὰ συμ.) been also divided together with the substrate? To answer this question, it is necessary to refer to the distinction between the potential and the actual.

[4] He aims at showing (a) that the minute parts of a πάθημα (e. g. a colour), when divided κατὰ συμβεβηκός with its substrate, may become indeed imperceptible ἐνεργείᾳ, but always (unless they perish with their

not [actually] see its ten-thousandth part in a grain of millet, 446 a
although sight has embraced the whole grain within its scope ;
and it is owing to this, too, that the sound contained in
a quarter-tone escapes notice, and yet one hears the whole
strain,[1] inasmuch as it is a continuum ; but the interval
between the extreme sounds [that bound the quarter-tone]
escapes the ear [being only potentially audible, not actually].
So, in the case of other objects of sense, extremely small constituents are unnoticed ; because they are only potentially not 5
actually [perceptible, e. g.] visible, unless [2] when they have been
parted from the wholes. So the foot-length too exists potentially [3] in the two-foot length, but actually only when it has been
separated from the whole. But objective increments so small
as those above might well, if separated from their totals,
[instead of achieving ' actual ' existence] be dissolved in their
environments, like a drop of sapid moisture poured out into
the sea. But even if this were not so [sc. with the objective
magnitude], still, since the [subjective] increment of sense- 10

substrate, like a drop in the ocean) remain perceptible (as the particle to
which each part cleaves is αἰσθητόν) δυνάμει ; and(b)that when, by aggregation
of particles or otherwise, these potential perceptibles again become actual,
their εἴδη reappear limited as before : never having been really changed in
quality, and therefore never multiplied, for the εἴδη as such have not been
divided. To this [b] 23-30 (πᾶν . . . τούτοις) is prefatory.

[1] μέλος, see Chappell, p. 87: we must not here think of a melody, or a *series*
of notes, in a scale—but of the *continuous* raising or lowering (ἀπότασις) of
the tone of a voice or string. The δίεσις (here = quarter tone) was the
conventional unit of measurement. It is itself an interval, but so small
that the parts of which it consists are not distinguishable by the ear.
τὸ τοῦ μ. πρὸς τοὺς ἐσχ΄τους φθ.='the interval consisting of the δίεσις.'

[2] Reading (with EMY) μὴ χωρὶς ᾖ.

[3] He wishes to remove a possible ground of misunderstanding. The foot-
length too is, like these small parts, only potentially existent while in the
two-foot length: but, unlike them, when separated it is (supply ὑπάρχει, not
ἐνυπάρχει) then first actually existent, while these may not even then be
actually existent, but may be dissolved, &c. But Aristotle's present point
(introduced by οὐ μὴν ἀλλ') is that magnitudes stand on a different footing
from πάθη, and must be distinguished in the αἰσθητά (which are both). The
mere ὑπεροχὴ αἰσθήσεως has at no time any existence except as in a whole,
and so its object—a correspondingly small πάθημα αἰσθητόν—actually exists
only in a substrate. It has not, like a magnitude (e. g. ἡ ποδιαία), a
separate existence. But unless the substrate of it perishes, it is always
potentially perceptible ; and when the small parts are reaggregated, it
will become actually perceptible again—in the total. There is great pro-
bability in Prof. Bywater's emendation διαιρεθείσῃ (sc. τῇ δίποδι). ἡ ποδιαία
is here the unit ; and not this but the δίπους is what really requires bisection.
To make διαιρεθεῖσα = separated from = χωρισθεῖσα, is not quite satisfactory.

perception is not perceptible [1] in itself, nor capable of separate existence (since it exists only potentially in the more distinctly perceivable whole of sense-perception), so neither will it be possible to perceive [actually] its correlatively small object [sc. its quantum of πάθημα or sensible quality] when separated from the object-total. But yet this [small object] is to be considered as perceptible: for it is both potentially so already [i.e. even when alone], and destined to be actually [2] so when it has 15 become part of an aggregate. Thus, therefore, we have shown that some magnitudes and their sensible qualities escape notice, and the reason why they do so, as well as the manner in which they are still perceptible or not perceptible in such cases. Accordingly then, when these [minutely subdivided] sensibles have once again become *aggregated* in a whole in such a manner, relatively to one another, as to be perceptible actually, and not merely because they are in the whole, but even apart from it, it follows necessarily [from what has been already stated [3]] that their sensible qualities, whether colours 20 or tastes or sounds, are limited in number.

One might ask:—do the objects of sense-perception, or the movements proceeding from them ([since movements there are,] in whichever of the two ways [viz. by emanations or by stimulatory κίνησις] sense-perception takes place), when these are actualized for perception, always arrive first at a spatial middle point [between the sense-organ and its object], as Odour evidently does, and also Sound? For he who is nearer [to the odorous object] perceives the Odour sooner [than he who is 25 farther away], and the Sound of a stroke reaches us some time after it has been struck. Is it thus also with an object seen, and with Light? Empedocles, for example, says that the Light from the Sun arrives first in the intervening space before it comes

---

[1] There is no need to read αἰσθητική if we think of the just noticeable differences of sensation in modern 'Psychophysik'. Indeed αἰσθητική would not suit the sense here, but rather give rise to a tautology.

[2] [a] 14. Magnitudes (like the foot-length) actually exist only when apart from their wholes; but πάθη have no such actual existence apart from the μεγέθη in which they inhere: their actual existence only comes about when the objects to which they belong are or become large enough to be actually perceived. Hence there is no discrepancy between this place and [a] 5-7 above, where αἰσθητά as magnitudes are spoken of.

[3] Sc. in 445[b] 25-29. What they were potentially, in their latent state, they show when actualized in an aggregate.

to the eye, or reaches the Earth. This might plausibly seem
to be the case. For whatever is moved [in space],[1] is moved
from one place to another; hence there must be a corresponding interval of time also in which it is moved from 30
the one place to the other. But any given time is divisible 446 b
into parts; so that we should assume a time when the sun's
ray was not as yet seen, but was still travelling in the middle
space.

Now, even if it be true that the acts[2] of 'hearing' and
'having heard', and, generally, those of 'perceiving' and
'having perceived', form co-instantaneous wholes,[3] in other
words, that acts of sense-perception do not involve a process
of becoming, but have their being none the less without
involving such a process;[4] yet, just as, [in the case of sound], 5
though the stroke which causes the Sound has been already
struck, the Sound is not yet at the ear (and[5] that this last is
a fact is further proved by the transformation which the letters
[viz. the consonants as heard] undergo [in the case of words
spoken from a distance], implying that the local movement
[involved in Sound] takes place in the space between [us and
the speaker] ; for the reason why [persons addressed from
a distance] do not succeed in catching the sense of what is
said is evidently that the air [sound wave] in moving towards
them has its form changed) [granting this, then, the
question arises]: is the same also true in the case of Colour
and Light? For certainly it is not true that the beholder 10
sees, and the object is seen, in virtue of some merely abstract
relationship between them, such as that between equals.
For if it were so, there would be no need [as there is] that
either [the beholder or the thing beheld] should occupy some

---

[1] We must here bear in mind that there are other kinds of κίνησις
besides locomotion (φορά) ; see below 446[b] 28.

[2] The ἐνέργειαι of these αἰσθήσεις are instantaneous, yet their stimuli
move in a medium and take time. Is the case the same with Seeing, and
Light? The apodosis to καὶ εἰ [b] 2 begins below at ἆρ' οὖν [b] 9, but is
prefaced by the clause ὥσπερ . . . ἀκοῇ [b] 5-6, to which the οὕτω of [b] 9 refers.

[3] ἅπαν ἅμα = 'all at once.' The smallest ἐνέργεια of an αἴσθησις is
perfect in itself. ἅπαν is best taken as 'acc. of inner object' after the
verbs.

[4] Cf. Phys. Θ. 258[b] 17, de Coelo, A. 280[b] 27.

[5] [b] 6 δηλοῖ to [b] 9 ἀέρα is parenthetical, and would have been placed in
a note by a modern writer.

particular place; since to the equalization of things their being near to, or far from, one another makes no difference.

Now this [travelling through successive positions in the medium] may with good reason take place as regards Sound 15 and Odour, for these, like [their media] Air and Water, are continuous, but the movement[1] of both is divided into parts. This too is the ground of the fact that the object which the person first in order of proximity hears or smells is the same as that which each subsequent person perceives, while yet it is not[2] the same.

Some, indeed, raise a question also on these very points; they declare it impossible that one person should hear, or see, or smell, the same object as another, urging the impossibility 20 of several persons in different places hearing or smelling [the same object], for the one same thing would [thus] be divided from itself. The answer is that, in perceiving the object which first set up the motion—e.g. a bell, or frankincense, or fire— all perceive an object numerically one and the same ; while, of course, in the special object perceived they perceive an object numerically different for each, though specifically the same for all ; and this, accordingly, explains how it is that many persons together see, or smell, or hear [the same object]. These things 25 [the odour or sound proper] are not bodies, but an affection or process of some kind (otherwise this [viz. simultaneous perception of the one object by many] would not have been, as it is, a fact of experience), though, on the other hand,[3] they each imply a body [as their cause].

But [though sound and odour may travel,] with regard to Light the case is different. For Light has its *raison d'être* in the being[4] [not *becoming*] of something, but it is not a move-

---

[1] All sensibles, therefore ψόφος and ὀσμή, are continuous quantities, cf. 449ᵃ 20 seqq., capable of infinite subdivision. κίνησις is essentially continuous for Aristotle, that is it is divisible εἰς ἀεὶ διαιρετά. The κίνησις, or stimulus-movement, of sound and odour propagates itself from part to part of its medium, and so 'is divided' among the parts successively traversed by it.

[2] The senses in which it is and is not are explained just below ᵇ 21-25.

[3] οὐδ' (if correct) 446ᵇ 26 somewhat alters the point of view given at οὔτε ᵇ 25.

[4] For what follows cf. 418ᵇ 20-26. The reading τῷ εἶναι ='owing to the fact that something *is* (not *becomes*)'. With τῷ ἐνεῖναι there would be a distinct allusion to the πυρῶδές τι, and the παρουσία, of 439ᵃ 19 : τὸ

ment.[1] And in general, even in qualitative change the case is different from what it is in local movement [both being different species of κίνησις]. Local movements, of course,[2] arrive first 30 at a point midway before reaching their goal (and Sound, it is currently believed, is a movement of something locally moved), but we cannot go on to assert this [arrival at a point midway] 447 a in like [3] manner of things which undergo qualitative change. For this kind of change may conceivably take place in a thing all at once, without one half of it being changed before the other; e.g. it is conceivable that water should be frozen simultaneously in every part. But still, for all [4] that, if the body which is heated or frozen is extensive,[5] each part of it successively is affected by the part contiguous, while the part first changed in quality is so changed by the cause itself 5 which originates the change, and thus the change throughout the whole need not take place coinstantaneously and all at once. Tasting would have been as smelling now is, if we

ἐνεῖναι would be nearly the same in sense. τῷ εἶναι χ γίγνεσθαι : there is no process involved. φῶς (or φωτισμός) is, for Aristotle, not a κίνησις in *any* sense—not even an ἀλλοίωσις. For even some ἀλλοιώσεις may travel, when the medium is extensive, as the illustrations show; but illumination does not.

[1] The τε . . . καί following οὐδέ is impossible to translate except by a periphrasis, e. g. 'We must not even couple qualitative change with local movement,' as if they were similar in the respect under discussion; i. e. we must distinguish the obvious travelling of the one, and the possible simultaneousness of the change in the other.

[2] εὐλόγως = 'as the name φορά implies,' or *ex vi termini*. For the kinds of κίνησις see 406ᵃ 12. Plato, *Parmen.* 13 B, had distinguished ἀλλοίωσις and φορά.

[3] οὐκέτι ὁμοίως : i. e. with the same universality as in the case of φορά. For some ἀλλοιώσεις are instantaneous, though some are not. But for his having denied that φῶς is a κίνησις we might suppose him in the sequel to mean that it belongs to the former class of κινήσεις. However, the use of εἶναι precludes its being a κίνησις, for εἶναι χ γίγνεσθαι, and therefore χ κινεῖσθαι in *all* its forms. So Alexander (p. 133, 10 Wendland) understands Aristotle to mean. The reference to ἀλλοίωσις seems intended to show that as this can be simultaneous so *a fortiori* can φωτισμός, which is not a κίνησις but depends on εἶναι. The attempt to regard Aristotle here as having meant that φῶς is a special kind of ἀλλοίωσις is benevolent, but creates great confusion in the passage. Ziaja has tried to make out that both here and in *de Anima* the controversy with Empedocles is interpolated and spurious. It is disappointing, to the Aristotelean—that is all.

[4] οὐ μὴν ἀλλ'. Though the simultaneity of ἀλλοίωσις is conceivable, it is not necessary.

[5] That this cannot affect the case of light appears from *de Anima*, 418ᵇ 24-5.

lived in a liquid medium, and perceived [the sapid object] at
a distance, before touching it.

Naturally, then,[1] the parts of media[2] between a sensory
10 organ and its object are not all affected at once—except in the
case of Light [illumination], for the reason [3] above stated, and
also in the case of seeing,[4] for the same reason; for Light
is an efficient cause of seeing.

CHAPTER VII

Another question respecting sense-perception is as follows:
assuming, as is natural, that of two [simultaneous] sensory
stimuli the stronger always tends to extrude the weaker [from
consciousness], is it conceivable or not that one should be
able [5] to discern [6] two objects coinstantaneously in the same
15 individual time? The above assumption explains why persons
do not perceive what is brought before their eyes, if they are
at the time deep in thought, or in a fright, or listening to
some loud noise. This assumption, then, must be made, and
also the following: that it is easier to discern each object of
sense when in its simple form than when an ingredient in

---

[1] We should have expected δή (marking, as usual, the conclusion) not
δέ after εὐλόγως. So Alexander quoting ('εὐλόγως δή, φησι'), but Biehl
does not notice this.

[2] ὧν = τούτων ἅ. The genitive is partitive, depending on πάιτα. Alexander wrongly makes ὧν refer to τὰ αἰσθητά. μεταξὺ τοῦ αἰσθητηρίου = μ.
τοῦ αἰσθ. καὶ τῶν αἰσθητῶν, a construction regular in Aristotle. Cf. 440ᵃ 18.
There should be a comma, not a full stop, after εἰρημένον, ἐπὶ τοῦ ὁρᾶν
as well as ἐπὶ τοῦ φωτός being under the regimen of πλήν.

[3] That is, the reason given 446ᵇ 27 (τῷ εἶναί τι φῶς ἐστίν).

[4] The effect of χρῶμα on the διαφανές is the stimulus of seeing. Cf.
430ᵃ 16 τὸ φῶς ποιεῖ τὰ δυνάμει ὄντα χρώματα ἐνεργείᾳ ὄντα. If one asks
how Aristotle would reconcile the proposition in 438ᵇ 4 ἡ διὰ τούτου κίνησίς
ἐστιν ἡ ποιοῦσα τὸ ὁρᾶν with the doctrine here, that light is not a κίνησις and
that χρῶμα does not locally move towards the eye (see 446ᵇ 9), what is the
answer? Every κίνησις is ἐν χρόνῳ (235ᵃ 11) and every χρόνος is διαιρετός
(ibid.). How then does this κίνησις not travel in space? Viderit ipse
Aristoteles.

[5] The usual device for distinguishing δύνασθαι and ἐνδέχεσθαι has been
adopted: but it is not easy to believe that the former should be sound
here. The two are never elsewhere so combined in Aristotle.

[6] αἰσθάνεσθαι here and generally in this chapter = discern: for the two
objects must be kept distinct in perception, while perceived coinstantaneously. αἴσθησις is a δύναμις κριτική.

a mixture ; easier, for example, to discern wine when neat than when blended, and so also honey, and [in other provinces] a colour, or to discern the *nété*[1] by itself alone, than [when sounded with the *hypaté*] in the octave ; the reason being [20] that component elements tend to efface [the distinctive characteristics of] one another. Such is the effect [on one another] of all ingredients of which, when compounded, some one thing is formed.

If, then, the greater stimulus tends to expel the less, it necessarily follows that, when they concur, this greater should itself too be less distinctly perceptible than if it were alone, since the less by blending with it has removed some of its individuality, according to our assumption that simple objects are in all cases more distinctly perceptible.

Now, if the two stimuli are equal but heterogeneous, no [25] perception of either will ensue ; they will alike efface one another's characteristics. But in such a case the perception of either stimulus in its simple form is impossible. Hence either there will then be no sense-perception at all, or there will be a perception compounded of both and differing from either. The latter is what actually seems to result from ingredients blended[2] together, whatever may be the compound in which they are so mixed.

Since, then, from some concurrent [sensory stimuli] a resultant object is produced, while from others no such resultant is produced, and of the latter sort are those things which belong [30] to different sense provinces (for only those things are capable of mixture whose extremes are contraries, and no one compound **447 b** can be formed from, e. g., White and Sharp, except indirectly, i. e. not as a concord is formed of Sharp and Grave) ; there follows logically the impossibility of discerning such concurrent stimuli coinstantaneously. For we must suppose that the stimuli, when equal, tend alike to efface one another, since [5]

---

[1] *Nété* (= νεάτη) and *hypaté* were respectively the highest and the lowest notes in the octave. 'Although *hypaté* is the lowest string [of the lyre] in point of pitch and sound, it is the "highest" in the Greek sense, which is as to length. *Nété* on the contrary is highest as to sound, but is "lowest" when compared in length to any other.'—Chappell, *History of Music*, p. 36. So D. B. Monro, *Modes of Ancient Greek Music*, p. 31.

[2] τῶν κεραννυμένων, i. e. blended in the manner referred to 444[b] 3-12, or, as we should perhaps say, chemically.

DE SENSU

no one [form of stimulus] results from them; while, if they are unequal, the stronger alone is distinctly perceptible.

Again,[1] the soul would be more likely to perceive coinstantaneously, with one and the same sensory act, two things in the same sensory province, such as the Grave and the Sharp in sound; for the sensory stimulation in this one province is more likely to be unitemporal than that involving
10 two different provinces, as Sight and Hearing. But it is impossible to perceive two objects coinstantaneously in the same sensory act unless they have been mixed, [when, however, they are no longer two], for their amalgamation involves their becoming one, and the sensory act related to one object is itself one, and such act, when one, is, of course, coinstantaneous with itself. Hence, when things are mixed we of necessity perceive them coinstantaneously: for we perceive them by a perception actually one. For an object numerically one means that which is perceived by a perception actually one, whereas an object specifically one means that which is
15 perceived by a sensory act potentially one [i.e. by an ἐνέργεια of the same sensuous faculty]. If then the actualized perception is one, it will declare its data to be one object; they must, therefore, have been mixed. Accordingly, when they have not been mixed, the actualized perceptions which perceive them will be two; but [if so, their perception must be successive not coinstantaneous, for] in one and the same faculty the perception actualized at any single moment is necessarily one, only one stimulation or exertion of a single faculty being possible at a single instant, and in the case supposed here the faculty is one. It follows, therefore, that we cannot conceive
20 the possibility of perceiving two distinct objects coinstantaneously with one and the same sense.

But if it be thus impossible to perceive coinstantaneously two objects in the same province of sense *if they are really two*, manifestly it is still less conceivable that we should perceive coinstantaneously objects in two different sensory provinces, as White and Sweet. For it appears that when the

---

[1] b 6. There should be a full stop after ποιεῖ. A new paragraph then begins, consequently ἐπεὶ δέ or ἔτι seems required for ἐπεί. The apodosis is prefaced by οὐκ ἄρα b 20, and really begun at δῆλον ὅτι b 22.

Soul predicates numerical unity it does so in virtue of nothing 25
else than such coinstantaneous perception [of one object, in
one instant, by one ἐνέργεια]: while it predicates specific[1]
unity in virtue of [the unity of] the discriminating faculty of
sense together with [the unity of] the mode in which this
operates. What I mean, for example, is this; the same sense
no doubt discerns White and Black, [which are hence generically one] though specifically different from one another, and
so, too, a faculty of sense self-identical, but different from the
former, discerns Sweet and Bitter; but while both these
faculties differ[2] from one another [and each from itself] in
their modes of discerning either of their respective contraries,
yet in perceiving the co-ordinates in each province they 30
proceed in manners analogous to one another; for instance,
as Taste perceives Sweet, so Sight perceives White; and as 448 a
the latter perceives Black, so the former perceives Bitter.[3]

Again, if the stimuli of sense derived from Contraries are
themselves Contrary, and if Contraries cannot be conceived as
subsisting together in the same individual subject, and if
Contraries, e. g. Sweet and Bitter, come under one and the same
sense-faculty, we must conclude that it is impossible to discern 5
them coinstantaneously. It is likewise clearly impossible so
to discern such homogeneous sensibles as are not [indeed]
Contrary, [but are yet of different species]. For these are,
[in the sphere of colour, for instance], classed some with
White, others with Black, and so it is, likewise, in the other
provinces of sense; for example, of savours, some are classed
with Sweet, and others with Bitter. Nor can one discern
the components in compounds coinstantaneously (for[4] these

---

[1] For specific unity the αἴσθησις is one and also its manner of operating
is one. For generic, only the αἴσθησις is one. We must not suppose that
Aristotle here confuses εἶδος and γένος. Cf. 449ᵃ 18.

[2] Each sense proceeds in a different mode in discerning its specifically
different objects; ἑτέρως = ἕτερον τρόπον (sc. τοῦ κρίνειν) cf. ᵇ 26. So also
two different senses proceed differently in this respect. Yet, notwith-
standing this difference of mode, there is an analogy between the procedure
of ὄψις in perceiving white (the positive) and that of γεῦσις in perceiving
sweet (also positive). Cf. 431ᵃ 21 seqq. with Torstrik's commentary.

[3] The completion of the argument begun here is found below, 448ᵃ
13–19, hence it seems that this latter passage should be transferred to
follow 448ᵃ 1.

[4] λόγοι ... πέντε is parenthetic. Biehl's punctuation is wrong.

10 are ratios of Contraries, as e. g. the Octave or the Fifth) ; unless, indeed, on condition of perceiving them as one. For thus, and not otherwise, the ratios of the extreme sounds are compounded into one ratio ;[1] since we should have together the ratio, on the one hand, of Many to Few or of Odd to Even, on the other, that of Few to Many or of Even to Odd [and these, to be perceived together, must be unified].

If, then, the sensibles denominated co-ordinates though in 15 different provinces of sense (e.g. I call[2] Sweet and White co-ordinates though in different provinces) stand yet more aloof, and differ more, from one another than do any sensibles in the same province ; while Sweet differs from White[3] even more than Black does from White, it is still less conceivable that one should discern them [viz. sensibles in different sensory provinces whether co-ordinates or not] coinstantaneously than sensibles which are in the same province. Therefore, if co-instantaneous perception of the latter be impossible, that of the former is *a fortiori* impossible.

20 Some of the writers who treat of concords assert that the sounds combined in these do not reach us simultaneously, but only appear to do so, their real successiveness being unnoticed whenever the time it involves is [so small as to be] imperceptible. Is this true or not ? One might perhaps, following this up, go so far as to say that even the current opinion that one sees and hears coinstantaneously is due merely to the fact that the intervals of time [between the really successive perceptions of sight and hearing] escape observation. But this can scarcely be true, nor is it conceivable that any portion of 25 time should be [absolutely] imperceptible, or that any should be absolutely unnoticeable ; the truth being that it is possible[4] to perceive every instant of time. [This is so] ; because, if it is inconceivable that a person should, while perceiving him-

---

[1] The ratios involved in each of the great concords are 'reciprocal' quantities which multiplied together give unity. Thus in the Octave $\frac{1}{2} \times \frac{2}{1} = 1$; in the Fourth $\frac{3}{4} \times \frac{4}{3} = 1$; in the Fifth $\frac{2}{3} \times \frac{3}{2} = 1$. This same operation combines the opposites Few χ Many and Even χ Odd.

[2] Adopting καλῶ. Biehl's reading is untranslatable, except in a very awkward fashion.   [3] *Vide* Biehl's corrigenda.

[4] To demonstrate this directly Aristotle might have again employed his distinction between actuality and potentiality. But he chooses here the method of *reductio ad absurdum*

self or aught else in a continuous time, be at any instant
unaware of his own existence; while,[1] obviously, the assumption, that there is in the time-continuum a time so small as
to be absolutely imperceptible, carries the implication that
a person would, during such time, be unaware of his own
existence, as well as of his seeing and perceiving; [this
assumption must be false].

Again,[2] if there is any magnitude, whether time or thing,
absolutely imperceptible owing to its smallness, it follows that 30
there would not be either a thing which one perceives, or a
time in which one perceives it, unless in the sense that in some
part of the given time he sees some part of the given thing.   For 448 b
[let there be a line αβ, divided into two parts at γ, and let this
line represent a whole object and a corresponding whole time.
Now,] if one sees the whole line, and perceives it during
a time which forms one and the same continuum, only [3] in the
sense that he does so in some portion of this time, let us
suppose the part γβ, representing a time in which by sup- 5
position he was perceiving nothing, cut off from the whole.
Well, then, he perceives *in* a certain part [viz. in the re-
mainder] of the time, or perceives *a part* [viz. the remainder]
of the line, after the fashion in which one sees the whole earth
by seeing some given part of it, or walks in a year by walking
in some given part of the year.   But [by hypothesis] in the part
βγ he perceives nothing: therefore, in fact, he is said to
perceive the whole object and during the whole time simply
because he perceives [some part of the object] in some part of
the time αβ.   But [4] the same argument holds also in the case
of αγ [the remainder, regarded in its turn as a whole]; 10

---

[1] a 26-30.   εἰ is to be supplied again with ἔστι a 28.   This is Aristotle's
first argument.   The second (a 30-448b 12) shows that, on the given
assumption, the perception of any whole would be impossible.
[2] a 30.   Omit, as Biehl suggests, καὶ εἰ αἰσθάνεται before ἔτι.   If it is
retained, with οὐκ before the preceding αἰσθάνεται, we must render ' and
does not perceive, although he perceives ', for οὐ . . . καὶ εἰ could not (as if
it were οὐδὲ . . . εἰ) be translated ' not even perceives whether he perceives '.
[3] Read with Alexander (W. 150, 13) οὕτω τῷ ἐν τούτου τινί (of which
τῶι νῦν τούτων τινί of EMY may be a corruption), and make apodosis begin
with ἀφῃρήσθω b 5.
[4] Since it is not really possible in any concrete case to divide a whole
object and the time of its perception, as we have divided the line,
secluding, as if known, the part not perceived and the time in which no
perception takes place.

for it will be found [on this theory of vacant times and imperceptible magnitudes] that one always perceives only, in some part of a given whole time, and perceives only some part of a whole magnitude, and that it is impossible to perceive any [really] whole [object in a really whole time; a conclusion which is absurd, as it would logically annihilate the perception of both Objects and Time].

Therefore we must conclude that all magnitudes are perceptible, but their actual dimensions do not present themselves immediately in their presentation as objects One sees the sun, or a four-cubit rod at a distance, as a magnitude, but their exact dimensions are not given in their visual presentation : nay, at times an object of sight appears indivisible, but [vision, like other special senses, is fallible respecting 'common sensibles', e. g. magnitude, and] nothing that one sees is really
15 indivisible. The reason of this has been previously explained.[1]
It is clear then, from the above arguments, that no portion of time is imperceptible.

But we must here return to the question proposed above for discussion, whether it is possible or impossible to perceive several objects coinstantaneously ; by 'coinstantaneously' I mean perceiving the several objects in a time one and indivisible relatively to one another, i. e. indivisible in a sense consistent with its being all a continuum.[2]

---

[1] Viz. in the passage 445ᵇ 2–446ᵇ 20. ἡ δὲ αἰτία here is the αἰτία of the proposition ἅπαντα ... ὅσα ἐστίν ᵇ 12–13. In the passage referred to Aristotle showed (a) that all αἰσθητά were directly or indirectly magnitudes and as such divisible in infinitum, and (b) that all magnitudes are perceptible either actually or potentially, i. e. are αἰσθητά. This implies that the magnitudes of αἰσθητά are not always determinately perceived, for sometimes an αἰσθητόν is only potentially divisible, not actually. He nowhere in the de Sensu or anywhere else proves what he says, ᵇ 14 ἀλλ' οὐ ... But it follows from what he says that μέγεθος is one of the things about which ἀπατῶνται—men's perception misleads them.

[2] ᵇ 18 seqq. Omit οὐ τῷ ἀτόμῳ in ᵇ 21 as a piece of dittography, and, reading with Alexander καὶ οὕτως ἀτόμῳ, transfer the clause καὶ οὕτως ... συνεχεῖ (which in its traditional place makes no sense, whether ἀτόμῳ be referred to χρόνῳ as some take it, or to μορίῳ ψυχῆς, as others) to follow πρὸς ἄλληλα ᵇ 20, as an explanation of the term ἀτόμῳ χρόνῳ πρὸς ἄλληλα. The text thus becomes τὸ δ' ἅμα λέγω ἐν ἑνὶ καὶ ἀτόμῳ χρόνῳ πρὸς ἄλληλα, καὶ οὕτως ἀτόμῳ ὡς παντὶ ὄντι συνεχεῖ. No time is absolutely ἄτομος for Aristotle, and he lacks a word to express our 'individual', which is what is here really meant by ἄτομος. Hence the need of the explanation given of it. By ἀτόμῳ πρὸς ἄλληλα (cf. πρὸς αὐτά 446ᵃ 17) is meant that the time of discerning one of the two objects is identical with that of discerning

First,[1] then, is it conceivable that one should perceive the 20 different things coinstantaneously, but each with a different part of the Soul? Or [must we object] that,[2] in the first place, to begin with the objects of one and the same sense, e. g. Sight, if we assume it [the Soul *qua* exercising Sight] to perceive one colour with one part, and another colour[3] with a different part, it will have a plurality of parts the same in species, [as they must be,] since the objects which it thus perceives fall within the same genus?[4]

25

the other: that they are discerned together in the same individual time. Keeping the vulgate reading, we may perhaps translate 'with another part of the soul, and not with the indivisible part, though with a part which is individual in the sense that it is all continuous'. But the notion of the old commentators that here, and in 451ᵃ 26, the πρῶτον αἰσθητήριον is referred to is very questionable.

[1] ᵇ 20. πρῶτον μέν here corresponds to εἰ δὲ δή in 449ᵃ 5, where Aristotle begins his own solution. The πρῶτον μέν of ᵇ 22 corresponds not to ἔτι ᵇ 29, but to εἰ δέ of 449ᵃ 2, where the case of two different senses actualized through different parts of soul is taken up and dismissed. In ᵇ 24, after πλείω, τε should be kept (against Bäumker), as this corresponds to ἔτι in ᵇ 29, where the second part of the argument against the hypothesis of different parts of soul ' energizing' in simultaneous discernment through one sense is introduced. For ἔτι answering τε after an interval and with changed point of view cf. Eucken, *de usu particularum apud Aristotelem*, p. 13.

[2] ᵇ 22. ἢ ⟨λεκτέον⟩ ὅτι is strange. ἢ ὅτι generally answers to τί or διὰ τί.

[3] ᵇ 24. χρῶμα here merely = the ' object in general ' of each of the visual parts of soul assumed to operate at once. We need not suppose reference to colours of different species; ἄλλου is not ἑτέρου, nor ἄλλῳ, ἑτέρῳ.

[4] ᵇ 25. See Alexander, pp. 157, 13–158, 16 (Wendland). The 'parts of soul' are, by this hypothesis, so many αἰσθητήρια *of the same species*, since each has χρῶμα for object. Their αἰσθητά being of the same *genus* makes the αἰσθητήρια to be of the same species—not genus. Hence the καὶ γάρ. All αἰσθητήρια, as such (i. e. by the definition 424ᵃ 24, where even Rodier incorrectly construes as if he had τὸ πρῶτον, and finds mention of the πρῶτον αἰσθητήριον) are of the same genus, but each αἰσθητήριον differs in species from each other as it has a different genus of αἰσθητά for its object. If two αἰσθητήρια had the same genus of αἰσθητά (or rather two absolutely similar genera, e. g. if each had χρῶμα) for object, these αἰσθητήρια would be εἴδει ταὐτά, as in the case suggested by the objection. The point of the present objection lies in this unparcimonious multiplication of specifically identical *parts* of soul operating through each sense when discerning several objects together. The point of the next objection 448ᵃ 28 ἔτι κτλ. lies in the correlative multiplication of genera, and hence of *sciences* that would follow. For each of the 'parts' of soul would be a faculty of sense with its own ἐναντία under it; and thus under each of our 'five senses' would be not one science (as Aristotle teaches), but as many sciences as there were genera or pairs of contraries: the absurdity being that these pairs would be of the same kind, only repeated for each of the different co-operant parts of soul. From the above it appears that Biehl's adoption of ταῦτα after εἴδει ᵇ 25, connecting the latter with πλείω as dative of respect, is wrong. The καὶ γάρ ᵇ 25 cannot be explained

Should any one [to illustrate how the Soul might have in it two different parts specifically identical, each directed to a set of αἰσθητά the same in genus with that to which the other is directed] urge that, as there are two eyes, so there may be in the Soul something analogous, [the reply is] that of the eyes, doubtless, some one organ is formed, and hence their actualization in perception is one; but if this is so in the Soul, then, in so far as what is formed of both [i. e. of any two specifically identical parts as assumed] is one, the true perceiving subject also will be one, [and the contradictory of the above hypothesis (of different parts of Soul remaining engaged in simultaneous perception with one sense) is what emerges from the analogy]; while if the two parts of Soul remain separate, the analogy of the eyes will fail, [for of these some one is really formed].

Furthermore, [on the supposition of the need of different parts of Soul, co-operating in each sense, to discern different 30 objects coinstantaneously], the senses will be each at the same time one and many, as if we should say that they were each a set of diverse sciences; for neither will an 'activity' exist without its proper faculty, nor without activity will there be sensation.[1]

449 a But if the Soul does not, in the way suggested [i.e. with different parts of itself acting simultaneously], perceive in one

without ταὐτά: and εἴδει and γένει have here their proper Aristotelean significance. Read also, with Bitterauf, ἃ ἐν for the πάλιν of EMY.
[1] Instead of one αἴσθησις (e. g. ὄψις) with its present variety of ἐνέργειαι, i. e. *sensiones*, we should have, in each, many αἰσθήσεις, related severally, as so many δυνάμεις, to different parts of soul. For the ἐνέργειαι under each αἴσθησις would no longer run up into one δύναμις, but be held apart from one another, and imply each a δύναμις (i. e. a faculty of perceiving ἐναντία) to itself. This would (as Alexander says) be as absurd as having 'several sciences of the same theorem'; for, since to each genus of αἰσθητά a single ἐπιστήμη corresponds, on this hypothesis there would be as many ἐπιστῆμαι of the same kind as there were δυνάμεις (faculties of perceiving contraries) under (or in) each αἴσθησις. For the hypothesis being that, e. g. to see any two χρώματα at once, two different parts of soul should be employed, and this implying two faculties of colour-perception exactly alike in their αἰσθητά, we should have, under *each* of the two, the contraries White X Black. This would be totally needless, except for the purpose of meeting the above psychological ἀπορία, which (as Aristotle shows 449ᵃ 5 seqq.) can be solved otherwise, consistently with the unity of each αἴσθησις as a faculty, and of the soul itself as a whole. By the proposed solution the unity not only of each sensory faculty, and, in the sequel, of the soul itself, but also of each science would be totally abolished.

and the same individual time sensibles of the same sense, *a
fortiori* it is not thus that it perceives sensibles of different
senses. For it is, as already stated, more conceivable that
it should perceive a plurality of the former together in this
way than a plurality of heterogeneous objects.

If then, as is the fact, the Soul with one part perceives 5
Sweet, with another, White, either that[1] which results from these
is some one part, or else there is no such one resultant. But
there must be such an one, inasmuch as the general faculty of
sense-perception is one.[2] What one object, then, does that one
faculty [when perceiving an object, e.g., as both White and
Sweet] perceive?[3] [None]; for assuredly no one object arises
by composition of these [heterogeneous objects, such as White
and Sweet]. We must conclude, therefore, that there is, as
has been stated before, some one faculty in the soul with which
the latter perceives all its percepts, though it perceives[4] each 10
different genus of sensibles through a different organ.

May we not, then, conceive this faculty which perceives
White and Sweet to be one *qua* indivisible [sc. *qua* combining
its different simultaneous objects] in its actualization, but
different, when it has become divisible [sc. *qua* distinguishing
its different simultaneous objects] in its actualization?

---

[1] ª 6. τὸ ἐκ τούτων: cf. 448ᵇ 28 τὸ ἐξ ἀμφοῖν, where also the form of
expression seems to put it beyond question that there is *some* resultant,
the only question being whether or not this resultant is *one*.

[2] ª 7. That the general faculty of perception is one has been already
shown in *de Anima*, 426ᵇ 8-29; where too (426ᵇ 29-427ª 16) it is explained how a faculty numerically one can perceive opposites simultaneously without losing its numerical oneness. The difficulty is solved
there as here by the doctrine that its numerical oneness is consistent with
plurality in the relations in which it manifests itself.

[3] ª 8. For what follows cf. 431ª 17-431ᵇ 2. The negative answer to the
question—τίνος οὖν ἐκεῖνο ἑνός;—is all-important. If the conjoint percepts
here too (as in the cases stated above, e. g. 448ª 10) formed a μῖγμα, or
ran into one, simultaneous discernment of different objects could not be
made out at all. But while τὸ γλυκύ and τὸ λευκόν are held together
in the unity of τὸ αἰσθητικὸν πάντων (ª 17), they are kept distinct in the
object. Just as in πράγματα (objects in space) such qualities are present
together, yet not confused or combined, so in the αἴσθημα, or immediate
impression of them (and also in the φάντασμα, or subsequent representa-
tion), they are present together, yet discerned as different by the unity
of the *sensus communis* to which they are simultaneously presented. In
this solution of the ἀπορία Aristotle confines himself to the more difficult
case (cf. 447ᵇ 6, 22, 448ª 13-19, 449ª 2-5), that of heterogeneous sensibles;
which being settled, that of the homogeneous follows.

[4] ª 10. After ἄλλο δὲ κτλ. supply αἰσθάνεται, not αἰσθάνεσθαι.

Or is what occurs in the case of the perceiving Soul conceivably analogous to what holds true in that of the things
15 themselves? For the same numerically one thing is white
and sweet, and has many other qualities, [while its numerical
oneness is not thereby prejudiced] if the fact is not that the
qualities are really separable in the object from one another,
but that the *being* of each quality is different [from that of
every other].[1] In the same way therefore we must assume
also, in the case of the Soul, that the faculty of perception in
general is in itself numerically one and the same, but different
[differentiated] in its *being*; different, that is to say, in genus
as regards some[2] of its objects, in species as regards others.
Hence too, we may conclude that one can perceive [numeri-
cally different objects] coinstantaneously with a faculty which
20 is numerically one and the same, but not the same in its
relationship [sc. according as the objects to which it is directed
are not the same].

That every sensible object is a magnitude, and that nothing
which it is possible to perceive is indivisible, may be thus
shown.[3] The distance whence an object could not be seen

---

[1] τὸ εἶναι (in full τὸ εἶναι λευκῷ or γλυκεῖ) here='being *in relationship*', i. e.
relationship of the objects to the faculty of perception. In [a] 18 εἶναι
(sc. αἰσθητικῷ)='relationship of the faculty of perception to that of conception (according as the former perceives the different genera of αἰσθητά)'.
This explains the change from τὸ εἶναι [a] 18 to λόγῳ [a] 20. It is our *conceiving*
faculty that distinguishes τὸ αἰσθητικὸν πάντων in its relationships to its
different classes of objects, in which therefore it differs λόγῳ or *notione* :
it is τὸ αἰσθητικὸν πάντων that distinguishes λευκόν and γλυκύ, which differ
in their mode of manifestation to sense, in each particular experience.
Hence Bonitz (*Ind. Arist.* 221[a] 56), is hardly right in identifying τὸ εἶναι
and λόγος here.

[2] For the construction of the genitive cf. 455[a] 21 ; supply αἰσθητικῷ here
on the analogy of αἰσθήσει there. τὸ αἰσθητικόν is said to differ γένει or εἴδει
according as its αἰσθητά differ γένει or εἴδει. This is remarkable. Should
not the second ἕτερον be ἑτέρων? Then τῶν μὲν . . . τῶν δέ would simply
explicate ἑτέρων—the objects which are different some in genus, some in
species: the αἰσθητικόν would be different and its objects would be different.
This would make all clear.

[3] [a] 21-31. This argument is from the first *ad hominem*. Any one who
believes (as Aristotle does not) in an αἰσθητὸν ἀδιαίρετον must believe that it
can be situated in an indivisible place, i. e. in a mathematical point. For
such a person (not, however, for Aristotle himself) the ἔσχατον καὶ πρῶτον
. . . ὅθεν ([a] 24), being identical, form such a 'place'. But the alleged
αἰσθητὸν ἀδιαίρετον, if supposed to be set in this place, will be found to
possess self-contradictory attributes ; e.g., if an object of vision, it will be
at the same time visible and invisible ; which is impossible.
For Aristotle himself the πρῶτον καὶ ἔσχατον could not in reality run

is indeterminate, but that whence it is visible is determinate. We may say the same of the objects of Smelling and Hearing, and of all sensibles not discerned by actual contact. Now, there is, in the interval of distance, some extreme place, the last from which the object is invisible, and the first from 25 which it is visible. This place, beyond which if the object be one cannot perceive it, while if the object be on the hither side one must perceive it, is, I presume, itself necessarily indivisible. Therefore, if any sensible object be indivisible, such object, if set in the said extreme place whence imperceptibility ends and perceptibility begins, will have to be both visible and invisible at the same time ; but this is impossible. 30

This concludes our survey of the characteristics of the organs of Sense-perception and their objects, whether regarded in general or in relation to each organ. Of the remaining subjects, we must first consider that of memory and remembering.

into a point. Between visibility and non-visibility (so far as these depend on distance) there are for him an infinite number of gradations, corresponding successively to successive possible removals of the object through consecutive points in the ἀπόστημα or line of distance. These gradations towards invisibility represent so many degrees of potential visibility.

DE MEMORIA ET REMINISCENTIA

CHAPTER I

449 b WE have, in the next place, to treat of Memory and Remembering, considering its nature, its cause, and the part of
5 the soul to which this experience, as well as that of Recollecting, belongs. For the persons who possess a retentive memory
are not identical with those who excel in power of recollection ;
indeed, as a rule, slow people have a good memory, whereas
those who are quick-witted and clever are better at recollecting.

We must first form a true conception of the objects of
10 memory, a point on which mistakes are often made. Now to remember the future is not possible, but this is an object of opinion
or expectation (and indeed there might be actually a science of
expectation, like that of divination, in which some believe) ;
nor is there memory of the present, but only sense-perception.
For by the latter we know not the future, nor the past, but the
15 present only. But memory relates to the past. No one would
say that he remembers the present, when [1] it is present, e. g.
a given white object at the moment when he sees it ; nor
would one say that he remembers an object of scientific contemplation at the moment when he is actually contemplating
it, and has it full before his mind ;—of the former he would say
only that he perceives it, of the latter only that he knows it.
But when one has scientific knowledge, or perception, apart
20 from the actualizations of the faculty concerned, he thus ' remembers ' [that [2] the angles of a triangle are together equal to
two right angles]; as to the former, that he learned it, or thought
it out for himself, as to the latter, that he heard, or saw, it, or
had some such sensible experience of it. For whenever one
exercises the faculty of remembering, he must say within himself, ' I formerly heard (or otherwise perceived) this,' or ' I
formerly had this thought '.

---

[1] The next clause shows that here ὅτε not ὅτι is the true reading.
[2] This is spurious.

Memory is, therefore, neither Perception nor Conception, but a state [1] or affection of one of these, conditioned by lapse of 25 time. As already observed, there is no such thing as memory of the present while present, for the present is object only of perception, and the future, of expectation, but the object of memory is the past. All memory, therefore, implies a time elapsed; consequently only those animals which perceive time remember, and the organ whereby they perceive time is also that whereby they remember.

The subject [2] of 'presentation' has been already considered 30 in our work *de Anima*.[3] Without a presentation intellectual activity is impossible. For there is in such activity an incidental 450 a affection identical with one also incidental in geometrical demonstrations. For in the latter case, though we do not for the purpose of the proof make any use of the fact that the quantity in the triangle [for example, which we have drawn] is determinate, we nevertheless draw it determinate in quantity. So likewise when one exerts the intellect [e. g. on the subject of first principles], although the object may not be quantitative, 5 one envisages it as quantitative, though he thinks it in abstraction from quantity; while, on the other hand, if the object of

---

[1] ἕξις conjoined, as here, with πάθος can only have its usual Aristoteican meaning of a mode of ποιότης, a *state*. The definition of memory implies that in its genesis an αἴσθησις (or ὑπόληψις) has undergone something (πάθος) owing to lapse of time since the ἐνέργεια. The residue of the αἴσθησις (or ὑπόληψις) *so affected* has become a φάντασμα (or set of κινήσεις capable of yielding a φάντασμα) related to the original αἴσθησις as its εἰκών. This settled state of relationship, to be explained and defined more precisely in 451ᵃ 16, is what ἕξις here means. The *qualification* or *modification* effected by lapse of time in the residue of the αἴσθησις (or ὑπόληψις) and resulting in the settled state, is denoted by the combined words ἕξις and πάθος. ἕξις, of course, can, and does in a few places, mean 'having'. Cf. Aristotle, *Met*. 1022ʰ 4-12 and 1022ᵇ 15-21, where this word is explained, as = (*a*) 'having', (*b*) διάθεσις καθ' ἥν εὖ ἥ κακῶς διάκειται τὸ διακείμενον, καὶ ἤ καθ' αὑτὸ ἤ πρὸς ἄλλο. Such a ἕξις as that of μνήμη is described in the last words. It is a ἕξις καθ' ἥν μνημονικῶς διάκειταί τις πρὸς τὰ μνημονευτά, as ἐπιστήμη is a ἕξις καθ' ἥν διάκειταί τις ἐπιστημονικῶς πρὸς τὰ ἐπιστητά. Bonitz, *Arist. Stud.* v. p. 29, is mistaken when he makes ἕξις and πάθος here undistinguishable. ἕξις adds the notion of 'relativity' to a past. This—how a present state of mind can pick up a past—is the real epistemological 'crux', and Aristotle, with his usual unerring insight, singles it out as what peculiarly demands explanation.

[2] For apod. to ἐπεί see 450ᵃ 12 note. Most translators render φαντασία 'imagination,' but this, from the pyschologist's point of view, is liable to objection.

[3] Cf. 427ᵇ 29 seqq.

the intellect is essentially of the class of things that are quantitative, but indeterminate, one envisages it as if it had determinate quantity, though subsequently, in thinking it, he abstracts from its determinateness. Why we cannot exercise the intellect on any object absolutely apart from the [1] continuous, or apply it even to non-temporal [2] things unless in
10 connexion with time,[3] is another question. Now, one must cognize magnitude [4] and motion by means of the same faculty by which one cognizes [5] time [i.e. by that which is also the faculty of memory], and the presentation [involved in such cognition] is an affection of the *sensus communis*; whence this follows, viz. that the cognition of these objects [magnitude, motion, time] is effected by the [said *sensus communis*, i.e. the] primary faculty of perception. Accordingly,[6] memory [not merely of sensible, but] even of intellectual [7] objects involves a presentation: hence we may conclude that it belongs to the faculty of intelligence [8] only incidentally, while

---

[1] τοῦ is generic: it should not be struck out, as Freudenthal proposes.

[2] The heavenly bodies and their 'eternal' laws, as well as the non-temporal (or 'eternal') truths of mathematics. Cf. 221ᵇ 3 seqq., 1044ᵇ 7.

[3] χρόνος is *essentially continuous*, not an ἀριθμός, despite its definition as ἀριθμὸς κινήσεως κτλ.

[4] Cf. 232ᵃ 24 μέγεθος δ' ἐστὶν ἅπαν συνεχές.

[5] Freudenthal's translation—'Grösse und Bewegung muss aber der vorstellen der Zeit vorstellt'—is, though correct in a sense, grammatically difficult. Besides what is the meaning of saying ᾧ ⟨ἀναγκαῖον⟩ χρόνον γνωρίζειν? Supply γνωρίζει. The point of the text is to identify the faculty which perceives time (which has been shown to be that of memory) with that which supplies the φαντάσματα for the use of νόησις. This is done by identifying both with that which perceives κίνησις in general—the empirical type and basis of continuity: for even time is ἀριθμὸς κινήσεως, and partakes in its continuity (ἀριθμός here not implying that time itself is an arithmetical number essentially discontinuous). Freudenthal is astray in thinking καὶ κίνησιν unintelligible except on his view of the construction.

[6] ἡ δὲ μνήμη ... ἐστιν resumes, or sums up the result of, the protasis commenced at ἐπεί 449ᵇ 30, and thus prefaces ὥστε ᵃ 13, which commences the apodosis.

[7] Since νοητά involve φαντάσματα, as shown 450ᵃ 1–10, the memory of them involves and depends upon the same φαντάσματα. For such μνήμη is the ἕξις or πάθος of νόησις (included under ὑπόληψις 449ᵇ 24) when time has elapsed, and the ἐνέργεια has ceased. Though the νοητά may be 'eternal,' or at least non-temporal, the faculty which perceives time (τὸ πρῶτον αἰσθητικόν) is that which supplies their empirical basis, and therefore the ground of remembering them.

[8] Far the easiest correction of the νοουμένου of all MSS. is Prof. Bywater's ⟨δια⟩νοουμένου. Cf. 459ᵃ 8 οὐδὲ τοῦ διανοουμένου τὸ πάθος τοῦτο ὃ

directly and essentially it belongs to the primary faculty of sense-perception.

Hence not only human beings and the beings which possess 15 opinion or intelligence, but also certain other animals, possess memory. If memory were a function of [pure] intellect, it would not have been as it is an attribute of many of the lower animals, but probably, in that case, no mortal beings [1] would have had memory; since, even as the case stands, it is not an attribute of them all, just because all have not the faculty of perceiving time. Whenever one actually remembers having seen or heard, or learned, something, he includes in this act (as 20 we have already observed) the consciousness of 'formerly'; and the distinction of 'former' and 'latter' is a distinction in time.

Accordingly, if asked, of which among the parts of the soul memory is a function, we reply: manifestly of that part to which 'presentation' appertains; and all objects capable of being presented [viz. αἰσθητά] are immediately and properly objects of memory, while those [viz. νοητά] which necessarily involve [but *only* involve] presentation are objects of memory 25 incidentally.

One might ask how it is possible that though the affection [the presentation] alone is present, and the [related], fact absent, the latter—that which is not present—is remembered. [This question arises], because it is clear that we must conceive that which is generated through sense-perception in the sentient soul, and in the part of the body[2] which is its seat,— viz. that affection the state whereof we call memory—to be some such thing as a picture. The process of movement 30

καλοῦμεν ἐνυπνιάζ,ν, where τοῦ διανοουμένου is used in answer to the question raised 458ᵇ 1 in reference to τοῦ νοητικοῦ. τὸ διανοεῖσθαι can include Reason as well as reasoning.

[1] Reading θνητῶν, not θηρίων as Biehl after Rassow. Memory is limited to beings which have the sense of time (τὸ αἰσθητικόν), none of whom possess pure intellect; so that if it were a purely intellectual function, οἱ ἀθάνατοι might have it, but οἱ θνητοί (or τὰ θνητά) could not.

[2] It is an affection of soul and body conjointly, like all affections treated of in the *Parva Naturalia*. The clause τὸ ... εἶναι is difficult, but may be right. That thing, the ἕξις of which is μνήμη, is a φάντασμα 451ᵃ 15, and μνήμη itself is a ἕξις ἢ πάθος of an αἴσθησις or ὑπόληψις 449ᵇ 25. What then is the πάθος here the ἕξις of which is μνήμη? We must conclude it to be the φάντασμα (which in 450ᵃ 10 we saw to be πάθος τῆς κοινῆς αἰσθήσεως), to be described later on as εἰκών of its original. The word πάθος here does not mean an affection of the particular αἴσθησις or ὑπόληψις, as in 449ᵇ 25,

[sensory stimulation] involved in the act of perception stamps in, as it were, a sort of impression of the percept, just as 450 b persons do who make an impression with a seal.[1] This explains why, in those who are strongly moved owing to passion, or time of life, no mnemonic impression is formed ; just as no impression would be formed if the movement of the seal were to impinge on running water ; while there are others in whom, owing to the receiving surface [2] being frayed, as 5 happens to [the stucco on] old [chamber] walls, or owing to the hardness of the receiving surface, the requisite impression is not implanted at all. Hence both very young and very old persons are defective in memory ; they are in a state of flux, the former because of their growth, the latter, owing to their decay. In like manner, also, both those who are too 10 quick and those who are too slow have bad memories. The former are too soft,[3] the latter too hard [in the texture of their receiving organs], so that in the case of the former the presented image [though imprinted] does not remain in the soul, while on the latter it is not imprinted at all.

But then, if this truly describes what happens in the genesis of memory, [the question stated above arises :] when one remembers, is it this impressed affection that he remembers, or is it the objective thing from which this was derived ? If the former, it would follow that we remember nothing which 15 is absent ; if the latter, how is it possible that, though perceiving directly only the impression, we remember that absent thing which we do not perceive ? Granted that there is in us something like an impression or picture, why should the perception of the mere impression be memory of something else, instead of being related to this impression alone ? For when one actually remembers, this impression is what he

but an affection of the αἰσθητικὴ ψυχή. τὸ πάθος is here, therefore, in apposition to τὸ γιγνόμενον διὰ τῆς κτλ. 450ᵃ 29, and τοιοῦτον οἷον ζωγρ. τι is the *whole* predicate after εἶναι.

[1] This explanation of memory with the simile of the seal-impression is taken almost literally from Plato, *Theaetetus*, 191 D.

[2] Before ψήχεσθαι supply τὸ δεχόμενοι from ᵇ 5. For the above interpretation of ψήχεσθαι cf. Galen Προτρεπτικός, § 19 τοὺς τοίχους . . . γραφαῖς κεκοσμῆσθαι.

[3] ὑγρότεροι. τὸ ὑγρόν, 'the moist' = the elemental quality which explained softness in bodies ; just as τὸ ξηρόν, 'the dry' (a notion fundamental also in τὸ σκληρόν) explained hardness.

contemplates, and this is what he perceives. How then does he remember what is not present? One might as well suppose it possible also to see or hear that which is not present. In reply, we suggest that this very thing is quite conceivable, 20 nay, actually occurs in experience. A picture[1] painted on a panel is at once a picture and a likeness: that is, while one and the same, it is both of these, although the 'being' of both is not the same, and one may contemplate it either as a picture, or as a likeness. Just in the same way we have to conceive that the mnemonic presentation within us is something which 25 by itself is merely an object of contemplation, while, in relation to something else, it is also a presentation of that other thing. In so far as it is regarded in itself, it is only an object of contemplation, or a presentation ; but when considered as relative to something else, e. g., as its likeness, it is also[2] a mnemonic token. Hence, whenever the residual sensory process[3] implied by it is actualized in consciousness, if the soul perceives this in so far as it is something absolute, it appears to occur as a mere thought or presentation ; but if the soul perceives it *qua* related to something else, then,— just as when one contemplates the painting in the picture as being a likeness, and without having [at the moment] seen 30 the actual Koriskos, contemplates it as a likeness of Koriskos, and in that case[4] the experience involved in this contempla- 451 a tion of it [as relative] is different from what one has when he contemplates it simply as a painted figure—[so in the case of memory we have the analogous difference, for], of the objects[5]

---

[1] The apodosis to οἷον κτλ. begins with οὕτω b 24. ζῷον here and below = 'picture' generally, not 'picture of animal'. This use of the word is as early as Empedocles (Karst. 372), and Herod. iv. 88. To restrict the meaning here to painted *animals* would spoil the illustration, since then ζῷον would be relative at once and from the first.

[2] Freudenthal thinks the καί unmeaning ; but on the contrary it is indispensable. The relative φάντασμα is *as it were* an εἰκών (for this is only a simile), and this is also a 'reminder'. So in 451ª 2 ὅτι εἰκών, μνημόνευμα, because it is an εἰκών it is a 'reminder'.

[3] Every such φάντασμα depends for its possibility on a κίνησις within the organs, which persists as a survival or relic of the original perception.

[4] The reading of Bekker τε ... τε (450b 31–451ª 1)—a rare mode of conjunction—might mark the parallelism between the cases. But EMY have τὸ ἐν for ἐν τε in 451ª 1, and this has been translated.

[5] τὸ ἐν is, by a sort of 'Attic' apposition, subdivided into the τὸ μέν and τὸ δέ which follow.

in the soul, the one [the unrelated object] presents itself simply as a thought, but the other [the related object], just because, as in the painting, it is a likeness, presents itself as a mnemonic token.

We can now understand why it is that sometimes, when we have such processes, based on some former act of perception, occurring in the soul, we do not know whether this really 5 implies our having had perceptions corresponding to them, and we doubt whether the case is or is not one of memory. But occasionally it happens that [while thus doubting] we get a sudden idea and recollect that we heard or saw something formerly. This [occurrence of the 'sudden idea'] happens whenever, from contemplating a mental object as absolute, one changes his point of view, and regards it as relative to something else.

The opposite [sc. to the case of those who at first do not recognize their phantasms as mnemonic] also occurs, as happened in the cases of Antipheron of Oreus and others suffering 10 from mental derangement; for they were accustomed to speak of their mere phantasms as facts of their past experience, and as if remembering them. This takes place whenever one contemplates what is not a likeness as if it were a likeness.

Mnemonic exercises aim at preserving one's memory of something by repeatedly reminding him of it; which implies nothing else [on the learner's part] than the frequent contemplation of something [viz. the 'mnemonic', whatever it may be] as a likeness, and not as out of relation.

15 As regards the question, therefore, what memory or remembering is, it has now been shown that it is the state of a presentation, related as a *likeness* to that of which it is a presentation; and as to the question of which of the faculties within us memory is a function, [it has been shown] that it is a function of the primary faculty of sense-perception, i. e. of that faculty whereby we perceive time.

CHAPTER II

Next comes the subject of Recollection,[1] in dealing with
which we must assume as fundamental the truths elicited 20
above in our introductory discussions.[2] For recollection is not
the ' recovery ' or ' acquisition '[3] of memory ; since at the
instant when[4] one at first learns [a fact of science] or experiences [a particular fact of sense], he does not thereby ' recover '
a memory, inasmuch as none has preceded, nor does he acquire

---

[1] In the first paragraph of this chapter Aristotle is occupied with
correcting what he thinks the imperfect views of μνήμη as σωτηρία
αἰσθήσεως, and of ἀνάμνησις as τὸ τὴν μνήμην ἀναπολεῖν, expressed in the
Philebus 34 A-B. There is no reference, whatever to the metaphysical
' reminiscence ' theory of the *Meno* and *Phaedo*, as Thurot thinks. See
note on 451[b] 6.

[2] τοῖς ἐπιχειρηματικοῖς λόγοις. In translating this, the authority of Bonitz
(*Index*, 99[a] 40) has been followed. The expression may, however, refer
to the current discussions and assumptions (e. g. in the Platonic school)
on the subject of memory. But appearances are in favour of Bonitz'
view here. Cf. especially 449[b] 15-29 where the notion of memory as implying
lapse of time is developed. On this implication too the notion of Recollection rests. On this point the significance of γάρ [a] 20 turns. For
ἀνάμνησις is not μνήμης λῆψις just because the establishment of the ἔξις or
πάθος, in which μνήμη consists, requires lapse of time ; while it is not
μνήμης ἀνάληψις because *before* time has elapsed since the experience there
is no μνήμη to be recovered, while *after* time has elapsed the μνήμη may
be revived by processes that are not ἀναμνήσεις—by re-learning or re-
experiencing, instead of by an internal effort.

[3] That ἀνάμνησις is not λῆψις μνήμης is argued, with reference to
a supposed initial moment of the μάθησις or πάθησις regarded as continuous processes, in [a] 21-25 ὅταν . . . ἐγγίνεται [with a parenthetic hit
(οὔτ' ἀναλ.—προγέγονεν) at the theory of ἀνάληψις] and with reference to the
final moment, when the μάθησις or πάθησις is supposed to be perfected, in
ἔτι . . . μνημονεύει [a] 25-31. Next it is shown, 451[b] 3 (ἔτι) to 451[b] 6 (ἀκολουθεῖ),
that since μνήμη (or μνημονεύειν) is possible without ἀνάμνησις, λῆψις μνήμης
again fails as a definition ; for ἀνάμνησις always implies the *recovery* of an
interrupted μνήμη. Finally it is shown [b] 6-10 (οὐδὲ . . . ἀναμιμνήσκεσθαι)
that even ἀνάληψις μνήμης is not an adequate definition of ἀνάμνησις,
because one may recover μνήμη by re-learning or re-experiencing (re-
perceiving, &c.). For two reasons then, this last and that given paren-
thetically above, 451[a] 22 (οὐδεμία γὰρ προγέγονεν), ἀνάμνησις is not merely
ἀνάληψις μνήμης. But the short parenthetical argument is used with
reference merely to the moment of the original experience (at which if
one does not acquire μνήμην, *a fortiori* he does not recover it), whereas
the argument 451[b] 6-10 is used with reference to the later period when
μνήμη has now been established.

[4] [a] 21=μάθῃ . . . πάθῃ, and [a] 23 ἐγγένηται. We must attend to the
meaning of the aorists, which is carefully calculated here by the writer.

one *ab initio*. It is only at the instant when the aforesaid state[1] or affection [of the αἴσθησις or ὑπόληψις ; see 449ᵇ 24] is implanted in the soul that memory exists, and therefore
25 memory is not itself implanted concurrently with the continuous implantation of the [original][2] sensory experience.

Further: at the very individual and concluding[3] instant when first [the sensory experience or scientific knowledge] has been completely implanted, there is then already[4] established in the person affected the [sensory] affection, or the scientific[5] knowledge (if one ought to apply the term ' scientific knowledge' to the [mnemonic] state or affection ; and indeed one may well remember, in the 'incidental' sense, some of the

---

[1] ᵃ23. ἡ ἕξις καὶ τὸ πάθος. Here, if we should not read ἤ, we must take καί = ἤ. The mnemonic ἕξις and πάθος here are not to be taken for the primary experiences referred to in ᵃ 21, ᵃ 25, where the words τὸ πρῶτον are used to mark the difference. But πάθος is ambiguous, referring sometimes (as in ᵃ 26) to the primary affection of the subject of a sensory experience, sometimes (as in 449ᵇ 25) to the mnemonic affection which this experience itself undergoes by lapse of time. In ᵃ 24 it has both meanings.

[2] Therefore the disputed definitions fail with regard to the initial stage, not only as to recollection, but even as to memory, of which also they betray a misconception.

[3] Kampe's explanation (after Themistius) of τῷ ἀτόμῳ καὶ ἐσχάτῳ here as 'das letzte und untheilbare Sinnesorgan' is unsatisfactory. ἐσχάτῳ denotes the limit of the completion of the experience—the πάθησις. or μάθησις. [We agree with Kampe and Themistius (241. 29, ed. Spengel), and would translate : 'has come to be present in the individual and ultimate organ.' Edd.]

[4] There is no tautology, and, if there were, Freudenthal's τι before τῷ, ᵃ 25, would not stave it off. The point of the proposition ὅτε ἐγγέγονε, τότε ἐνυπάρχει ἤδη lies in the contrasted meaning of these two verbs : when once the πάθος or ἐπιστήμη has been perfectly engendered, thereupon or therein the foundation of memory—the immanence of the πάθος or ἐπιστήμη —is laid. The πάθος or ἐπιστήμη does not pass away, but abides as an ἀρχή in the mind, which is the force of ἐνυπάρχει. But memory itself is not there yet : time must first elapse.
To understand this passage we have to bear in mind Aristotle's definition of ἤδη as = τὸ ἐγγὺς τοῦ παρόντος νῦν ἀτόμου μέρος τοῦ μέλλοντος χρόνου 222ᵇ 7. Thus ἤδη here denotes *the very moment of the event* referred to in τῷ ἀτόμῳ καὶ ἐσχάτῳ ὅτε τὸ πρῶτον ἐγγέγονε, regarded as first in a coming series of moments. The experience occurs in the first moment, and in that and all succeeding moments the πάθος or ἐπιστήμη is found to be established. τὸ μὲν πάθος is balanced by τὸ δὲ μνημονεύειν ᵃ 29: the πάθος or ἐπιστήμη to which memory shall refer is now indeed implanted, but no time has yet passed. Before τὸ μνημονεύειν is possible, time must have passed. This πάθος is not the πάθος (or ἕξις) in which memory has been said to *consist*. The latter is a πάθος *of* the αἴσθησις or ὑπόληψις, i. e. a modification in their residual κινήσεις caused by lapse of time. The former is the original sensory experience to which memory shall refer.

[5] Sc. in the person who has learned it : after ἐπιστήμη understand τῷ μαθόντι.

things [i. e. τὰ καθόλου] which are properly objects of scientific[1]
knowledge); but to remember, strictly and properly speaking,[2] is an activity which will not be immanent until the 30
original experience has undergone lapse of time. For one
remembers, now what one saw or otherwise experienced
formerly; the moment of the original experience and the
moment of the memory of it are never identical.

Again,[3] [even when time has elapsed, and one can be said
really to have acquired memory, this is not necessarily
recollection, for firstly] it is obviously possible, without any 451 b
present act of recollection, to remember as a continued
consequence of the original perception or other experience;
whereas [4] when [after an interval of obliviscence] one recovers
some scientific knowledge which he had before, or some perception, or some other experience, the state of which we above
declared to be memory, it is then, and then only, that this
recovery may amount to a recollection of any of the things
aforesaid. But, [though, as observed above, remembering does 5
not necessarily imply recollecting], recollecting always implies

---

[1] ἐπιστήμη is a ἕξις ἀποδεικτική 1139[b] 31. In the sense in which it
is spoken of as δυνάμει (*Met.* 1087[a] 15, cf. Locke's 'Habitual Knowledge') it can subsist in the mnemonic ἕξις; for we may 'remember'
τὰ καθόλου κατὰ συμβεβηκός, as explained 450[a] 23-25. Ἔνια: *some* of the
objects of ἐπιστήμη; for this word was (like our 'science') extended to
include even ἡ πυκτική, and many other matters of the sort that can be
direct objects of memory. The question here raised about the term
ἐπιστήμη being used of a ἕξις shows how far ἕξις is from meaning a
'having' in this connexion.

[2] καθ' αὐτό, i. e. as distinct from τὸ κατὰ σ. μν., and as opposed to τὸ
ἐνυπάρχειν τὸ πάθος ἢ τὴν ἐπιστήμην. 'Incidental' as well as 'direct'
remembering involves time-lapse.

[3] Freudenthal is right in interpreting this argument as directed against
the proposition ἀνάμνησις = μνήμης λῆψις; for a person may have
acquired μνήμη but not parted with it, and ἀνάμνησις implies always at
least an interruption of μνήμη, though it implies more, as will be shown.
Freudenthal wrongly thinks that Aristotle will not allow ἀνάμνησις to involve
μνήμης ἀνάληψις at all—only a recovering of the ἐπιστήμη or αἴσθησις. But
the expression μνήμης ἀνάληψις was part of the traditional definition: ἀναλαμβάνειν μνήμην is used by Plato, *Phil.* 34 B, and Aristotle has no objection
to it as a definition, provided it be qualified by reference to the πλείων
ἀρχή of [b] 10 below. In accepting the expression, thus qualified, he may be
following the ἐπιχειρηματικοὶ λόγοι, in the sense referred to above in the note
on these words as alternative to that in which they are taken by Bonitz.

[4] There should not be a full stop, but only a colon, or comma, before
ἀλλά 451[b] 2. Just before, μνημονεύειν = μνημονεύοντα διατελεῖν, which is
contrasted here with τὸ ἀναλαμβάνειν τὴν ἐπιστήμην ἢ τὴν αἴσθησιν.

DE MEMORIA ET REMINISCENTIA

remembering,[1] and actualized memory follows [upon the successful act of recollecting].

But secondly,[2] even the assertion that recollection is the reinstatement in consciousness of something which was there before but had disappeared requires qualification. This assertion may be true, but it may also be false ; for the same person may twice learn [from some teacher], or twice discover [i. e. excogitate], the same fact. Accordingly, the act of recollecting ought [in its definition] to be distinguished from these acts ; i. e. recollecting must imply in those who recollect the presence of some spring [3] over and above that from which they originally learn.

10 Acts of recollection, as they occur in experience, are due to the fact that one movement has by nature another that succeeds it in regular order.

If this order be necessary, whenever a subject experiences the former [4] of two movements thus connected, it will [invariably] experience the latter ; if, however, the order be not necessary, but customary, only in the majority of cases will the subject experience the latter of the two movements. But it is a fact that there are some movements, by a single experience of which persons take the impress of custom more deeply 15 than they do by experiencing others many times ; hence [5]

---

[1] The text is correct : τὸ μνημονεύειν is a necessary 'incident' of τὸ ἀναμεμνῆσθαι, and the latter is accompanied by and implies a reinstatement of ἡ μνήμη. This last is both the condition and the consequence of ἀνάμνησις : the *condition*, for if there be no (potential) μνήμη, ἀναμ. is impossible (cf. 452ᵃ 7 οὐκέτι μέμνηται) ; the *consequence*, for ἀνάμν. results in the reviviscence of (actual) μνήμη. 'A man has not the power to recollect what is not in his mind,' said Dr. Johnson, 'but when a thing is in his mind he may remember it.'

[2] Even here Plato had been beforehand with Aristotle. Cf. *Phil.* 34 B ὅταν [ἡ ψυχὴ] ἀπολέσασα μνήμην . . . αὖθις ταύτην ἀναπολήσῃ πάλιν αὐτὴ ἐν ἑαυτῇ, where both the interval of obliviscence and the internal activity are required for the definition of Recollection. So in the *Meno* 85 D τὸ δ' ἀναλαμβάνειν αὐτὸν ἐν αὑτῷ ἐπιστήμην οὐκ ἀναμιμνήσκεσθαί ἐστιν ; πάνυ γε. Both in *Meno* 81 D and *Phaedo* 73 D recollection is conceived as a ζήτησις. Aristotle is superior to Plato chiefly in the detail with which he examines the process of ἀνάμνησις.

[3] For the meaning of πλείων ἀρχή see below, 452ᵃ 4-7, and 452ᵃ 11-12.

[4] Grammar and sense require ἐκείνην here.

[5] How can one reason (διό) from ἐνίους to ἔνια ? Try how one will, one cannot, with Biehl's text, avoid logical absurdity and confusion. Read ἐνίας (sc. κινήσεις) ᵇ 14, ἄλλας ᵇ 15, and ἕτερα ᵇ 16. Freudenthal in recommending also κινουμένας ᵇ 15 seems to miss seeing that the

upon seeing some things but once we remember them better than others which we may have seen frequently.

Whenever, therefore, we are recollecting, we are experiencing[1] certain [read τινάς with Freudenthal] of the antecedent movements until finally we experience the one after which customarily comes that which we seek. This explains why we hunt up the series[2] [of κινήσεις], having started in thought either from a present intuition or some other, and from something either similar, or contrary, to what we seek, or else from that which is contiguous[3] with it. Such is the empirical ground 20 of the process of recollection ; for the mnemonic movements involved in these starting-points are in some cases identical, in others, again, simultaneous, with those of the idea we seek, while in others they comprise a portion of them, so that the remnant which one experienced after that portion [and which still requires to be excited in memory] is comparatively small.

Thus, then, it is that persons seek to recollect, and thus, too, it is that they recollect even without the effort[4] of seeking to

construction is κινεῖταί τις κίνησίν τινα—not κινεῖται κίνησις. The κινοῦντι πολλά and κινήσῃ κίνησιν below 452ᵃ 9, and the σωματικόν τι κινεῖ 453ᵃ 22 stand on a different footing ; for there the person is supposed to be making active voluntary efforts to stir up or arouse some idea. Besides, the expression αἱ κινήσεις ἐθίζονται would be absurd : it is the persons that ἐθίζονται.

What Aristotle is thinking of here is the greater impressiveness of some experiences as compared with others : he is not alluding to the greater impressibility of some persons as compared with others ; but the idea that he must also have referred to the latter point is possibly what first corrupted the text. The use of μνημονεύομεν, however,—the first person standing for all persons—shows that the latter point was not intended here.

[1] Here κινούμεθα includes both the active and the passive sense. This twofold aspect is referred to below ᵇ 22-23 ζητοῦντες . . . καὶ μὴ ζητοῦντες.

[2] For the meaning of τὸ ἐφεξῆς (which is not a *continuum*) see *Phys.* 231ᵃ 22, 259ᵃ 16.

[3] i. e. as coefficient in one total idea. ' The association between the parts and the whole would be the typical form of all association. This fundamental law of all association of ideas might be called the law of totality.' See Höffding, *Psych.* p. 159, E. T. Such seems the force of the compound σύνεγγυς in ᵇ 20. By τὸ νῦν of course is meant not an abstract instant of time, but the concrete filling of an instant. We may begin by calling to mind what we were thinking of at *any* moment, or start from what we are thinking of *now*. Thus the time-factor in recollection is put in the forefront here, though not fully dealt with till 452ᵇ 7-453ᵃ 4.

[4] For such non-voluntary ἀνάμνησις cf. *infra* 453ᵃ 17-18. The train of ideas is part of the mechanism of nature, which the will avails itself of, but which may lead to recollection without an effort of will.

do so, viz. when the movement implied in recollection has
25 supervened on some other which is its condition. For, as a
rule, it is when antecedent movements of the classes here
described have first been excited, that the particular movement
implied in recollection follows. We need not examine a series
of which the beginning and end lie far apart, in order to see
how [by recollection] we remember [1]; one in which they lie
near one another [2] will serve equally well. For it is clear that
the method is in each case the same, that is, one hunts
up the objective series, without any previous search or previous
recollection. For [there is, besides the natural order, viz. the
order of the πράγματα, or events of the primary experience,
also a customary order, and] by the effect of custom the
mnemonic movements tend to succeed one another in a certain
30 order.[3] Accordingly, therefore, when one wishes to recollect,
this is what he will do : he will try to obtain a beginning of
movement whose sequel shall be the movement which he
desires to reawaken. This explains why attempts at recollection succeed soonest and best when they start from a
452 a beginning [of some objective series]. For, in order of succession,
the mnemonic movements are to one another as the objective
facts [from which they are derived]. Accordingly, things
arranged in a fixed order, like the successive demonstrations
in geometry, are easy to remember [or recollect],[4] while badly [5]
arranged subjects are remembered with difficulty.

Recollecting differs also in this respect from relearning,
5 that one who recollects will be able, somehow, to move,
solely by his own effort, to the term next after the starting-

---

[1] All ἀνάμνησις if successful ends in μνήμη—actual memory. Hence it
is idle to say that μεμνῆσθαι is confused with ἀναμιμνήσκεσθαι here or in
452[b] 7.
[2] τὰ σύνεγγυς, i. e. a train of ideas whose extremes—the mnemonic ἀρχή
and ἡ κίνησις 'ἐκείνη'—are not far apart *from one another*; τὰ πόρρω just
above is the opposite.
[3] There must not have been previous ζήτησις or ἀνάμνησις, for previous
ζήτησις or ἀνάμνησις would have tended to establish ἔθος, and to
prejudice, so far, our efforts to discover the natural τρόπος of ἀνάμνησις,
with which Aristotle is here concerned.
[4] The distinction of μνήμη and ἀνάμνησις cannot be preserved in εὐμνη-
μόνευτα and such compounds.
[5] τὰ φαῦλα here = τὰ χύδην of 1409[b] 5, τὰ μέτρα πάντες μνημονεύουσι μᾶλλον
τῶν χύδην.

point. When one cannot do this of himself, but only by external assistance, he no longer remembers [i. e. he has totally forgotten, and therefore of course cannot recollect]. It often happens that, though a person cannot recollect at the moment, yet by seeking he can do so, and discovers what he seeks. This he succeeds in doing by setting up many movements, until finally he excites one of a kind which will have for its sequel the fact he wishes to recollect. For remembering[1] 10 [which is the *condicio sine qua non* of recollecting] is the existence, potentially, in the mind of a movement capable of stimulating it to the desired movement, and this, as has been said, in such a way that the person should be moved [prompted to recollection] from within himself, i. e. in consequence of movements wholly contained within himself.

But one must get hold of a starting-point. This explains why it is that persons are supposed to recollect sometimes by starting from mnemonic *loci*.[2] The cause is that they pass swiftly in thought from one point to another, e. g. from milk 15 to white, from white to mist[3], and thence to moist, from which one remembers Autumn [the 'season of mists'], if this be the season he is trying to recollect.

[1] Freudenthal is quite wrong in thinking that we should read here ἀναμιμνήσκεσθαι, which indeed would rather require ἐνεργεῖν than ἐνεῖναι in what follows. See next note.

[2] Cf. 163ᵇ 28 (Bonitz' *Ind.* gives a wrong reference) καθάπερ γὰρ ἐν τῷ μνημονικῷ μόνον οἱ τόποι τεθέντες εὐθὺς ποιοῦσιν αὐτὰ μνημονεύειν. It was a well-known fact, and the Simonidean mnemonic art, or art of topical memory, was cultivated widely long before Aristotle's time, as well as ever since. Cf. Xen. *Symp.* iv. 62 (with Schneider's note); Cic. *de Orat.* ii. 86–88; *Auct. ad Herenn.* iii. 16 to end; Quintil. *Inst. Or.* xi. 2 (de memoria); Plato, *Hipp. Mai.* 285, where Hippias who has τὸ μνημονικόν boasts of his power to repeat fifty names after hearing them only once. Cf. also Aristotle himself *de An.* 427ᵇ 19 ὥσπερ οἱ ἐν τοῖς μνημονικοῖς τιθέμενοι καὶ εἰδωλοποιοῦντες, and 458ᵇ 20 οἷον οἱ δοκοῦντες κατὰ τὸ μνημονικὸν παράγγελμα τίθεσθαι τὰ προβαλλόμενα (where οἱ δοκοῦντες may be regarded as giving the impression present to the sleepers' minds). Why δοκοῦσιν and ἐνίοτε here, words which seem to express doubt of the pretensions of the professors of the mnemonic art? But on the whole it seems best not to adopt Sir W. Hamilton's ἀπ' ἀτόπων, very tempting as it is; for (*a*) the instances given here are not quite ἄτοπα, and (*b*) Aristotle habitually speaks with caution and reserve, often using such words as suggest hesitation even when he cannot really be in doubt. Freudenthal suggests τάχιστα for ἐνίοτε, but this can hardly be ventured.

[3] ἀήρ, for Aristotle, is naturally and distinctively white: it is the immixture of this that causes the whiteness of snow and foam. See Prantl, *Arist. de Coloribus*, p. 105. The history of the word in classical usage from Homer onwards shows that it properly meant thick or misty air.

It seems true in general that the middle point also among all things is a good mnemonic starting-point from which to reach any of them. For if one does not recollect before, he will do so when he has come to this, or, if not, nothing can help him ; as, e. g. if one were to have in mind the numerical [1] series
20 denoted by the symbols A, B, Γ, Δ, E, Ϲ,[2] Ι, H, Θ. For, if he does not remember what he wants at E,[3] then at E he remembers Θ [4] ; because from E movement in either direction is possible, to Δ or to Ϲ. But, if it is not for one of these that he is searching, he will remember [what he *is* searching for] when he has come to Γ, if he is searching for H or Ι.[5] But if [it is] not [for H or Ι that he is searching, but for one of the terms that remain], he will remember by going to A, and so in all cases [in which one starts from a middle point].
25 The cause of one's sometimes recollecting and sometimes not, though starting from the same point, is, that from the same starting-point a movement can be made in several directions, as, for instance, from Γ [6] to Ι or to Δ. If, then, the mind has

---

[1] Taking the series as numerical (see Smyly, *Cl. R.* June, 1906), the only alterations of MSS. readings are (*a*) the insertion of Ϲ after E, which is easy; (*b*) the alteration of E to Ϲ in ᵃ 22, which is also easy ; and (*c*) the insertion of τοῦ before Θ in ᵃ 20.

[2] For the use of this as a numerical symbol *in the time of* Aristotle there is evidence enough. The disappearance of numeral letters from our texts is due to the rule by which the Byzantine and even earlier copyists translated them into words.

[3] If the text is not here dittographic, it may mean, ' if E itself be not what he wants.'

[4] When he has come to E, the middle point, he will remember Θ ; i. e. being at 5 he moves to 4, and by the proximity of these in thought he gets 9. In Greek arithmetic in many cases the juxtaposition of symbols implies addition. Thus at E (which it has to be observed he does not ever abandon) he has also Δ, and so he has Θ. We may bring the case under the rule of τὸ σύνεγγυς 451ᵇ 18-20. What he would get if he moved upwards, viz. EϹ = 11, is not mentioned, as this lies outside the series.

[5] When he has come to Γ (still, of course, keeping hold of E) he similarly obtains H, i. e. 5 + 3, or else he obtains Ι by τὸ ἐναντίον (cf. 451ᵇ 19) thus : in the series 3, 5, 7, of which 5 is τὸ μέσον, either ἔσχατον with τὸ μέσον tends to bring to mind the other ἔσχατον. For this see *N. E.* 1106ᵃ 33 seqq. Thus it is that from Γ E here he gets (or may get) Ι. All the cases here given come, in fact, under two of the rules mentioned as governing recollection in 451ᵇ 18 seqq.

[6] From Γ he may go to Ι by ἐναντιότης as just explained, to Δ by proximity in the series (τὸ σύνεγγυς).

not [when starting from E] moved in an old path [1] [i. e. one
in which it moved when first having the objective experience,
and that, therefore, in which un-'ethized' φύσις would have it
again move], it tends to move to the more customary; for
[the mind having, by chance or otherwise, *missed* moving in
the 'old' way] Custom now [2] assumes the rôle of Nature.[3]
Hence the rapidity with which we recollect what we frequently [4] think about. For as regular sequence of events is
in accordance with nature, so, too, regular sequence is observed in the actualization of κινήσεις [in consciousness], and
here frequency tends to produce [the regularity of] [5] nature. 30
And since in the realm of nature occurrences [6] take place which 452 b

[1] [a] 27. The well-supported μή with διὰ παλαιοῦ has been here adopted.
The only change desirable would seem to be the insertion of τοῦ before παλαιοῦ.
Critics have not seen how the 'παλαιόν' may differ from the 'customary'.
Suppose I want to recollect the name of the Spartan who said χρήματα
χρήματ' ἀνήρ, and get, as a clue, the abbreviation 'Aristo.' I once knew
the name well, but since then my reading habits have changed. If my
thoughts leap along their old path (as they *naturally* should, with the
question and the clue to guide them) they bring me from Aristo to
'Aristodemus'. If, however, they miss the old track, they bring me to
some name with which I am now more familiar, e. g. 'Aristotle'. Custom
has superseded mere φύσις. Freudenthal, however, asks 'Aber ist nicht
eben τὸ συνηθέστερον ebenfalls eine Affection die man vor Alters gehabt
hat?' This is the *fons et origo erroris*.
[2] [a] 28. ἤδη, i. e. at once, upon the 'old' path having been missed,
custom takes the reins.
[3] [a] 30. There being many possible paths for the mind to move in from
Γ, while that taken by it in its old, i. e. original, experience is only one,
if it misses this old track, φύσις alone no longer rules: ἔθος also now has
a power of interfering, and even deciding where it shall move. Thus
the 'old' track and the 'customary' are contrasted; which is quite
intelligible, for the mind may have only moved *once* διὰ ⟨τοῦ⟩ παλαιοῦ, i. e.
from Γ to the desired goal, but *often* from Γ to other points. Therefore
when once ὁ ἀναμιμνησκόμενος, or ὁ ζητῶν, has missed the old track, he
loses the guidance of φύσις (for which see 451[b] 11) in his particular quest.
and falls under that of ἔθος.
[4] Reading ἃ πολλάκις [a] 28.
[5] ποιεῖ φύσιν. For the whole cf. *N. E.* II. i. 1103[a] 20 (with Stewart's
notes). φύσις here=*organic* nature; ἔθος=the realm of the actualization
of κινήσεις in perception, &c.
[6] 452[b] 1. E M Y omit μή before ὁμοίως [b] 2. We should, if we followed
these MSS., suppose Aristotle to mean that Nature as a theatre or subject
of 'freaks' is equally present in the sphere of Custom. This, however, is
foreign to the whole tenor of these tracts, in which φύσις (cf. the frequent
πέφυκε, especially in 451[b] 11) implies a power making for order and
regularity. For παρὰ φύσιν cf. 770[b] 9 seqq. ἔστι γὰρ τὸ τέρας (monstrous
birth) τῶν παρὰ φύσιν τι, παρὰ φύσιν δ' οὐ πᾶσαν κτλ. (which last words
show that *here* too he may be thinking only of *organic* nature). Cf.
767[b] 5, 1255[b] 1 seqq. For ἀπὸ τύχης cf. 1027[b] 12, but especially 197[a] 36

are even contrary to nature, or fortuitous, the same happens *a fortiori* in the sphere swayed by custom, since in this sphere natural law is not similarly established. Hence it is that [from the same starting-point] the mind receives an impulse to move sometimes in the required direction,[1] and at other times otherwise, [doing the latter] particularly when something else somehow deflects the mind from the right direction and attracts it to itself.[2] This last consideration explains too how it happens that, when we want to remember a name, we remember one somewhat like[3] it, indeed, but blunder in reference to [i. e. in pronouncing] the one we intended. Thus, then, recollection takes place.

But the point of capital importance is that [for the purpose of recollection] one should cognize,[4] determinately or indeterminately, the time-relation [of that which he wishes to recollect]. There is,—let it be taken as a fact,—something by which one distinguishes a greater and a smaller time; and it is reasonable to think that one does this in a way analogous

seqq. τὸ μὲν γὰρ ἀπὸ τύχης πᾶν ἀπὸ ταὐτομάτου, τοῦτο δ' οὐ πᾶν ἀπὸ τύχης· ἡ μὲν γὰρ τύχη καὶ τὸ ἀπὸ τύχης ἐστὶν ὅσοις καὶ τὸ εὐτυχῆσαι ἂν ὑπάρξειεν καὶ ὅλως πρᾶξις. διὸ καὶ ἀνάγκη περὶ τὰ πρακτὰ εἶναι τὴν τύχην. But he goes on (197ᵇ 33) ὅταν γὰρ γένηταί τι [ἐν τοῖς φύσει] παρὰ φύσιν, τότε οὐκ ἀπὸ τύχης ἀλλὰ μᾶλλον ἀπὸ ταὐτομάτου γεγονέναι φαμέν, with which cf. 289ᵇ 26 also. Here therefore τύχης = ταὐτομάτου.

[1] ἐκεῖ = ἐκεῖσε (which Aristotle does not use). Cf. the regular ἐκείνη for the κίνησις to be recollected, ἐκεῖθεν in next line, and ἐκεῖ just below 452ᵇ 10. So ἄλλως here virtually = ἄλλοσε (which also Aristotle does not use), though it comes awkwardly before the ἄλλως in a different sense just following.

[2] E M Y give αὐτός for αὐτόσε ᵇ 4, but this would make the person's will perverse, which would be foreign to the matter here. It is something *else* that misleads his thoughts. For αὐτόσε cf. Plato, *Rep.* 369 D. We cannot take ἀφέλκῃ intransitively, but might read ἀφέλκῃ ⟨τι⟩. Yet Aristotle often leaves the indefinite subject to be supplied. [ἀφέλκῃ without a subject, and αὐτόσε, are difficult. Perhaps we should read αὐτός and take ἀφέλκῃ intransitively. Edd.]

[3] παρόμοιον. It is easy to supply μνημονεύομεν from the preceding clause : there is no difficulty in the accusative, for παρόμοιον = παρόμοιόν τι (rather than ὄνομα), and besides even if ὄνομα were supplied it could stand, as μνημονεύειν takes accusative even with such 'outer' object. Cf. 1409ᵇ 5 τὰ μέτρα πάντες μνημονεύουσι μᾶλλον τῶν χύδην.

[4] γνωρίζειν properly = to 'cognize' (or get into the mind) ✕ νοεῖν = to have in mind. The determinate cognition of time is explained and illustrated (down to ᵇ 24) by the mathematical mode of determining distance. Then, from ᵇ 30, the indeterminate mode of estimating it is considered. Knowing the time is a prime help towards recollecting the other circumstances of an event. The time-association is a chief element in the memory-idea. Aristotle's time-κινήσεις in what follows may perhaps, as an assumption, be compared with Lotze's 'local signs'.

to that in which one discerns [spatial] magnitudes. For it 10
is not by the mind's reaching out towards them, as some say
a visual ray from the eye does [in seeing], that one thinks [1] of
large things at a distance in space (for even if they are not there,
one may similarly think them); but one does so by a proportionate mental movement. For there are in the mind the
like figures and movements [i. e. 'like' to those of objects and
events]. Therefore, when one thinks the greater objects,
in what will his thinking those [2] differ from his thinking the
smaller? [In nothing,] because all the internal though
smaller are as it were proportional to the external. Now,
as we may assume within a person something proportional 15
to the forms [3] [of distant magnitudes], so, too, we may
doubtless assume also something else proportional to their
distances. As, therefore, if one has [psychically] the movement in AB, BE,[4] he constructs in thought [i. e. knows
objectively] ΓΔ, since AΓ and ΓΔ bear equal ratios respectively [5]
[to AB and BE], [so [6] he who recollects also proceeds]. Why
then does he construct ΓΔ rather than ZH? Is it not because [7]

[1] νοεῖ: the νόησις referred to here and below is of course carried on
by the help of φαντάσματα.

[2] b 13 read with EMY ὅταν τὰ μείζω νοῇ, ὅτι ἐκεῖνα νοεῖ ἢ τὰ ἐλάττω;
ὅτι νοεῖ being used for more usual infin. after διοίσει. One feels that ἐκεῖνα
must refer as elsewhere to the real or 'outward things'.

[3] b 15 εἴδεσιν. This reminds us of the def. of αἴσθησις (424 a 18) as
δεκτικὸν τῶν αἰσθητῶν εἰδῶν ἄνευ τῆς ὕλης. The word is more general than
σχήματα, including 'forms' of events as well as of objects, stored (without
the matter) for use in imagination and memory.

[4] See Figure. BE=the psychic analogue of the εἶδος of a real object; AB
=the analogue (the ἄλλο of b 16) of its ἀπόστημα; ΓΔ = the real object; AΓ =
its real distance. τὴν AB sc. κίνησιν. All the lines are lines of 'movement',
by moving in which the mind 'constructs' real things and distances. νοεῖν
is used here of the inner or representative lines (the given data), ποιεῖν,
except in b 21, of the outer objects constructed in thought, or, in other
words, objectively known. Possibly ποῆσαι should be read for νοῆσαι
in b 21. The epistemological implications of ποιεῖν here are interesting.

[5] Not the same as saying AΓ : ΓΔ : : AB : BE, for so we should not have
καί, but ὡς ἡ AΓ πρὸς τὴν ΓΔ, οὕτω s ἡ AB πρὸς τὴν BE. The proposition =
AΓ : AB : : ΓΔ : BE, as required by the reasoning.

[6] The application of the geometrical illustration (prefaced by ὥσπερ b 9
above) to memory is left to the reader, and the apodosis did not need to
be expressed.

[7] Manifestly AB : BE : : AΓ : ΓΔ. But if AΓ : AB were unknown, ΓΔ
could not be determined. We have, however (thanks to the power
ᾧ κρίνει b 8 above) the ratio of AΓ : AB, viz. Θ : I. Thus ΓΔ is determined;
for when the mind moves in the κίνησις AB, BE, it moves at the same time
in that of the determinative ratio Θ:I. In constructing ZH it moves similarly
in BE, but now the concurrent determinative ratio is K : Λ. We know

as AΓ[1] is to AB, so is Θ to I? These movements therefore [sc. in AB, BE, *and* in Θ : I] he has simultaneously. But if he wishes to construct to thought ZH, he has in mind BE in like manner as before [when constructing ΓΔ], but now, instead of [the movements of the ratio] Θ : I, he has in mind [those of the ratio] K : Λ ; for K : Λ : : ZA : BA.

When, therefore, the 'movement' corresponding to the object and that corresponding to its time concur, then one actually remembers. If one supposes [himself to move in these different but concurrent ways] without really doing so, he supposes himself to remember. For one may be mistaken, and think that he remembers when he really does not. But it is not possible, conversely, that when one actually remembers he should not suppose himself to remember, but should remember unconsciously. For remembering, as we have conceived it, essentially implies consciousness of itself. If, however, the movement corresponding to the objective fact takes place without that corresponding to the time, or, if the latter takes place without the former, one does not remember.[2]

The movement answering to the time is of two kinds. Sometimes in remembering a fact one has no determinate time-notion of it, no such notion as that, e.g., he did something or other on the day before yesterday[3] ; while in other cases he has

AB, BE, and that AB : BE : : AΓ : ΓΔ ; ∴ ΓΔ = $\dfrac{\text{AΓ} \cdot \text{BE}}{\text{AB}}$. But Θ : I gives AΓ in terms of AB ; e. g., AΓ = ABx. Hence ΓΔ = $\dfrac{\text{BE} \cdot \text{AB}x}{\text{AB}}$ = BEx. Similarly, ZH would appear in terms of BE ; e.g. as BEy.

[1] [b] 19 AΓ of the codices is right, as is I of EMY in [b] 20. [The above explanation of [b] 17-24 is, in form, due to Professor Smyly. It is the same in principle as that given by the translator (*Greek Theories of Elementary Cognition*, pp. 320-1 n.), but it is simpler, and requires less change in the letters of the MSS.]

[2] Biehl's paragraphing is here wrong. ὅταν . . . μέμνηται [b] 23-29 should run on with what precedes, for all this has been intended to show the importance of the time for memory and therefore for recollecting. What follows, on the other hand, is explanatory.

[3] The οἷον clause refers to μέτρῳ—not to οὐ μέτρῳ. Hence there is no need of Freudenthal's insertion ὅτι μέντοι ποτὲ ἐποίησεν : no need as far as

a determinate notion of the time. Still, even though one does not remember with actual determination of the time, he genuinely remembers, none the less. Persons are wont to say that they remember [something], but yet do not know when [it occurred, as happens] whenever they do not know determinately the exact length of time implied in the 'when'.

It has been already stated that those who have a good memory are not identical with those who are quick at recollecting. But the act of recollecting differs from that of remembering, not only chronologically [1], but also in this, that many also of the other animals [as well as man] have memory, but, of all that we are acquainted with, none, we venture to say, except man, shares in the faculty of recollection. The cause of this is that recollection is, as it were, a mode of inference.[2] For he who endeavours to recollect *infers* that he formerly saw, or heard, or had some such experience, and the process [by which he succeeds in recollecting] is, as it were, a sort of investigation. But to investigate in this way belongs naturally to those animals alone which are also endowed with the faculty of deliberation ; [which proves what was said above], for deliberation is a form of inference.

That the affection is corporeal, i. e. that recollection is a searching for an 'image' in a corporeal substrate, is proved by the fact that in some persons, when, despite the most

sense goes ; for critically the question is on a different footing, as Biehl's apparatus shows.

[1] κατὰ τὸν χρόνον. For τὸ ἀναμιμνήσκεσθαι is not only logically but chronologically posterior to τὸ μνημονεύειν. Μνήμη is the presupposition of ἀνάμνησις. A memory must have been grounded, and one must (potentially) *remember*, before one can *recollect.* Cf. 451[b] 1 seqq., 452[a] 7.

[2] The συλλογισμός here is an inference from effect to cause—from the φάντασμα to its origin in past experience, and the process is compared to the ζήτησις involved in deliberation, for which cf. *N. E.* iii. 1112[b] 20-24 ὁ γὰρ βουλευόμενος ἔοικε ζητεῖν καὶ ἀναλύειν τὸν εἰρημένον τρόπον ὥσπερ διάγραμμα ... ἡ δὲ βούλευσις πᾶσα ζήτησις, καὶ τὸ ἔσχατον ἐν τῇ ἀναλύσει πρῶτον εἶναι ἐν τῇ γενέσει. Thus, in ἀνάμνησις, ἀνάλυσις of the φάντασμα, by the help of associations, brings back ὁ ἀναμιμνησκόμενος to the πρᾶγμα. ἀνάμνησις proceeds analytically to account for the φάντασμα. The only *deductive* factor in the process is the major, that every such φάντασμα must have a cause (viz. an 'experience') or be capable of being accounted for. This starts the process of ζήτησις. While βούλευσις ends by finding out *the way to act*, ἀνάμνησις ends by placing the φάντασμα in its relation to past experience. The συλλογισμός here = the deductive inference which starts the ζήτησις + the ζήτησις itself. 'Syllogism,' as a rendering, is hopelessly wrong. 'Reasoning' would serve but 'inference' seems best.

strenuous application of thought, they have been unable to
recollect, it [viz. the ἀνάμνησις = the effort at recollection]
excites a feeling of discomfort, which, even though they
abandon the effort at recollection,[1] persists in them none
the less ; and especially in persons of melancholic temperament. For these are most powerfully moved by presentations.

20 The reason why the effort of recollection is not under the
control of their will is that, as those who throw a stone cannot
stop it at their will when thrown, so he who tries to recollect
and 'hunts' [after an idea] sets up a process in a material
part, [that] in which resides the affection.[2] Those who
have moisture around that part which is the centre of sense-
perception suffer most discomfort of this kind. For when
once the moisture has been set in motion it is not easily

25 brought to rest, until the idea which was sought for has again
presented itself, and thus the movement has found a straight
course.[3] For a similar reason bursts of anger or fits of terror,
when once they have excited such motions, are not at once
allayed, even though the angry or terrified persons [by efforts
of will] set up counter motions, but the passions continue
to move them on, in the same directior as at first, in opposition
to such counter motions. The affection resembles also that in
the case of words, tunes, or sayings, whenever one of them has
become inveterate on the lips. People give them up and

30 resolve to avoid them ; yet again and again they find themselves humming the forbidden air, or using the prohibited word.

453 b   Those whose upper parts are abnormally large, as is the
case with dwarfs, have abnormally weak memory, as compared
with their opposites, because of the great weight which they

---

[1] If ἀναμιμνήσκεσθαι ᵃ 18 is co-ordinated with τὸ παρενοχλεῖν, καὶ [οὐκέτ']
being made copulative, the subject changes from τὴν ἀνάμνησιν to ἐνίους,
and there are other difficulties ; but the sense would be in keeping with
ᵃ 25 (ἕως ἂν ἐπέλθῃ τὸ ζητούμενον) and with a well-known fact, for which cf.
Prof. James's *Principles of Psychology*, i. 681 : 'Something we have made
the most strenuous efforts to recall, but all in vain, will, soon after we
have given up the attempt, saunter into the mind as innocently as if it had
never been sent for.'

[2] In which memory consists, see 449ᵇ 25, 450ᵃ 10.

[3] Cf. Diog. of Apollonia, apud Theophr. *de Sens.* § 45, Diels, *Vorsokrat.*
p. 345, καὶ γὰρ τοῖς ἀναμιμνησκομένοις τὴν ἀπορίαν εἶναι περὶ τὸ στῆθος, ὅταν δὲ
εὕρωσι, διασκίδνασθαι καὶ ἀνακουφίζεσθαι τῆς λύπης. Circular motion tended
to continue : motion in a straight line, to cease. Cf. 261ᵃ 27–263ᵃ 3.

have resting upon the organ of perception, and because their mnemonic movements are, from the very first, not able to keep true to a course, but are dispersed, and because, in the effort 5 at recollection, these movements do not easily find a direct onward path. Infants and very old persons have bad memories, owing to the amount of movement going on within them ; for the latter are in process of rapid decay, the former in process of vigorous growth ; and we may add that children, until considerably advanced in years, are dwarf-like in their bodily structure. Such then is our theory as regards memory and remembering—their nature, and the particular organ of the soul by which animals remember ; also as regards recollection, 10 its formal definition, and the manner and causes of its performance.

CHAPTER I

WITH regard to sleep and waking, we must consider what they are; whether they are peculiar to soul or to body, or common to both; and if common, to what part of soul or body they appertain: further, from what cause it arises
15 that they are attributes of animals, and whether all animals share in them both, or some partake of the one only, others of the other only, or some partake of neither and some of both.

Further, in addition to these questions, we must also inquire what the dream is, and from what cause sleepers sometimes dream, and sometimes do not; or whether the truth is that sleepers always dream but do not always
20 remember (their dream); and if this occurs, what its explanation is.

Again, [we must inquire] whether it is possible or not to foresee the future (in dreams), and if it be possible, in what manner; further, whether, supposing it possible, it extends only to things to be accomplished by the agency of Man, or to those also of which the cause lies in supra-human agency, and which result from the workings of Nature, or of Spontaneity.
25 First, then, this much is clear, that waking and sleep appertain to the same part of an animal, inasmuch as they are opposites, and sleep is evidently a privation of waking. For contraries, in natural as well as in all other matters, are seen always to present themselves in the same subject, and to be affections of the same: examples are—health
30 and sickness, beauty and ugliness, strength and weakness, sight and blindness, hearing and deafness. This is also clear
454 a from the following considerations. The criterion by which we know the waking person to be awake is identical with that by which we know the sleeper to be asleep; for we assume that one who is exercising sense-perception is awake,

and that every one who is awake perceives either some external movement or else some movement in his own consciousness. If waking, then, consists in nothing else than 5 the exercise of sense-perception, the inference is clear, that the organ, in virtue of which animals perceive, is that by which they wake, when they are awake, or sleep, when they are asleep.

But since [1] the exercise of sense-perception [2] does not belong to soul or body exclusively, then (since the subject of actuality is in every case identical with that of potentiality, and what is called sense-perception, as actuality, is a movement of the soul through the body) it is clear that its [3] affection [4] is not an affection of soul exclusively, and that 10 a soulless body has not the potentiality [5] of perception [6]. [Thus sleep and waking are not attributes of pure intelligence, on the one hand, or of inanimate bodies, on the other.]

Now, whereas we have already elsewhere distinguished what are called the parts of the soul, and whereas the nutrient is, in all living bodies, capable of existing without the other parts, while none of the others can exist without the nutrient ; it is clear that [7] sleep and waking are not affections of such living 15 things as partake only of growth and decay, e. g. not of plants, because these have not the faculty of sense-perception,

---

[1] Since waking is not peculiar to soul or body, neither is sleeping ; for sleeping is the potentiality of waking, and if the actuality cannot be peculiar to body or to soul, neither can the potentiality be so. Sleep is an affection (πάθος) which renders 'potential' the αἴσθησις, whose actuality is waking. But instead of concluding 'neither is the πάθος peculiar to soul or body', or 'neither is the affection peculiar to soul, nor can a body without soul sleep', he winds up with the conclusion : 'nor is a body without soul *capable of sense-perception*'; which involves the other point ; and is really what he aims at. For to be capable of αἰσθάνεσθαι, without being actually αἰσθανόμενος, is to be asleep : to be incapable of it is to be incapable of sleeping as well as of waking. The nerve of the reasoning is contained in the parenthesis.

[2] i. e. in the form of ἐγρήγορσις.

[3] Sc. that of αἴσθησις.

[4] Sc. ὕπνος ; see 453ᵇ 28, 29.

[5] Cf. 454ᵇ 11-12, where also what is capable of sleeping is virtually *identified* with τὸ δυνατὸν αἰσθάνεσθαιχτὸ κατ᾽ ἐνέργ. αἰσθανόμενον.

[6] Sc. cannot sleep : Sleep, the πάθος, as the parenthesis shows, is here regarded as δύναμις, waking as ἐνέργεια, of αἴσθησις. Vide *de An.* II. i. 412ᵃ 23-26.

[7] The clauses preceding δῆλον ὅτι are only the preamble, not the reason, of what follows. For ὡς . . . ὅτι cf. 443ᵃ 23, 24.

whether or not this be capable of separate [1] existence ; in its potentiality, indeed, and in its relationships, it *is* separable [sc. from τὸ θρεπτικόν].

Likewise it is clear that [of those which either sleep or wake] there is no animal which is always awake or always asleep, but that both these affections belong [alter-
20 nately] to the same animals. [2] For if there be an animal not endued with sense-perception, it is impossible that this should either [3] sleep or wake ; since both these are affections

---

[1] Capable of existing separately from τὸ θρεπτικόν and the vegetative functions. With τῷ εἶναι cf. 448ᵃ 20 (note), where τῷ λόγῳ explains it. Nowhere in the world can Aristotle find τὸ αἰσθητικόν apart from τὸ θρεπτικόν. He cannot say that it is χωριστὸν ἁπλῶς, or χωριστὸν τόπῳ, or μεγέθει, yet it is separate τῷ εἶναι, i.e. in its relationship to objects. It is separate also τῇ δυνάμει. This difference may be expressed by saying that τὸ θρεπτικόν is a δύναμις θρεπτική, τὸ αἰσθητικόν a δύναμις αἰσθητική. τῇ δυνάμει therefore = 'in respect of its potentiality as part of soul', or briefly ' as a faculty '.

[2] τοῖς αὐτοῖς τῶν ζώων = 'the same animals ', as in 450ᵃ 15 ἑτέροις τῶν ζ.= ' different animals '.

[3] The difficulty of this whole passage becomes acute here. The traditional translation involves a misuse of οὔτε before the infinitive. The grammatical version would be — ' it cannot either sleep or wake,' οὔτε . . . οὔτε explicating οὐ. As the text stands this would make no sense. Inserting μή before ἔχον we could restore sense and grammar. This has been assumed in the translation. It is to be observed that the μὲν after ὅσα in ᵃ 15 has no answering δέ. But Aristotle would naturally have gone on from ' plants ' to the case of animals which stood on the border line. Having said that φυτά (which have not the organ of sense-perception) cannot sleep or wake, he would naturally say that if there be any animal which has not perception it too cannot sleep or wake. In 778ᵇ 23-779ᵃ 10 he considers such animals, viz. ἔμβρυα, which (he there says) do not sleep but do something like it, ' just like plants.' In *Pol.* 1335ᵇ 24, too, he refers to these before the stage of αἴσθησις, before which stage ἐμποιεῖσθαι δεῖ τὴν ἄμβλωσιν. In another respect the received translation is wrong, for εἴ τί ἐστι ζῷον ἔχον αἴσθησιν does not really = ' if an animal is, &c. ', but ' if there be any animal having αἴσθησις ': the former would be represented rather by εἰ ἔστι ζῷον τὸ ἔχον αἴσθησιν. Thus, too, γάρ ᵃ 21 first gets any meaning, by making it refer to οὐ γὰρ . . . ἔχουσι in ᵃ 17. Then, however, it appears that ὁμοίως . . . ταῦτα ᵃ 19-2¹ is out of its place. If, however, we transfer this to ᵃ 24 after αἰσθητ'.οῦ we find the next words tautological. So that there is something almost certainly wrong with the text. I believe the insertion of μή to be required absolutely by the grammar, and critically justifiable by the consideration that it would have easily been lost owing to the appearance it has of contradicting Aristotle's well-known definition of ζῷον. At least its insertion has as good critical ground to stand upon as that of μή in 449ᵃ 3 ⟨μή⟩ αἰσθάνεται. The general sense of ᵃ 21-26 (οὐ γὰρ . . . ἐγρηγορέναι) is — ' For while *without* sensation no creature can do either, *with* sensation every creature must do both.'

An explanation of the passage from ᵃ 19 to ᵃ 32 communicated by Mr. Charles Cannan seems so valuable, based as it is on minute and

of the activity of the primary faculty of sense-perception.
But it is equally impossible also that either of these two affections should perpetually attach itself to the same animal, e.g.
that some species of animal should be always asleep or always 25
awake, without intermission ; for all organs which have a
natural function must lose power when they work beyond the
natural time-limit of their working period ; for instance, the
eyes [must lose power] from [too-long continued] seeing, and
must give it up ; and so it is with the hand and every other
member which has a function. Now, if sense-perception is the 30
function of a special organ, this also, if it continues perceiving
beyond the appointed time-limit of its continuous working
period, will lose its power, and will do its work no longer.
Accordingly, if the waking period is determined by this fact,
that in it sense-perception is free; if in the case of some 454 b
contraries one of the two must be present, while in the case of
others this is not necessary [1]; if waking is the contrary of
sleeping, and one of these two must be present to every animal:
it must follow that the state of sleeping is necessary. Finally,
if such affection is Sleep, and this is a state of powerlessness
arising from excess of waking, and excess of waking is in its 5

scholarly analysis of the sense and grammar, that his permission to print it
has been gladly accepted. Mr. Cannan suggests that in [a] 21 we should read
οὐ γὰρ εἴ τί ἐστι ζῷον, or ζῴου ⟨μόριον⟩, and explains [a] 19–32 as follows:
'But it is equally plain that there is nothing which has one of the two
always, but both affections belong to the same *parts* and *kinds* of
animals [*animals*, for plants are excluded above]. For [(a) as to *parts*]
it does not follow that, if some part of an animal has sense-perception,
it—the mere part—has the faculty either of sleeping or of waking ; for
both these affections are incident, not to a single organ, but to the
primary faculty of sense-perception [for example, the heart is not always
asleep and the brain always awake (cf. Michael, p. 44. 13, Arist. 453[b] 13),
for in the proper sense they do not sleep or wake at all] ; nor [(b) as
to *kinds*], on the other hand, can either sleeping or waking attach itself
for ever, to the exclusion of the other, to the same thing, in the sense
that some particular kind of animal [e.g. the weasel] is always awake,
and some other [e.g. the dormouse] is always asleep. For (ὅτι) all
things having a natural ἔργον become incapable in time of that ἔργον ;
therefore, that of which τὸ αἰσθάνεσθαι is an ἔργον will become incapable
of τὸ αἰσθάνεσθαι, and leave a blank which must be filled up with sleep,
its contrary.'

[1] Read in 454[b] 1 with EMY τῶν δ' ἐναντίων τῶν μὲν ἀνάγκη θάτερον ἀεὶ
παρεῖναι, τῶν δ' οὔ. There are certain pairs of contraries (e. g. κακία and
ἀρετή, cf. 1145[a] 25) one of which is not always predicable of living animals ;
while there are others of which one must be always present, and to this
class belong sleep and waking.

origin sometimes morbid, sometimes not, so that the powerlessness or dissolution of activity will be so or not ; it is
inevitable that every creature which wakes must also be
capable of sleeping, since it is impossible that it should continue actualizing its powers perpetually.

So, also, it is impossible for any animal to continue always
10 sleeping. For sleep is an affection of the organ[1] of sense-
perception—a sort of tie or inhibition of function imposed on
it, so that every creature that sleeps must needs have the
organ of sense-perception. Now, that alone which is capable
of sense-perception in actuality has the faculty of sense-
perception ; but to realize this faculty, in the proper and
unqualified sense, is impossible while one is asleep. All
sleep, therefore, must be susceptible of awakening. Accord-
15 ingly, almost all other animals are clearly observed to partake
in sleep, whether they are aquatic, aerial, or terrestrial, since
fishes of all kinds, and molluscs, as well as all others which have
eyes, have been seen sleeping. ' Hard-eyed ' creatures and
insects manifestly assume the posture[2] of sleep ; but the sleep
of all such creatures is of brief duration, so that often it might
20 well baffle one's observation to decide whether they sleep[3]
or not. Of testaceous animals, on the contrary, no direct
sensible evidence is as yet forthcoming to determine whether
they sleep, but if the above reasoning be convincing to any
one, he who follows it will admit this[4] [viz. that they do so].

That, therefore, all animals sleep may be gathered from
these considerations. For an animal is defined as such by
25 its possessing sense-perception ; and we assert that sleep is,
in a certain way, an inhibition of function, or, as it were, a tie,
imposed on sense-perception, while its loosening or remission
constitutes the being awake. But no plant can partake in
either of these affections, for without sense-perception there

---

[1] What affects the *organ*, affects the *faculty*, and there is no need to
press the distinction here.

[2] If we cannot see that they are asleep, we can see them 'couching'.
The notion of κοίτη in κοιμώμενα is important ; the allusion to it contains
the point here.

[3] μετέχουσι τοῦ καθεύδειν, *not* = καθεύδουσι. The point is that *mere* observation cannot decide the *general* question : but with the *a priori*
argument (ὁ λεχθεὶς λόγος) it helps to convince.

[4] [Read τοῦτο for τούτῳ, with Bywater, *J. P.* xxviii. 243. Edd.]

is neither sleeping nor waking. But creatures which have
sense-perception have likewise the feeling of pain and plea- 30
sure, while those which have these have appetite as well ; but
plants have none of these affections. A mark of this[1] is
that the nutrient part does its own work better when 455 a
(the animal) is asleep than when it is awake. Nutrition
and growth are then especially promoted, a fact which
implies that creatures do not need sense-perception to assist
these processes.

CHAPTER II

We must now proceed to inquire into the cause why one
sleeps and wakes, and into the particular nature of the sense-
perception, or sense-perceptions, if there be several, on which
these affections depend. Since, then, some animals possess 5
all the modes of sense-perception, and some not all, not, for
example, sight, while all possess touch and taste, except such
animals as are imperfectly developed, a class of which we
have already treated in our work on the soul ; and since an
animal when asleep is unable to exercise, in the simple sense,
any particular[2] sensory faculty whatever, it follows that in 10
the state called sleep the same affection must extend to all[3]
the special senses ; because, if it attaches itself to one of them
but not to another, then an animal while asleep may perceive
with the latter ; but this is impossible.

Now, since every sense has something peculiar, and also
something common ; peculiar, as, e. g., seeing is to the sense
of sight, hearing to the auditory sense, and so on with the 15
other senses severally ; while all are accompanied by a common power, in virtue whereof a person perceives *that* he sees
or hears (for, assuredly, it is not by the special[4] sense of sight
that one sees that he sees ; and it is not by mere taste, or

---

[1] Separableness of the nutrient from the sentient faculty.

[2] Sleep is an affection of the general faculty τὸ αἰσθητικὸν πάντων,
which does not preclude such exercise of this as takes place in
dreaming.

[3] The text is exceedingly doubtful : cf. ᵃ 25 *infra* (where the conclusion
of the matter is given) διὸ καὶ πᾶσιν ὑπάρχει τοῖς ζῴοις, and also the words
εἰ γὰρ τῷ πάσας τι πεπονθέναι ᵃ 27-8.

[4] But by the 'general' sense, *qua* related to the 'special'.

sight, or both together that one discerns, and has the faculty of
discerning, that sweet things are different from white things,
but by a faculty connected in common with all the organs of
20 sense ; for there is one sensory function, and the controlling
sensory faculty is one, though differing as a faculty of perception [1] in relation to each genus of sensibles, e. g., sound or
colour); and since this [common sensory activity] subsists in
association chiefly with the faculty of touch (for this [touch]
can exist apart from all the other organs of sense, but none
of them can exist apart from it —a subject of which we
25 have treated in our speculations concerning the Soul) ; it is
therefore evident that waking and sleeping are an affection
of this [common and controlling organ of sense-perception].
This explains why they belong to all animals, for touch
[with which this common organ is chiefly connected], alone,
[is common] to all [animals].

For if sleeping were caused by the *special* senses having
each and all undergo some affection, it would be strange
that these senses, for which it is neither necessary nor in
a manner possible to realize their powers simultaneously,
30 should necessarily all go idle and become motionless simultaneously.   For the contrary experience, viz. that they
should not go to rest altogether, would have been more
reasonably anticipated.   But, according to the explanation
just given, all is quite clear regarding those also.   For, when
the sense organ which controls all the others, and to which
all the others are tributary, has been in some way affected,
455 b that these others should be all affected at the same time
is inevitable, whereas, if one of the tributaries becomes powerless, that the controlling organ should also become powerless
need in no wise follow.

It is indeed evident from many considerations that sleep
does not consist in the mere fact that the special senses do
not function or that one does not employ them ; and that
it does not consist merely in an inability to exercise the
5 sense-perceptions ; for such is what happens in cases of
swooning.   A swoon means just such impotence of percep-

---

[1] τὸ δ' εἶναι αἰσθήσει ἕτερον.   Cf. 459ᵃ 16 τὸ δ' εἶναι φανταστικῷ, αἰσθήσει
governs τοῦ γένους.   Cf. 449ᵃ 18 (note).

tion, and certain other cases of unconsciousness also are of this nature. Moreover, persons who have the blood-vessels in the neck compressed become insensible. But sleep supervenes when such incapacity of exercise has neither arisen in some casual organ of sense, nor from some chance cause, but when, as has been just stated, it has its seat in the 10 primary organ with which one perceives objects in general.[1] For when this has become powerless all the other sensory organs also must lack power to perceive ; but when one of them has become powerless, it is not necessary for this also to lose its power.

We must next state the cause to which it is due, and its quality as an affection. Now, since there are several types of cause (for we assign equally the 'final', the 'efficient', 15 the 'material', and the 'formal' as causes), in the first place, then, as we assert that Nature operates for the sake of an end, and that this end is a *good*[2] ; and that to every creature which is endowed by nature with the power to move, but cannot with pleasure[3] to itself move always and continuously, rest is necessary and beneficial ; and since, taught by experi- 20 ence, men apply to sleep this metaphorical[4] term, calling it a 'rest' [from the strain of movement implied in sense-perception] : we conclude that its end is the conservation of animals. But the waking state is for an animal its highest end, since the exercise of sense-perception or of thought is the highest end for all beings to which either of these appertains ; inasmuch as these are best, and the highest end is what is best : whence it follows that sleep belongs of necessity to 25 each animal. I use the term 'necessity' in its conditional sense, meaning that if an animal is to exist and have its own proper nature, it must have certain endowments ; and, if these

---

[1] See 449ᵃ 17 τὸ αἰσθητικὸν πάντων.

[2] ἀνάπαυσις is an end, i.e. *a* good ; but *the* end, i. e. the highest end, of animal life is τὸ αἰσθ. καὶ τὸ φρονεῖν, to which ὕπνος is subordinated. Cf. *infra* ᵃ 23-25. The ἀγαθόν τι is distinguished from τὸ τέλος.

[3] Anaxagoras held that all αἴσθησις is μετὰ λύπης. Theophr. *de Sens.* § 29. Cf. also Aristotle, *N. E.* 1154ᵇ 7 ἀεὶ γὰρ πονεῖ τὸ ζῷον ὥσπερ καὶ οἱ φυσιολόγοι μαρτυροῦσι, τὸ ὁρᾶν, τὸ ἀκούειν φάσκοντες εἶναι λυπηρόν.

[4] The metaphor is plain enough in the Greek word ἀνάπαυσις. No word in English seems to meet the case so well as 'rest'. EM give καταφοράν, which, however, it would be difficult to translate here. But cf. καταφέρεται, 456ᵇ 24.

are to belong to it, certain others likewise must belong to it [as their condition].

The next question to be discussed is that of the kind of movement or action, taking place within their bodies, from 30 which the affection of waking or sleeping arises in animals. Now, we must assume that the causes of this affection in all other animals are identical with, or analogous to, those which operate in sanguineous animals ; and that the causes operating in sanguineous animals generally are identical with those operating in man. Hence we must consider the entire subject in the light of these instances [afforded by sanguineous 456 a animals, especially man]. Now, it has been definitely settled already in another work that sense-perception in animals originates in the same part of the organism in which movement originates. This locus of origination is one of three determinate loci, viz. that which lies midway between the head and the abdomen. This in sanguineous animals is the region of the heart ; for all sanguineous animals have 5 a heart ; and from this it is that both motion and the controlling sense-perception originate. Now, as regards movement, it is obvious that that of breathing and of the cooling process generally takes its rise there ; and it is with a view to the conservation of the [due amount of] heat in this part that nature has formed as she has both the animals which respire, and those which cool themselves by moisture. Of this 10 [cooling process] *per se* we shall treat hereafter. In bloodless animals, and insects, and such as do not respire, the 'connatural spirit'[1] is seen alternately puffed up and subsiding in the part which is in them analogous [to the region of the heart in sanguineous animals]. This is clearly observable in the holoptera [insects with undivided wings] as wasps and bees ; also in flies and such creatures. And since to move 15 anything, or do anything, is impossible without strength, and holding the breath produces strength—in creatures which inhale, the holding of that breath[2] which comes from without,

---

[1] τὸ σύμφυτον πνεῦμα, i. e. the πνεῦμα which is naturally inherent, as opposed to that inhaled (τὸ θύραθεν ἐπείσακτον).

[2] ἡ θύραθεν is short for ἡ τοῦ θύραθεν πνεύματος κάθεξις, as ἡ σύμφυτος also = ἡ τοῦ συμφύτου πνεύματος κάθεξις.

but, in creatures which do not respire, of that which is connatural (which explains why winged insects of the class
holoptera, when they move, are perceived to make a humming noise, due to the friction of the connatural spirit collid-
ing with the diaphragm); and since movement [1] is, in every 20
animal, attended [2] with some sense-perception, either internal
or external [3], in the primary organ of sense, [we conclude]
accordingly that if sleeping and waking are affections of this
organ, the place in which, or the organ in which, sleep and
waking originate, is self-evident [being that in which move- 25
ment and sense-perception originate, viz. the heart].

Some persons move in their sleep, and perform many acts
like waking acts, but not without a phantasm or an exercise
of sense-perception; for a dream is in a certain way a sense-
impression. But of them we have to speak later on. Why
it is that persons when aroused remember their dreams, but
do not remember these acts which are like waking acts, has
been already explained in the work 'Of Problems'.

CHAPTER III

The point for consideration next in order to the preceding 30
is:—What are the processes in which the affection of waking
and sleeping originates, and whence do they arise? Now,
since it is when it has sense-perception that an animal must
first *take* [4] food and receive growth, and in all cases food in its
ultimate form is, in sanguineous animals, the natural sub- 35
stance blood, or, in bloodless animals, that which is analogous
to this; and since the veins are the place of the blood, while 456 b
the origin of these is the heart—an assertion which is proved
by anatomy—it is manifest that, when the external nutriment

[1] κινεῖται ... αἰσθητηρίῳ. Aristotle does not mean that whenever one
has an αἴσθησις he moves (or is moved) locally. The κινεῖται here and
the κινεῖν [a] 15 refer to *local* movement, involving output of bodily energy,
not to the κίνησις (or stimulation) of sense.
[2] [a] 20 If instead of γινομένης ([a] 20) γενομένης were read, the movement
should be regarded as *prompted* by the perception—a very important
difference.
[3] οἰκείας ἢ ἀλλοτρίας: arising either from an intra-organic or an extra-
organic stimulus.
[4] i.e. *qua* animal; before this, in the embryonic stage, it grows and is
nourished like a vegetable.

enters the parts fitted for its reception, the evaporation arising
from it enters into the veins, and there, undergoing a change,
5 is converted into blood, and makes its way to their source
[the heart]. We have treated of all this when discussing
the subject of nutrition, but must here recapitulate what was
there said, in order that we may obtain a scientific view of the
beginnings of the process, and come to know what exactly
happens to the primary organ of sense-perception to account
for the occurrence of waking and sleep. For sleep, as has
10 been shown, is not any given impotence of the perceptive
faculty ; for unconsciousness, a certain form of asphyxia, and
swooning, all produce such impotence. Moreover it is an established fact that some persons in a profound trance have still had
the imaginative faculty in play. This last point, indeed, gives
rise to a difficulty ; for if it is conceivable that one who had
swooned should in this state fall asleep, the phantasm also which
then presented itself to his mind might be regarded as a dream.
15 Persons, too, who have fallen into a deep trance, and have
come to be regarded as dead, say many things while in
this condition. The same view, however, is to be taken of
all these cases, [i. e. that they are not cases of sleeping or
dreaming].

As we observed above, sleep is not co-extensive with any and
every impotence of the perceptive faculty, but this affection is
one which arises from the evaporation attendant upon the
20 process of nutrition. The matter evaporated must be driven
onwards to a certain point, then turn back, and change its
current to and fro, like a tide-race in a narrow strait. Now,
in every animal the hot naturally tends to move [and carry
other things] upwards, but when it has reached the parts above,
[becoming cool, see 457 ^{b} 30] it turns back again, and moves
downwards in a mass. This explains why fits of drowsiness are
especially apt to come on after meals ; for the matter, both the
25 liquid and the corporeal, which is borne upwards in a mass, is
then of considerable quantity. When, therefore, this comes to
a stand it weighs a person down and causes him to nod, but
when it has actually sunk downwards, and by its return has re-
pulsed the hot, sleep comes on, and the animal so affected is
presently asleep. A confirmation of this appears from consider-

ing the things which induce sleep ; they all, whether potable 30
or edible, for instance poppy, mandragora, wine, darnel, produce
a heaviness in the head ; and persons borne down [by sleepi-
ness] and nodding [drowsily] all seem affected in this way,
i. e. they are unable to lift up the head or the eye-lids.   And
it is after meals especially that sleep comes on like this, for
the evaporation from the foods eaten is then copious.   It also
follows certain forms of fatigue ; for fatigue operates as a
solvent, and the dissolved matter acts, if not cold, like food 35
prior to digestion.   Moreover, some kinds of illness have **457 a**
this same effect ; those arising from moist and hot secretions,
as happens with fever-patients and in cases of lethargy.[1]
Extreme youth also has this effect ; infants, for example,
sleep a great deal, because of the food being all borne upwards
—a mark whereof appears in the disproportionately large size 5
of the upper parts compared with the lower during infancy,
which is due to the fact that growth predominates in the
direction of the former.   Hence also they are subject to
epileptic [2] seizures ; for sleep is like epilepsy, and, in a sense,
actually is a seizure of this sort.   Accordingly, the beginning 10
of this malady takes place with many during sleep, and their
subsequent habitual seizures occur in sleep, not in waking
hours.   For when the spirit [evaporation] moves upwards in
a volume, on its return downwards it distends the veins, and
forcibly compresses the passage through which respiration is
effected.   This explains why wines are not good for infants
or for wet nurses (for it makes no difference, doubtless, 15
whether the infants themselves, or their nurses, drink them),
but such persons should drink them [if at all] diluted with
water and in small quantity.   For wine is spirituous, and of all
wines the dark more so than any other.   The upper parts,
in infants, are so filled with nutriment that within five months
[after birth] they do not even turn the neck [sc. to raise the
head] ; for in them, as in persons deeply intoxicated, there is
ever a large quantity of moisture ascending.   It is reasonable, 20

---

[1] If ἐν be right, λήθαργος may be either a substantive or an adjective
in agreement with πυρετοῖς understood.
[2] Not merely childish fits and convulsions, but *epileptic* fits.   The
word in this sense is as old as Hippocrates, and the facts here stated are
all medical truths.

too, to think that this affection is the cause of the embryo's
remaining at rest in the womb at first. Also, as a general rule,
persons whose veins are inconspicuous, as well as those who
are dwarf-like, or have abnormally large heads, are addicted
to sleep. For in the former the veins are narrow, so that
it is not easy for the moisture to flow down through them ;
while in the case of dwarfs and those whose heads are ab-
25 normally large, the impetus of the evaporation upwards is
excessive. Those [on the contrary] whose veins are large
are, thanks to the easy flow through the veins, not addicted
to sleep, unless, indeed, they labour under some other affection which counteracts [this easy flow]. Nor are the 'atrabilious' addicted to sleep, for in them the inward region is
cooled so that the quantity of evaporation in their case is not
great. For this reason they have large appetites, though
30 spare and lean ; for their bodily condition is as if they
derived no benefit from what they eat. The dark bile, too,
being itself naturally cold, cools also the nutrient tract, and
the other parts wheresover such secretion [bile] is potentially
present [i. e. tends to be formed].

457 b   Hence it is plain from what has been said that sleep is
a sort of concentration, or natural recoil,[1] of the hot matter
inwards [towards its centre], due to the cause above mentioned. Hence restless movement is a marked feature in the
case of a person when drowsy. But where it [the heat in the
upper and outer parts] begins to fail, he grows cool, and
owing to this cooling process his eye-lids droop. Accord-
5 ingly [in sleep] the upper and outward parts are cool, but

---

[1] What is meant is otherwise expressed, 458ᵃ 10 συνεωσμένη κτλ.
ἀντιπερίστασις is not here used in its strict sense, in which it involves real
'circulation'. Hence τις goes with it as well as with σύνοδος. ἀντιπερίστασις is defined by Simplicius as a circular process in which ' when a body
is pushed out of its place that which has expelled it occupies the place,
while that which has been thrust out pushes the adjoining body from its
place, until the last moved in this series finds itself in the place of the
first, which extruded something else '. It depends on the fact that there
is no vacuum. (Cf. 266ᵃ 25 seqq., 459ᵇ 2, 472ᵇ 17 ; Zeller, *Plato* (E.T.),
p. 430 ; Zeller, *Arist.* i. 515, ii. 378, n.) So Aristotle explained physical
facts like the motion of projectiles. Plato, *Tim.* 79 B–E, uses the word
περιωθεῖν for what A. refers to ἀντιπερίστασις. We see the effect of the
process when on suddenly opening a door in a room the opposite door
shuts, or vice versa. Reference to this explains τῆς ἀρχῆς 454ʰ 2, *q.v.*

the inward and lower, i. e. the parts at the feet and in the interior of the body, are hot.

Yet one might found a difficulty on the facts that sleep is most oppressive in its onset after meals, and that wine, and other such things, though they possess heating properties, are productive of sleep,[1] for it is not probable that sleep should be a process of cooling while the things that cause sleeping are themselves hot. Is the explanation of this, then, to be found in the fact that, as the stomach when empty is hot, while replenishment cools it by the movement it occasions, so the passages and tracts in the head are cooled as the 'evaporation' ascends thither? Or, as those who have hot water poured on them feel a sudden shiver of cold, just so in the case before us, may it be that, when the hot substance ascends, the cold rallying to meet it cools [the aforesaid parts], deprives their native heat of all its power, and compels it to retire? Moreover, when much food is taken, which [i. e. the nutrient evaporation from which] the hot substance carries upwards, this latter, like a fire when fresh logs are laid upon it, is itself cooled, until the food has been digested.

For, as has been observed elsewhere,[2] sleep comes on when the corporeal element [in the 'evaporation'] is conveyed upwards by the hot, along the veins, to the head. But when that which has been thus carried up can no longer ascend, but is too great in quantity[3] [to do so], it forces the hot back again and flows downwards. Hence it is that men sink down [as they do in sleep] when the heat which tends to keep them erect (man alone, among animals, being naturally erect) is withdrawn; and this, when it befalls[4] them, causes unconsciousness, and afterwards[5] phantasy.

Or are the solutions thus proposed barely conceivable accounts of the refrigeration which takes place, while, as

---

[1] [b] 9. There should be only a comma after τοιαῦτα. δέ here gives the argument from the opponent's point of view, and = 'for'.

[2] De Part. An. ii. 7, 653[a] 10.

[3] A new factor—*mechanical* pressure—is here introduced.

[4] ἐπιπεσόν sc. τὸ ὑπεσπάσθαι τὸ θερμόν. Bonitz, *Ind.* 267[a] 32 makes τὸ θερμόν alone agree with ἐπιπεσόν, and so Freudenthal translates ' wiedereindringend erzeugt das Warme Bewusstlosigkeit'. ἐπιπίπτειν expresses a hostile attack, an onset.

[5] 'Afterwards', i. e. when the process of διάκρισις sets in; cf. 461[a] 25.

a matter of fact, the region of the brain is, as stated elsewhere, the main determinant of the matter? For the brain,
30 or in creatures without a brain that which corresponds to it,
is of all parts of the body the coolest. Therefore, as moisture
turned into vapour by the sun's heat is, when it has ascended
to the upper regions, cooled by the coldness of the latter, and
becoming condensed, is carried downwards, and turned into
458 a water once more; just so the excrementitious evaporation, when
carried up by the heat to the region of the brain, is condensed
into a 'phlegm' (which explains why catarrhs are seen to
proceed from the head); while that evaporation which is
5 nutrient and not unwholesome, becoming condensed, descends
and cools the hot. The tenuity or narrowness of the veins
about the brain itself contributes to its being kept cool, and
to its not readily admitting the evaporation. This, then, is
a sufficient explanation of the cooling which takes place,
despite the fact that the evaporation is exceedingly hot.

10   A person awakes from sleep when digestion is completed:
when the heat, which had been previously forced together in
large quantity within a small compass from out the surrounding part, has once more prevailed, and when a separation has
been effected [1] between the more corporeal and the purer
blood.[2] The finest and purest blood is that contained in the
head, while the thickest and most turbid is that in the lower
15 parts. The source of all the blood is, as has been stated
both here and elsewhere, the heart. Now of the chambers in
the heart the central communicates with each of the two
others. Each of the latter again acts as receiver from each,
respectively, of the two vessels,[3] called the 'great' and the
'aorta'. It is in the central chamber that the [above-men-
20 tioned] separation takes place. To go into these matters
in detail would, however, be more properly the business of
a different treatise from the present. Owing to the fact that
the blood formed after the assimilation of food is especially

---

[1] Sc. in the heart; see below a 19.
[2] Contained in the 'evaporated substance' now collected back into the
heart.
[3] To use the term 'artery' here in translation would mislead any mere
English reader into thinking that Aristotle knew the difference between
arteries and veins.

in need of separation, sleep [then especially] occurs [and lasts] until the purest part of this blood has been separated off into the upper parts of the body, and the most turbid into the lower parts. When this has taken place animals awake from sleep, being released from the heaviness consequent on taking food.

We have now stated the *cause*[1] of sleeping, viz., that it consists in the recoil by[2] the corporeal element, upborne by the connatural heat, in a mass upon the primary sense-organ ; we have also stated *what*[3] sleep is, having shown that it is a seizure of the primary sense-organ, rendering it unable to actualize its powers ; arising of necessity (for it is impossible for an animal to exist if the conditions which render it an animal be not fulfilled), i. e., for the sake of its conservation[4] ; since remission of movement tends to the conservation of animals.

[1] This gives the cause ὅθεν ἡ κίνησις, or *efficient* cause : the kinetic energy of τὸ θερμόν. The *material* cause is τὸ ἀναθυμιώμενον, and the other material conditions, regarded statically, i. e. in abstraction from their κίνησις.

[2] ἡ . . . ἀντιπερίστασις sc. γιγνομένη. In 458ᵇ 1 τὸ θερμόν is used for τὸ σωματῶδες τὸ ἀναφ. ὑπὸ τοῦ συμφύτου θερμοῦ here. The agency which causes the recoil is the cold of the brain : hence ὑπό ᵃ 26 = (not ' caused by ', but) 'undergone by'. The ὑπό in this sense is curious, but ἀντιπερίστασις (corresponding to ἀντιπεριστῆναι, not to ἀντιπεριστάναι) is a sort of manœuvre effected by the substance.

[3] i. e. its definition or *formal* cause.

[4] σωτηρία is the *final* cause.

DE SOMNIIS

CHAPTER I

WE must, in the next place, investigate the subject of the
dream, and first inquire to which of the faculties of the soul it
presents itself, i. e. whether the affection is one which pertains to the faculty of intelligence or to that of sense-perception; for these are the only faculties within us by which we
acquire knowledge.

If, then, the exercise of the faculty of sight is actual seeing,
that of the auditory faculty, hearing, and, in general that of
the faculty of sense-perception, perceiving; and if there are
5 some perceptions common to the senses, such as figure, magnitude, motion, &c., while there are others, as colour, sound,
taste, peculiar [each to its own sense]; and further, if all
creatures, when the eyes are closed in sleep, are unable to see,
and the analogous statement is true of the other senses, so
that manifestly we perceive nothing[1] when asleep; we may
conclude that it is not by sense-perception we perceive
a dream.

But neither is it by opinion that we do so. For [in
10 dreams] we not only assert, e. g., that some object approaching is a man or a horse [which would be an exercise of
opinion], but that the object is white or beautiful, points
on which opinion without sense-perception asserts nothing

---

[1] 458ᵇ 8. Read after Christ's conj. οὐδὲν ἐν. We do not perceive anything in sleep with the *particular* or *special* senses, but the πρῶτον αἰσθητικόν
is active in the dream, i. e. we perceive, in a way to be explained
in these chapters, with the *general* sense as re-presentative faculty.
Biehl wrongly marks the apodosis at ὥστε ᵇ8: it really begins at οὐκ
ἄρα γε ᵇ9. The ὥστε clause states the consequence of the fact contained
in the clause commencing ἀδυνατεῖ δέ, and therefore belongs to the
premisses. 'We cannot by sense perceive either the κοινά or the ἴδια
in sleep, so that we cannot then perceive anything at all; therefore it
is not by sense that we perceive a dream (not, that is, by *special* sense,
as afterwards to be explained).' Such is the argument.

either truly or falsely. It is, however, a fact that the soul
makes such assertions in sleep. We seem to see equally well
that the approaching figure is a man, and that it is white.
[In dreams], too, we think something else, over and above 15
the dream presentation, just as we do in waking moments
when we perceive something ; for we often also reason about
that which we perceive. So, too, in sleep we sometimes have
thoughts other than the mere phantasms immediately before
our minds. This would be manifest to any one who should
attend and try, immediately on arising from sleep, to remember [his dreaming experiences]. There are cases of persons 20
who have seen such dreams, those, for example, who believe
themselves to be mentally arranging a given list of subjects
according to the mnemonic rule. They frequently find
themselves engaged in something else besides the dream, viz.
in setting a phantasm which they envisage into its mnemonic
position.[1] Hence it is plain that not every 'phantasm' in sleep
is a mere dream-image, and that the further thinking which we 25
perform then is due to an exercise of the faculty of opinion.

So much at least is plain on all these points, viz. that
the faculty by which, in waking hours, we are subject to
illusion when affected by disease, is identical with that which
produces illusory effects in sleep. So, even when persons are
in excellent health, and know the facts of the case perfectly
well, the sun, nevertheless, appears[2] to them to be only a
foot wide. Now, whether the presentative faculty of the
soul be identical with, or different from, the faculty of sense- 30
perception, in either case the illusion does not occur without
our actually seeing or [otherwise] perceiving something. Even

---

[1] The word φάντασμα here and in [b] 24 is, according to Freudenthal, a
generalized ' vorstellung ', of the nature of a concept. But as we see from
458[b] 18 and 462[a] 29 its proper application is to the dream-image. Here
that which is παρὰ τὸ ἐνύπνιον is not the mere φάντασμα, but the activity
of thought expressed in τίθεσθαι εἰς τὸν τόπον φάντασμα, this clause being
in apposition to ἄλλο τι, which it explains. In [b] 24, however, φάντασμα
seems to refer to that activity.

[2] δοκεῖ is here used improperly for the more correct φαίνεται. See
de An. 428[b] 1-3 φαίνεται μὲν ὁ ἥλιος ποδιαῖος, πέπεισται δ' εἶναι μείζω τῆς
οἰκουμένης. See also 460[b] 18. We cannot suppose Aristotle to be here
alluding to the unscientific opinion of those who (like Epicurus and his
school afterwards) insisted that the sun is only so large as it seems to
the eye. Cf. Kant's reference to the 'persistent illusion' of sense on
this point (of the size of the sun or moon).

to see wrongly or to hear wrongly can happen only to one
who sees or hears something real, though not exactly what he
supposes.   But we have assumed that in sleep one neither
459 a sees, nor hears, nor exercises any sense whatever.   Perhaps
we may regard it as true that the dreamer sees nothing, yet
as false that his faculty of sense-perception is unaffected, the
fact being that the sense of seeing and the other senses may
possibly be then in a certain way affected, while each of these
affections, as duly as when he is awake, gives its impulse in
5 a certain manner to his [primary] faculty of sense, though
not in precisely the same manner[1] as when he is awake.
Sometimes, too, opinion says [to dreamers] just as to those
who are awake, that the object seen is an illusion ; at other
times it is inhibited, and becomes a mere follower of the
phantasm.

It is plain therefore that this affection, which we name
' dreaming ', is no mere exercise of opinion or intelligence,
10 but yet is not an affection of the faculty of perception in the
simple sense.[2]   If it were the latter it would be possible
[when asleep] to hear and see in the simple sense.

How then, and in what manner, it takes place, is what we
have to examine.   Let us assume, what is indeed clear
enough, that the affection [of dreaming] pertains to sense-
perception as surely as sleep itself does.   For sleep does not
pertain to one organ in animals and dreaming to another ;
both pertain to the same organ.

15   But since we have, in our work on the Soul,[3] treated of
presentation,[4] and the faculty of presentation is identical

---

[1] οὐχ ... ὥσπερ : not directly from the αἰσθητόν, but indirectly or me-
diately from the residual κίνησις—the αἴσθημα ὑπόλοιπον.

[2] αἰσθάνεσθαι ἁπλῶς : opp. κατὰ πρόσθεσιν, ' with a difference or qualification.'   Dreaming is afterwards shown to be αἰσθάνεσθαι in a secondary
sense, or κατὰ συμβεβηκός, i. e. in virtue of the residual κινήσεις left in the
organs after αἴσθησις has departed.

[3] 427b 27-429a 9.

[4] The word ' imagination ', owing to popular and psychological associations, is unfitted to be a rendering of φαντασία here, and ' presentation ' is now a recognized term χ re-presentation.   For the operation
of φαντασία in ordinary αἴσθησις see 460b 18, where φαίνεται = to have a
presentation—a φάντασμα—not a re-presentation.   Presentation differs
from αἴσθησις (in which it is involved).   It is the aspect in which that
which αἴσθησις apprehends is put before the mind's eye, so to speak.
αἴσθησις takes the εἴδη ἄνευ ὕλης of αἰσθητά, and ' presents ' them as

with [1] that of sense-perception, though the essential notion of
a faculty of presentation is different from that of a faculty
of sense-perception ; and since presentation is the movement
set up by a sensory faculty when actually discharging its
function, while a dream appears to be a presentation (for
a presentation which occurs in sleep—whether simply [2] or in 20
some particular way—is what we call a dream): it manifestly
follows that dreaming is an activity of the faculty of sense-
perception, but belongs to this faculty *qua* presentative.

CHAPTER II

We can best obtain a scientific view of the nature of the
dream and the manner in which it originates by regarding it
in the light of the circumstances attending sleep. The objects 25
of sense-perception corresponding to each sensory organ produce sense-perception in us, and the affection due to their
operation is present in the organs of sense not only when
the perceptions are actualized, but even when they have
departed.

What happens in these cases may be compared with what
happens in the case of projectiles moving in space. For in
the case of these the movement continues even when that
which set up the movement is no longer in contact [with the 30
things that are moved]. For that which set them in motion
moves [3] a certain portion of air, and this, in turn, being moved
excites motion in another portion ; and so, accordingly, it is
in this way that [the bodies], whether in air or in liquids,
continue moving, until they [4] come to a standstill.

material of thought or opinion. This explains how τὸ εἶναι φανταστικῷ (the
essential notion of a faculty of presentation) differs from τὸ εἶναι αἰσθητικῷ.
See 449ᵃ 16-20, 454ᵃ 19, 455ᵃ 21, with notes.

[1] i. e. inseparable *numero*, and in concrete existence, from it.

[2] ἁπλῶς : without specifying particular conditions : τρόπον τινά, i. e. in
the way defined 462ᵃ 29, where the φάντασμα of the dream is said to be
formed ἀπὸ τῆς κινήσεως τῶν αἰσθημάτων : the case to which the dream proper
is here restricted.

[3] ἐκίνησεν not ʻconsuetudinal aorist ʼ, but referring to the time of κινῆσαν.
Still it may be rendered as in the text.

[4] ἕως ἂν στῇ sc. τὰ φερόμενα. While their movement lasts it is to this
cause it is due. The emphasis lies on τοῦτον τὸν τρόπον. The movement lasts until the last thing (portion of air) has come into the place of
the first movement—ἕως τῆς ἀρχῆς. See next note but one.

This we must likewise assume to happen in the case of qualitative change[1]; for that part which [for example] has been heated by something hot, heats [in turn] the part next to it, and this propagates the affection continuously onwards until the process has come round to its point of origination.[2] This must also happen in the organ wherein the exercise of sense-perception takes place, since sense-perception, as realized in actual perceiving, is a mode of qualitative change. This explains why the affection continues in the sensory organs, both in their deeper and in their more superficial parts, not merely while they are actually engaged in perceiving, but even after they have ceased to do so. That they do this, indeed, is obvious in cases where we continue for some time engaged in a particular form of perception, for then, when we shift the scene of our perceptive activity, the previous affection remains; for instance, when we have turned our gaze from sunlight[3] into darkness. For the result of this is that one sees nothing, owing to the motion excited by the light still subsisting in our eyes. Also, when we have looked steadily for a long while at one colour, e. g. at white or green, that to which we next transfer our gaze appears to be of

---

[1] Not merely, as with projectiles, in change of place.

[2] ἕως τῆς ἀρχῆς. The process of ἀλλοίωσις in a material body is like that of ἀντιπερίστασις (see note 457ᵇ 2), which ends when the last thing moved takes the place vacated by the first. This place is ἡ ἀρχή: i. e. the place ὅθεν ἡ κίνησις ἄρχεται. Something is here supposed to occur in the process of heating analogous to what occurs in the case of the projectile. The heat having been applied (and then withdrawn—this is the meaning), something (corresponding to the displaced part of the air) is displaced by it in τὸ πλησίον, which becomes hot, while that which was displaced again retires, and so on (κατ' ἀνταλλαγὴν τῶν τόπων, as Simplic. would say) until the process ends where it began. The air in successive parts retires before the stone; what retires before τὸ θερμόν? τὸ ψυχρόν or ἡ ψυχρότης, which for Aristotle was a positive. The conclusion of the process in the case of the stone is a state of rest—the stopping of the stone. What is it in the case of θέρμανσις (a word which Bonitz omits in his Index, though it occurs 1067ᵇ 12 q.v.)? The answer is—ἡ θερμότης τοῦ ὅλου. With this the κίνησις (involved in the ἀλλοίωσις) ceases: for ἔστιν οὐχ ἡ θερμότης κίνησις, ἀλλ' ἡ θέρμανσις (1067ᵇ 12). We cannot look for an exact parallel to all this in the case of αἴσθησις, which at most is only ἀλλοίωσίς τις: yet something analogous to ἀντιπερίστασις seems to occur in the κινήσεις that, as it were, 'circulate' between the external 'points of sense' (eye, ear, &c.) and the κύριον, between which poles the κινήσεις and the inhibiting forces (their negatives) move.

[3] If we had been gazing at the sun itself we should not 'see nothing', but continue to see the sun, as stated below 459 ᵇ 13.

the same colour.   Again if, after having looked at the sun
or some other brilliant object, we close the eyes, then, if
we watch carefully, it appears in a right line with the direction 15
of vision (whatever this may be), at first in its own colour ; then
it changes to crimson, next to purple, until it becomes black
and disappears.   And also when persons turn away from
looking at objects in motion, e. g. rivers, and especially those
which flow very rapidly, they find that the visual stimulations [1] still present themselves, for the things really at rest are 20
then seen moving : persons become very deaf after hearing
loud noises, and after smelling very strong odours their power
of smelling is impaired ; and similarly in other cases.   These
phenomena manifestly take place in the way above described.[2]

That the sensory organs are acutely sensitive to even a
slight qualitative difference [in their objects] is shown by
what happens in the case of mirrors ; a subject to which, 25
even taking it independently, one might devote close [3] consideration and inquiry.   At the same time it becomes plain
from them that as the eye [in seeing] is affected [by the
object seen], so also it produces a certain effect upon it.
'Speculorum enim admodum nitidorum, si forte mulieres
menstruae inspexerint, superficies sanguinea quasi nebula 30
offunditur ; et novo quidem speculo haud facile est eiusmodi maculam detergere, veteri autem facilius.   Quod fit

---

[1] καὶ . . . μεταβάλλουσιν.   Cf. 460ᵇ 28–32 αἱ κινήσεις αἱ ἀπὸ τῶν . . .
γινόμεναι . . . φαίνονται.   From this we learn that αἱ here agrees with
κινήσεις, and that φαίνονται (which occurs in the clauses just before and
after) is to be supplied in the sense of ἔτι φαίνονται.   μεταβάλλουσιν here
cannot be as Mich. takes it = 'undergo ἀλλοίωσις', persistency of impression
after transfer of gaze being the point of the sentence, not μεταβολή
on the part of the κινήσεις (as with the colour images just before changing
to their complementaries, negatives, &c.).   We have had it in this sense
of 'transfer' just above ᵇ 13, where μεταβάλωμεν serves as aor. subj. of
μεταφέρειν ᵇ 8.   The full construction then would be : καὶ αἱ ἀπὸ τῶν κινου-
μένων δὲ ⟨γινόμεναι κινήσεις ἔτι φαίνονται⟩ μεταβάλλουσιν ⟨τὴν ὄψιν ἀπὸ
τῶν κινουμένων⟩ οἷον κτλ.   Of course 'δέ copulat, καί intendit'.   It is a
matter of indifference for sense or grammar whether after οἷον we supply
αἱ, or μεταβάλλουσι.   There is no need to suspect the αἱ as a piece of
dittography after καί in ᵇ 18.   In 460ᵇ 28 the conclusion of the whole
argument is set forth.
[2] i.e. by the persistence of the qualitative change implied in all perception.
[3] It is simplest to take περὶ οὗ καθ' αὑτό with σκέψαιτο ἄν, and understand
of course τὴν διάνοιαν (or something equivalent) in the usual way with
ἐπιστήσας.

propterea quia visus, ut diximus, non modo patitur quippiam,
aere agente, sed etiam facit et agit, id quod debent omnia
quae sunt splendida. Visus enim ipse illorum est quae
splendida sunt et colorem habent. Oculi igitur, ut con-
sentaneum est, eadem qua quaelibet alia pars corporis ratione
5 se habent; suapte enim natura sunt venosi,[1] unde fit ut, dum
menstrua perturbatione quadam sanguinis et inflammatione
profluunt, oculi mulierum, quamvis nos quidem mares, dum
intuemur, res fugiat (eadem [2] enim seminis quae menstruorum
natura), mutationem subeant; illis autem motus vicinus aer
eum quoque, qui supra speculum continuus diffunditur, aera
10 nescio qualem reddit, nempe talem qualiscumque iam antea
est ipse redditus; hic porro superficiem speculi pariter afficit.
Ut enim vestimenta, [sic specula] quo sunt puriora, eo citius
sordescunt. Quaecunque enim pura sunt, si maculam acce-
perint, aperte ostendunt, et purissimum quidque exhibet vel
minimas turbationes. Aes vero speculare imprimis, propter
lēvitatem quidem tactum qualemcunque sentit (aëris autem
15 tactum oportet pro fricatione quadam et quasi expressione
vel ablutione haberi); propterea autem quod purum est,
manifeste in eo apparet tactus quantuluscumque. Quod vero
tarde e novis speculis maculae discedunt, id fit quia speculum
eiusmodi lēve et purum est; namque per talia in altum et
20 omnifariam insinuatur infectus; in altum quidem propterea
quod pura sunt, omnifariam autem propter levitatem. Contra
in veteribus speculis macula idcirco non residet, quod neque
perinde in ea penetrat, et summa tantummodo attingit.'

From this therefore it is plain that stimulatory motion is
set up even by slight differences, and that sense-perception
is quick to respond to it; and further that the organ which
25 perceives colour is not only affected by its object, but also

---

[1] φλεβώδεις ὄντες as if ὀφθαλμοί not ὄμματα had preceded.
[2] The object of the parenthetic words is to explain not the ἔνεστι, but
the fact that, although ἔνεστι, it escapes *our* notice. This is due to the
fact that the ἀλλοίωσις required for perception depends on the presence
of opposites (cp. *de An.*, where the doctrine πάσχει τὸ ἀνόμοιον [ὑπὸ τοῦ
ἀνομοίου] πεπονθὸς δ' ὅμοιόν ἐστιν is laid down as fundamental). Owing
to the identity of φύσις here the requisite ἀνομοιότης does not exist:
hence ἡ ἐν τοῖς ὄμμασι τῶν γ. ἡμῖν ἄδηλος. This seems plain enough; but
the words in the translation have been so collocated as to exhibit it in
the clearest light.

reacts upon it.   Further evidence to the same point is afforded by what takes place in wines, and in the manufacture of unguents.   For both oil, when prepared, and wine become rapidly infected by the odours of the things near them ; they not only acquire the odours of the things thrown 30 into or mixed with them, but also those of the things which are placed, or which grow, near the vessels containing them.

In order to answer our original question, let us now, therefore, assume one proposition, which is clear from what 460 b precedes, viz. that even when the external object of perception has departed, the impressions it has made persist, and are themselves objects of perception ; and [let us assume], besides, that we are easily deceived respecting the operations of sense-perception when we are excited by emotions,[1] and different persons according to their different emotions ; for example, the coward when excited by fear, the amorous 5 person by amorous desire ; so that, with but little resemblance to go upon, the former thinks he sees his foes approaching, the latter, that he sees the object of his desire ; and the more deeply one is under the influence of the emotion, the less similarity is required to give rise to these illusory impressions. Thus too, both in fits of anger, and also in all states of appetite, all men become easily deceived, and more so the more their 10 emotions are excited.   This is the reason too why persons in the delirium of fever sometimes think they see animals on their chamber walls, an illusion arising from the faint resemblance to animals of the markings thereon when put together in patterns ; and this sometimes corresponds with the emotional states of the sufferers, in such a way that, if the latter be not very ill, they know well enough that it is an illusion ; but if the illness is more severe they actually move 15 according to the appearances.[2]   The cause of these occur-

---

[1] ἐν πάθεσιν ὄντες . . . ὁ δειλός, κτλ. The δειλός = the person whose disposition or character inclines him to take fright ; the φόβος = the fright he gets into at any particular time. So with ὁ ἐρωτικός and his ἔρως. πάθη here not = ' passions ', as this word is generally understood in psychological English. See Höffding (E.T.), p. 282, where ' passion ' and ' emotion ' are defined. For πάθος χ ἕξις, see N.E. 1105^b 21–26.

[2] πρὸς αὐτά : they regulate their movements with a view to them or with relation to them : i.e. move away from them or towards them, as if they were real.

rences is that the faculty in virtue of which the controlling sense judges is not identical with that in virtue of which presentations come before the mind. A proof of this is, that the sun presents itself as only a foot in diameter, though often something[1] else gainsays the presentation.
20 Again, when the fingers are crossed, the one object [placed between them] is felt [by the touch] as two; but yet we deny that it is two; for sight is more authoritative than touch. Yet, if touch stood alone, we should actually have pronounced the one object to be two. The ground of such false judgments is that any appearances whatever present themselves, not only when its object stimulates a sense, but also when the sense by itself alone[2] is stimulated,
25 provided only it be stimulated in the same manner[3] as it is by the object. For example, to persons sailing past the land seems to move,[4] when it is really the eye that is being moved by something else [the moving ship].

CHAPTER III

From this it is manifest that the stimulatory movements based upon sensory impressions, whether the latter are derived from external objects or from causes within the body, present them-
30 selves[5] not only when persons are awake, but also then, when

---

[1] As some senses are more authoritative than others, so τὸ κρῖνον is more authoritative than τὸ φανταστικόν, and even than any particular sense. The judgment, which recognizes the superior authority of sight and makes us say (φαμέν) that the objects are *not* two, but one, is what Aristotle here wishes to emphasize.

[2] Without an object.

[3] The importance of this in explaining the illusion of dreams appears fully in 461ᵇ 28-9.

[4] κινεῖσθαι, κινουμένης are here both used of local movement, while κινοῦντος, κινουμένης, just above were used of sense-stimulation.

[5] Biehl's text has been translated. ἐγρηγο,ότων: we have a gen. absol. (not a dative after φαίνονται) because when awake people do not notice them, although they are there. The εἰσιν supplied by Mich. in first clause is not necessary. ᵇ 29 τῶν αἰσ'ημάτων: the impressions of sense as distinct from the exercises of sense—αἰσθήσεις. τῶν θύραθεν . . . τῶν ἐκ τοῦ σ. impressions derived from objects in space around us Χ impressions of our bodily states, e. g. twinges of pain, &c. αἰσθημάτων *agrees* with τῶν καὶ τῶν. Ἐνυπαρχουσῶν in Biehl's text must be wrong, for we cannot believe in his anacoluthia. The case is not like φλεβώδεις ὄντες, 460ᵃ 5 ; for there, at least, there is a new sentence, and the subject is grammatically different. Fut we cannot part with αἰσθημάτων here : αἰσθήσεων would contradict 459ᵃ 27 ἀπελθουσῶν and 460ᵇ 2 (ἀπελθόντων);

this affection which is called sleep has come upon them, with even greater[1] impressiveness.   For by day, while the senses and the intellect are working together,[2] they (i. e. such movements) are extruded from consciousness or obscured, just as 461 a a smaller is beside a larger fire, or as small beside great pains or pleasures, though, as soon as the latter have ceased, even those which are trifling emerge into notice.   But by night [i. e. in sleep] owing to the inaction of the particular senses, and their powerlessness to realize themselves, which arises from the reflux of the hot from the exterior parts to the 5 interior, they [i. e. the above 'movements'] are borne in[3] to the head quarters of sense-perception, and there display themselves as the disturbance (of waking life) subsides.   We must suppose that, like the little eddies which are being ever formed in rivers, so the sensory movements are each a continuous process, often remaining like what they were when first 10 started, but often, too, broken into other forms by collisions with obstacles.   This [last mentioned point], moreover, gives the reason why no dreams occur in sleep immediately after meals, or to sleepers who are extremely young, e.g., to infants. The internal movement in such cases is excessive, owing to the heat generated from the food.   Hence, just as in a liquid, if one vehemently disturbs it, sometimes no reflected image 15 appears, while at other times one appears, indeed, but utterly

the doctrine being that dreams are based ἀπὸ τῶν αἰσθημάτων or ἀπὸ τῶν κινήσεων τῶν αἰσθημάτων, the αἰσθήσεις of which have departed. Cf. 461ᵃ 19 and 462ᵃ 30. We should, therefore (in spite of MSS.), read ἐνυπάρχουσιν, with Bywater, *J. P.* xxviii. 243, 461ᵇ 30. Besides it is emphatically not the αἰσθήσεις but their κινήσεις or αἰσθήματα that abide within : cf. 459ᵃ οὐ μόνον ἐνυπάρχει ἐν τοῖς αἰσθητηρίοις ἐνεργουσῶν τῶν αἰσθήσεων, ἀλλὰ καὶ ἀπελθουσῶν. Keeping Biehl's text, however, φαίνονται 460ᵇ 32 goes with the preceding clause also, even without zeugma : for the κινήσεις can be said φαίνεσθαι ἐγρηγορότων = to 'present themselves' *when* people are awake, though they do not φαίνονται ἐγρηγορόσιν, i.e. appear *to* or get noticed by them.

[1] καὶ μᾶλλον. The trans. '*even* more' has the advantage of requiring φαίνονται to be supplied but once, viz. in the οὐ μόνον clause. We get a perfectly good construction by making καί the copula, but then must supply φαίνονται twice. Besides καὶ μᾶλλον=*vel magis* is a stock expression.

[2] Συνεργουσῶν should be ἐνεργουσῶν of which it is an attempted correction in EMY ; (1) it perverts Aristotle's meaning, as the *co*-operation of αἰσθ. and διάνοια is not necessary for the extrusion of the κινήσεις ; (2) Aristotle nowhere else uses συνεργεῖν absolutely, nor can we supply here ταῖς κινήσεσιν ; (3) cf. 461ᵃ 5, *alibi*, where ἐνεργεῖν is used *de re eadem*.

[3] καταφέρονται, borne *in* (to the κύριον αἰσθ.) from τὰ αἰσθητήρια, in which ἐνυπάρχουσιν.

distorted, so as to seem quite unlike its original ; while, when
once the motion has ceased, the reflected images are clear
and plain ; in the same manner during sleep the phantasms,
or residuary movements, which are based upon the sensory
impressions, become sometimes quite obliterated by the
20 above described motion when too violent ; while at other
times the sights are indeed seen, but confused and weird. and
the dreams [which then appear] are unhealthy, like those
of persons who are atrabilious, or feverish, or intoxicated with
wine.   For all such affections, being spirituous, cause much
commotion and disturbance.   In sanguineous animals, in pro-
25 portion as the blood becomes calm, and as its purer are
separated from its less pure elements, the fact that the
movement, based on impressions derived from each of
the organs of sense, is preserved in its integrity, renders the
dreams healthy, causes a [clear] image to present itself,
and makes the dreamer think, owing to the effects borne in
from the organ of sight, that he actually sees, and owing to
those which come from the organ of hearing, that he really
30 hears ; and so on with those also which proceed from the
other sensory organs.   For it is owing to the fact that
the movement which reaches the primary organ of sense
comes from them, that one even when awake believes him-
461 b self to see, or hear, or otherwise perceive ; just as it is from
a belief that the organ of sight is being stimulated,[1] though
in reality not so stimulated, that we sometimes erroneously
declare ourselves to see, or that, from the fact that touch
announces two movements, we think that the one object is
two.   For, as a rule, the governing sense affirms the report
of each particular sense, unless another particular sense, more
5 authoritative, makes a contradictory report.   In every case
an appearance presents itself, but what appears does not in
every case seem real, unless when the deciding faculty is
inhibited, or does not move with its proper motion.   Moreover, as we said that different men are subject to illusions,
each according to the different emotion present in him, so it is
that the sleeper, owing to sleep, and to the movements then
going on in his sensory organs, as well as to the other facts

---

[1] By objective visual impressions.

of the sensory process, [is liable to illusion], so that the 10
dream presentation, though but little like it, appears as some
actual given thing. For when one is asleep, in proportion as
most of the blood sinks inwards to its fountain [the heart],
the internal [sensory] movements, some potential, others
actual [1] accompany it inwards. They are so related [in
general] that, if anything move the blood, some one
sensory movement will emerge from it, while if this perishes
another will take its place ; while to one another also they 15
are related in the same way as the artificial frogs in water
which severally rise [in fixed succession] to the surface in the
order in which the salt [which keeps them down] becomes
dissolved. The residuary movements are like these : they are
within the soul potentially, but actualize themselves only
when the impediment to their doing so has been relaxed ;
and according as [2] they are thus set free, they begin to move
in the blood which remains in the sensory organs, and which
is now but scanty,[3] while they possess verisimilitude after the
manner of cloud-shapes, which in their rapid metamorphoses 20
one compares now to human beings and a moment afterwards
to centaurs. Each of them is however, as has been said, the
remnant of a sensory impression taken when sense was
actualizing itself ; and when this, the true impression,[4] has
departed, its remnant is still immanent, and it is correct to say
of it, that though not actually Koriskos, it is like Koriskos.
For [5] when the person was actually perceiving, his controlling 25

---

[1] The 'actual' are those in consciousness at the time when one is falling
asleep : the potential, those which had before that subsided into latency.
Cf. 461ª 1.

[2] λυόμεναι : i. e. successively and severally : pres. part. has its force
(all through these tracts such points are most carefully observed).

[3] The most favourable condition, disturbance being at its minimum.

[4] τοῦ αἰσθήματος τοῦ ἀληθοῦς has here and in what follows to be
carefully distinguished from τὸ αἴσθημα = the impression merely, when
the αἰσθητόν is gone.

[5] Mich. explains δέ as = γάρ, rightly ; for the ὁμοιότης of the ὑπόλειμμα
is derived from that of the ἀληθὲς αἴσθημα. But he is wrong when he
makes ὅτε ᾐσθάνετο = ὅτε ἐν τῷ ὕπνῳ οὐ κατείχετο ὑπὸ τοῦ αἵματος. The
past tense might have warned him against doing so. Both this and
the ἂν μὴ παντελῶς refer to what happens in waking and normal
consciousness. The detection of a dream as such in sleep is mentioned below (462ª 3) as an exceptional occurrence, and not part of the
dream proper ; to introduce it here would only confuse, not illustrate

and judging sensory faculty did not call it [1] Koriskos, but, prompted by this [impression], called the genuine person yonder Koriskos. Accordingly, this sensory impulse, which, when actually perceiving, it [the controlling faculty] so describes (unless completely inhibited by the blood), it now [in dreams], when quasi-perceiving, [2] receives from the movements persisting in the sense-organs, and mistakes it — an impulse that is merely like the true [3] [objective] impression — for the true impression itself, while the effect 30 of sleep is so great that it causes this mistake to pass unnoticed. Accordingly, just as if a finger be inserted beneath the eyeball without being observed, one object will

---

as Aristotle means to do. Mich. is right, however, in making οὐ δὴ . . . αἵματος δηλωτικὸν τοῦ ὅτε δὲ ἠσθάνετο. Biehl, in stating that Mich. read μή after ὥσπερ, [b] 27, makes a mistake. Wendland's (Mich., p. 73. 12) note is 'ὥσπερ cum Arist. EMSUY (ὥσπερ μὴ L).' See next note but one.

[1] The impression synchronous with actual perception.

[2] ὥσπερ αἰσθανόμενον. In the translation the text of Biehl has not been followed. The retention (with Biehl, after L) of μή after ὥσπερ [b] 27, or its omission (with Mich. and EMYSU), makes a great difference. It ought to be omitted : ὥσπερ αἰσθανόμενον is in sense opposed to καὶ αἰσθανόμενον [b] 26, and to ὅτε ἠσθάνετο [b] 24, as the dreaming to the waking consciousness. When one was actually percipient, the κύριον did not confound even τὸ αἴσθημα τὸ ἀληθές with Κορίσκος ὁ ἀληθινός, nor does it when actually percipient ever do so unless under some pathological condition ; yet (see 460 [b] 25) in the quasi-percipient state of sleep, when not perceiving τὸ αἴσθημα τὸ ἀληθές at all, but only its ὑπόλειμμα, it is moved with this same movement (τοῦτο κινεῖται, cf. 463[b] 18), and made to treat this (the ὑπόλειμμα) not only as if it were τὸ ἀληθὲς αἴσθημα, but as if it were a real thing. After αἰσθητηρίοις [b] 29 there should be only a comma. The waking αἴσθημα is only οἷον Κορίσκος, not actually K. The remanent αἴσθημα too is, but only in a secondary degree, οἷον K. Yet so great is the power of sleep that the critical faculty, which in waking moments (unless inhibited completely) does not mistake even the genuine αἴσθημα for its object, when asleep confounds distinctions, and mistaking the remanent αἴσθημα for the object, is unaware of this mistake.

[3] [b] 29, αὐτῷ with ὅμοιον. ἀληθές here and above is to be kept distinct from ἀληθινός, as 'truthful' from 'genuine', according to the usual meanings of these words. ὁ ἀληθινὸς K. = the genuine Koriskos : τὸ ἀληθὲς αἴσθημα = the impression which tells truth, i. e. the immediate impression of K. yonder, as distinct from the ὑπόλειμμα, which speaks of him as if there when he is not there. Hence it is that ἀληθές and αὐτῷ should not be referred to the external thing. Two degrees of error (whence the strong expression τοσαύτη ἡ δύναμις) are usual in dreams : (a) the αἴσθημα τὸ ὑπόλοιπον is confounded with τὸ αἴσθημα τὸ ἀληθές ; (b) no distinction is drawn between τὸ αἴσθημα τὸ ἀληθές and τὸ πρᾶγμα τὸ ἀληθινόν. This fine analysis is (or may have been) founded on Plato, Republic, 476 c τὸ ὀνειρώττειν ἆρα οὐ τόδε ἐστίν, ἐάν τε ἐν ὕπνῳ τις ἐάν τ' ἐγρηγορὼς τὸ ὅμοιόν τῳ μὴ ὅμοιον ἀλλ' αὐτὸ ἡγῆται εἶναι ᾧ ἔοικεν;

not only present two visual images, but will create an opinion
of its being two objects ; while if it [the finger] be observed, the
presentation will be the same, but the same opinion will not
be formed of it ; exactly so it is in states of sleep: if the
sleeper perceives that he is asleep, and is conscious of
the sleeping state during which the perception comes before
his mind, it presents itself still, but something within him 5
speaks to this effect: ' the image of Koriskos presents itself,
but the real Koriskos is not present '; for often, when one is
asleep, there is something in consciousness which declares
that what then presents itself is but a dream. If, however,
he is not aware of being asleep, there is nothing which will
contradict the testimony of the bare presentation.

That what we here urge is true, i. e. that there are such
presentative movements in the sensory organs, any one may
convince himself, if he attends to and tries to remember the 10
affections we experience when sinking into slumber or when
being awakened. He will sometimes, in the moment of
awakening, surprise the images which present themselves to
him in sleep, and find that they are really but movements
lurking in the organs of sense. And indeed some very young
persons, if it is dark, though looking with wide open eyes,[1]
see multitudes of phantom figures moving before them, so that
they often cover up their heads in terror.

From all this, then, the conclusion to be drawn is, that the 15
dream is a sort of presentation, and, more particularly, one
which occurs in sleep ; since the phantoms just mentioned
are not dreams, nor is any other a dream which presents
itself when the sense-perceptions are in a state of freedom.
Nor is every presentation which occurs in sleep necessarily
a dream. For in the first place, some persons [when asleep]
actually, in a certain way, perceive sounds, light, savour, and 20
contact ; feebly, however, and, as it were, remotely. For
there have been cases in which persons while asleep, but with
the eyes partly open, saw faintly in their sleep (as they
supposed) the light of a lamp, and afterwards, on being
awakened, straightway recognized it as the actual light of
a real lamp ; while, in other cases, persons who faintly heard

---

[1] διαβλέποντες χ ὑποβλέποντες, 462ᵃ 22.

₂₅ the crowing of cocks or the barking of dogs identified these clearly with the real sounds as soon as they awoke. Some persons, too, return answers to questions put to them in sleep. For it is quite possible that, of waking or sleeping, while the one is present in the ordinary sense, the other also should be present in a certain way. But none of these occurrences[1] should be called a dream. Nor should the true thoughts,[2] as distinct from the mere presentations, which occur in sleep [be called dreams]. The dream proper is a presentation based ₃₀ on the movement of sense impressions, when such presentation occurs during sleep, taking sleep in the strict sense of the term.

There are cases of persons who in their whole lives have 462 b never had a dream, while others dream when considerably advanced in years, having never dreamed before. The cause of their not having dreams appears somewhat like that which operates in the case of infants, and [that which operates] immediately after meals. It is intelligible enough that no ₅ dream-presentation should occur to persons whose natural constitution is such that in them copious evaporation is borne upwards, which,[3] when borne back downwards, causes a large quantity of motion. But it is not surprising that, as age advances, a dream should at length appear to them. Indeed, ₁₀ it is inevitable that, as a change is wrought[4] in them in proportion to age or emotional experience, this reversal [from non-dreaming to dreaming] should occur also.

---

[1] Those due to this ambiguous condition.

[2] ἀληθεῖς ἔννοιαι : .e. g. when one says to himself 'this is only a dream'. Cf. *supra* 462ᵃ 6.

[3] Reading ἡ . . . καταφερομένη ποιεῖ with I S U and Themistius. Biehl's text is wrong, for it implies that the *upward* movement of the ἀναθυμίασις causes sleep. Cf. *supra* 456ᵇ 26-8.

[4] If we keep γινομένης (which suits καθ' ἡλικίαν) we must give it its continuative or progressive sense. This progressive change keeps pace with their change of age, and with the succession of (or vicissitudes of) πάθη which they experience. κατὰ πάθος does not mean 'in consequence of something that has happened to them', or in consequence of some *one* emotion.

CHAPTER I

As to the divination which takes place in sleep, and is said
to be based on dreams, we cannot lightly either dismiss it with
contempt or give it implicit confidence. The fact that all persons, or many, suppose dreams to possess a special significance,
tends to inspire us with belief in it [such divination], as founded 15
on the testimony of experience ; and indeed that divination in
dreams should, as regards some subjects, be genuine, is not
incredible, for it has a show of reason ; from which one might
form a like opinion also respecting all other dreams. Yet the
fact of our seeing no probable cause to account for such
divination tends to inspire us with distrust. For, in addition to 20
its further unreasonableness, it is absurd to combine [1] the idea
that the sender of such dreams should be God with the fact
that those to whom he sends them are not the best and wisest,
but merely commonplace persons. If, however, we abstract
from the causality of God, none of the other causes assigned
appears probable. For that certain persons should have foresight in dreams concerning things destined to take place at the
Pillars of Hercules, or on the banks of the Borysthenes, seems 25
to be something to discover the explanation of which surpasses
the wit of man. Well then, the dreams in question must be
regarded either as *causes*, or as *tokens*, of the events, or else as
coincidences; either as all, or some, of these, or as one only.
I use the word 'cause' in the sense in which the moon is

---

[1] b 20-22. Biehl's comma after πέμποντα is wrong, unless another
comma be put after ἀλογίᾳ. The clause πρὸς τῇ ἄλλῃ ἀλογίᾳ, which is
parenthetic, refers to the 'abandonment of reason' already noticed in
μηδεμίαν αἰτίαν εὔλογον just before. Besides the general ἀλογία of referring
dreams to ὁ θεός, there is the special ἀτοπία of his sending them to poor
creatures, not to wise men (cf. 463^b 15). The constr. is : τό τε ... εἶναι
καὶ τὸ ... πέμπειν ; it is the conjunction of the two things that is peculiarly
ἄτοπον. Thus τε and καί are in their usual correlation here.

[the cause] of an eclipse of the sun, or in which fatigue is
30 [a cause] of fever; 'token' [in the sense in which] the entrance
of a [1] star [into the shadow] is a token of the eclipse, or [in
which] roughness of the tongue [is a token] of fever; while
by 'coincidence' I mean, for example, the occurrence of an
eclipse of the sun while some one is taking a walk; for the
463 a walking is neither a token nor a cause of the eclipse, nor
the eclipse [a cause or token] of the walking.   For this
reason no coincidence takes place according to a universal
or general rule.   Are we then to say that some dreams
are causes, others tokens, e. g. of events taking place in the
bodily organism?   At all events, even scientific physicians tell
5 us that one should pay diligent attention to dreams, and to
hold this view is reasonable also for those who are not
practitioners, but speculative philosophers.   For the movements which occur in the daytime [within the body] are,
unless very great and violent, lost sight of in contrast with the
10 waking movements, which are more impressive.   In sleep the
opposite takes place, for then even trifling movements seem
considerable.   This is plain in what often happens during sleep;
for example, dreamers fancy that they are affected by thunder
and lightning, when in fact there are only faint ringings in their
ears; or that they are enjoying honey or other sweet savours,
when only a tiny drop of phlegm is flowing down [the
15 oesophagus]; or that they are walking through fire, and
feeling intense heat, when there is only a slight warmth
affecting certain parts of the body.   When they are awakened,
these things appear to them in this their true character.
But since the beginnings of all events are small, so, it is
clear, are those also of the diseases or other affections about
20 to occur in our bodies.   In conclusion, it is manifest that these
beginnings must be more evident in sleeping than in waking
moments.

Nay, indeed, it is not improbable that some of the presentations which come before the mind in sleep may even be

---

[1] τὸν ἀστέρα = 'a star or *any* star': the star that *does* show out, whatever
star it be.   The article is generic.   The εἰσ- not = 'into our view' but =
'into the shadow,' when however, of course, it also comes into our view.
Bonitz, *Ind.*, queries εἰσελθεῖν here: why?   The first star we see
betokens the coming eclipse.

causes of the actions cognate to each of them. For as when we are about to act [in waking hours], or are engaged in any course of action, or have already performed certain actions, we often find ourselves concerned with these actions, or per- 25 forming them, in a vivid dream ; the cause whereof is that the dream-movement has had a way paved for it from the original movements set up in the daytime ; exactly so, but conversely, it must happen that the movements set up first in sleep should also prove to be starting-points of actions to be performed in the daytime, since the recurrence by day of the thought of these actions also has had its way paved for it in the images before the mind at night. Thus then it is 30 quite conceivable that some dreams may be tokens and causes [of future events].

Most [so-called prophetic] dreams are, however, to be classed as mere coincidences, especially all such as are ex- 463 b travagant, and those in the fulfilment of which the dreamers have no initiative, such as in the case of a sea-fight, or of things taking place far away. As regards these it is natural that the fact should stand as it does whenever a person, on mentioning something, finds the very thing mentioned come to pass. Why, 5 indeed, should this not happen also in sleep ? The proba- bility is, rather, that many such things should happen. As, then, one's mentioning a particular person is neither token nor cause of this person's presenting himself, so, in the parallel instance, the dream is, to him who has seen it, neither token nor cause of its [so-called] fulfilment, but a mere coincidence Hence the fact that many dreams have no 'fulfilment', for coincidences do not occur according to any universal or 10 general law.

CHAPTER II

On the whole, forasmuch as certain of the lower animals also dream, it may be concluded that dreams are not sent by God, nor are they designed for this purpose [to reveal the future]. They have a divine aspect,[1] however, for Nature [their cause]

---

[1] δαιμόνια μέντοι, ἡ γὰρ φύσις δαιμονία, ἀλλ' οὐ θεία. Bonitz (*Ind.* 464ᵃ 28) followed by L. and S. (*sub voc.* δαιμόνιος) explains φύσις here as ἡ τῶν ἄλλων ζῴων φύσις. Zeller, *Arist.* i. 421 (E. T.) takes the right view.

¹⁵ is divinely planned, though not itself divine.   A special proof [of their not being sent by God] is this : the power of foreseeing the future and of having vivid dreams is found in persons of inferior type, which implies that God does not send their dreams; but merely that all those whose physical temperament is, as it were, garrulous and excitable, see sights of all descriptions ; for, inasmuch as they experience many movements of every kind, they just chance to have visions resembling objective facts, their luck in these matters ²⁰ being merely like that of persons who play at even and odd.¹ For the principle which is expressed in the gambler's maxim : ' If you make many throws your luck must change,' holds good in their case also.

That many dreams have no fulfilment is not strange, for it is so too with many bodily symptoms and weather-signs, ²⁵ e. g., those of rain or wind.   For if another movement occurs more influential than that from which, while [the event to which it pointed was] still future, the given token was derived, the event [to which such token pointed] does not take place. So, of the things which ought to be accomplished by human agency, many, though well-planned, are by the operation of other principles more powerful [than man's agency] brought to nought. For, speaking generally, that which *was* about to happen is not in every case what now *is happening* ; nor is that which *shall* hereafter *be* identical with that which *is* now *going to* be. ³⁰ Still, however, we must hold that the beginnings from which, as we said,² no consummation follows, are *real* beginnings, and these constitute natural tokens of certain events, even though the events do not come to pass.

As for [prophetic] dreams which involve not such beginnings [sc. of future events] as we have here described, but such as are extravagant in times, or places, or magnitudes ; or those

---

If φύσις were to be thus limited we should have had αὐτῶν. Nature in general is δαιμονία as the province and theatre of God's final causation, and dreams (which are φυσικά) partake of the character of Nature their cause. The general difference between θεός and δαίμων, θεῖος and δαιμόνιον, (that the δαίμων is the offspring of the θεός, the δαιμόνιον the handiwork of the θεῖον) is here preserved.

¹ Reading ἁρτιάζοντες, Bekker's conj.

² οὐκ ἐτελέσθη : such is the force of the aor. For meaning of τινάς cf. notes 440ª 28.

involving beginnings which are not extravagant in any of
these respects,[1] while yet the persons who see the dream
hold not in their own hands the beginnings [of the event
to which it points]: unless the foresight which such dreams
give is the result of pure coincidence, the following
would be a better explanation of it than that proposed by Democritus, who alleges 'images' and 'emana- 5
tions' as its cause. As, when something has caused
motion in water or air, this [the portion moved] moves
another [portion of water or air], and, though the cause has
ceased to operate, such motion propagates itself to a certain
point, though there the prime movent is not present; just so
it may well be that a movement and a consequent sense-perception should reach sleeping souls from the objects from which 10
Democritus represents 'images' and 'emanations' as coming;
that such movements, in whatever way they arrive, should be
more perceptible at night [than by day], because when proceeding thus in the daytime they are more liable to dissolution (since at night the air is less disturbed, there being then
less wind); and that they shall be perceived within the body 15
owing to sleep, since persons are more sensitive even to slight
sensory movements when asleep than when awake. It is
these movements then that cause 'presentations', as a result
of which sleepers foresee the future even relatively to such
events as those referred[2] to above. These considerations
also explain why this experience befalls commonplace persons 20
and not the most intelligent. For it would have regularly occurred both in the daytime and to the wise had it been God
who sent it; but, as we have explained the matter, it is quite
natural that commonplace persons should be those who have
foresight [in dreams]. For the mind of such persons is not
given to thinking, but, as it were, derelict, or totally vacant,
and, when once set moving, is borne passively on in the direction taken by that which moves it. With regard to the fact
that some persons who are liable to derangement have this 25

---

[1] [a] 2. ἢ τούτων μὲν μηδέν: sc. ὑπεροπρίας τὰς ἀρχὰς ἐχόντων τῶν ἐνυπνίων.
Μηδέν is acc. of respect after ὑπεροπρίας understood from the previous
clause. Perhaps μηδενί would have been plainer; but the construction
is easy enough. Biehl by his proposed correction αὐτοῖς ... τοῖς ἰδοῦσι
would seem to construe as if μηδέν depended on ἐχόντων directly.

[2] i. e. those referred to 464ª 1-4.

foresight, its explanation is that their normal mental movements do not impede [the alien movements], but are beaten off by the latter. Therefore it is that they have an especially keen perception of the alien movements.

That certain persons in particular should have vivid dreams, e. g. that familiar friends should thus have foresight in a special degree respecting one another, is due to the fact that such friends are most solicitous on one another's behalf. 30 For as acquaintances in particular recognize and perceive one another a long way off, so also they do as regards the sensory movements respecting one another ; for sensory movements which refer to persons familiarly known are themselves more familiar. Atrabilious persons, owing to their impetuosity,[1] are, when they, as it were, shoot from a distance, expert at hitting ; 464 b while, owing to their mutability, the series of movements deploys quickly before their minds. For even as the insane recite, or con over in thought, the poems of Philaegides,[2] e. g. the Aphrodite, whose parts succeed in order of similitude, just so do they [the ' atrabilious '] go on and on stringing sensory movements together. Moreover, owing to their aforesaid 5 impetuosity, one movement within them is not liable to be knocked out of its course by some other movement.

The most skilful interpreter of dreams is he who has the faculty of observing resemblances. Any one may interpret dreams which are vivid and plain. But, speaking of ' resemblances ', I mean that dream presentations are analogous to the forms reflected in water, as indeed we have already stated. 10 In the latter case, if the motion in the water be great, the reflexion has no resemblance to its original, nor do the forms resemble the real objects. Skilful, indeed, would he be in interpreting such reflexions who could rapidly discern, and at a glance comprehend, the scattered and distorted fragments

---

[1] Which do not suffer them to wait until the object of their speculation is near them.

[2] Probably should be Φιλαινίδος, a name found in Lucian, *Pseudologista*, § 24, and Athenaeus 335 B-E. But what were the poems referred to? Did they go on like ' The House that Jack built ' ? Ath. and Luc. do not help to explain the point here, and Mich. and Pseudo-Them. add nothing to what our passage yields. Michael only contrasts the desultory manner of Euripides with the consistency of Philaegides in keeping to a theme.

of such forms, so as to perceive that one of them represents
a man, or a horse, or anything whatever. Accordingly, in the 15
other case also, in a similar way, some such thing as this
[blurred image] is all that a dream amounts[1] to; for the
internal movement effaces the clearness of the dream.

The questions, therefore, which we proposed as to the nature
of sleep and the dream, and the cause to which each of them
is due, and also as to divination as a result of dreams, in every
form of it, have now been discussed.

---

[1] ᵇ 15. The *troubled* dream 'has this effect', δύναται τοῦτο. The κἀκεῖ
prevents us from taking τοῦτο with τὸ ἐνύπνιον = 'the dream we speak of
has a certain effect.' To explain τι it is necessary, after Biehl's conjecture,
to read τοιοῦτο. There is no analogy for τοῦτό τι : τόδε τι is a totally different
kind of expression. But τοιοῦτό τι would be not only correct, but quite to
the point here. Not τι, but πως, should qualify ὁμοίως.

CHAPTER I

THE reasons for some animals being long-lived and others
20 short-lived, and, in a word, the causes of the length and
brevity of life call for investigation.

The necessary beginning to our inquiry is a statement of
the difficulties about these points. For it is not clear whether
in animals and plants universally it is a single or diverse
cause that makes some to be long-lived, others short-lived.
25 Plants too have in some cases a long life, while in others it
lasts but for a year.

Further, in a natural structure are longevity and a sound
constitution coincident, or is shortness of life independent of
unhealthiness? Perhaps in the case of certain maladies a
diseased state of the body and shortness of life are inter-
30 changeable, while in the case of others ill-health is perfectly
compatible with long life.

Of sleep and waking we have already treated; about life
and death we shall speak later on, and likewise about health
and disease, in so far as it belongs to the science of nature
465 a to do so. But at present we have to investigate the causes of
some creatures being long-lived, others short-lived. We
find this distinction affecting not only entire genera opposed
as wholes to one another, but applying also to contrasted sets[1]
of individuals within the same species.[2] As an instance of

---

[1] See next sentence, *sub fin.*

[2] Aristotle does not mention the opposition of species to species, but
passes at once from the maximum of difference (generic) to the minimum
(individual). In the next sentence, however, we have a case of specific
diversity (man and horse). It is strange for him to say that the difference
of man and horse in longevity is a difference κατὰ γένος, and that between
man and man (who must be individuals ὑφ' ἐν εἶδος) κατ' εἶδος. Unless
we translate in the fashion I have adopted we must believe that there is
a confusion in the first sentence between γένος and εἶδος, and that when
in the second he does distinguish between them Aristotle contradicts the
rest of his teaching.

the difference applying to the genus I give man and horse 5
(for mankind has a longer life than the horse), while within
the species there is the difference between man and man ; for
of men also some are long-lived, others short-lived, differing
from each other in respect of the different regions in which
they dwell. Races inhabiting warm countries have longer
life, those living in a cold climate live a shorter time. Like- 10
wise there are similar differences among individuals occupying
the same locality.

CHAPTER II

In order to find premisses for our argument, we must
answer the question, What is that which, in natural objects,
makes them easily destroyed, or the reverse? Since fire
and water, and whatsoever is akin thereto, do not possess 15
identical powers they are reciprocal causes of generation and
decay. Hence it is natural to infer that everything else
arising from them and composed of them should share in the
same nature, in all cases where things are not, like a house,
a composite unity formed by the synthesis of many things.

In other matters a different account must be given ; for
in many things their mode of dissolution is something
peculiar to themselves, e. g. in knowledge and health and 20
disease. These pass away even though the medium in
which they are found is not destroyed but continues to
exist; for example, take the termination of ignorance, which
is recollection or learning, while knowledge passes away into
forgetfulness, or error. But accidentally the disintegration of
a natural object is accompanied by the destruction of the
non-physical reality; for, when the animal dies, the health 25
or knowledge resident in it passes away too. Hence from
these considerations we may draw a conclusion about the
soul too ; for, if the inherence of soul in body is not a matter
of nature but like that of knowledge in the soul, there would
be another mode of dissolution pertaining to it besides that
which occurs when the body is destroyed. But since evidently 30
it does not admit of this dual dissolution, the soul must stand
in a different case in respect of its union with the body.

CHAPTER III

Perhaps one might reasonably raise the question whether there is any place where what is corruptible becomes incorruptible, as fire does in the upper regions where it meets with no opposite. Opposites destroy each other, and hence 5 accidentally, by their destruction, whatsoever is attributed to them is destroyed. But no opposite in a real substance is accidentally destroyed, because real substance is not predicated of any subject. Hence a thing which has no opposite, or which is situated where it has no opposite, cannot be destroyed. For what will that be which can destroy it, if destruction comes only through contraries, but no contrary to 10 it exists either absolutely or in the particular place where it is? But perhaps this is in one sense true, in another sense not true, for it is impossible that anything containing matter should not have in any sense an opposite. Heat and straightness can be present in every part of a thing, but it is impossible that the thing should be nothing but hot or white or straight; for, if that were so, attributes would have an 15 independent existence. Hence if, in all cases, whenever the active and the passive exist together, the one acts and the other is acted on, it is impossible that no change should occur. Further, this is so if a waste product is an opposite, and waste must always be produced; for opposition is always the source of change, and *refuse* is what remains of the previous opposite. But, after expelling everything of a nature actually opposed, would an object in this case also be imperishable? No, it 20 would be destroyed by the environment.

If then that is so, what we have said sufficiently accounts for the change; but, if not, we must assume that something of actually opposite character is in the changing object, and refuse is produced.

Hence accidentally a lesser flame is consumed by a greater 25 one, for the nutriment [1], to wit the smoke, which the former takes a long period to expend, is used up by the big flame quickly.

----

[1] Read ἦν τροφήν with Bywater, *Journal of Philol.* xxviii. p. 243, instead of Biehl's ἡ τροφὴ ἦν. This obviates the necessity of treating τὸν καπνόν as a gloss.

Hence [too] all things are at all times in a state of transition and are coming into being and passing away. The environment acts on them either favourably or antagonistically, and, owing to this, things that change their situation become more or less enduring than their nature warrants, but never are they eternal when they contain contrary qualities; for their matter is an immediate source of 30 contrariety, so that if it involves locality they show change of situation, if quantity, increase and diminution, while if it involves qualitative affection we find alteration of character.

CHAPTER IV

We find that a superior immunity from decay attaches 466 a neither to the largest animals (the horse has shorter life than man) nor to those that are small (for most insects live but for a year). Nor are plants as a whole less liable to perish than animals (many plants are annuals), nor have sanguineous animals the pre-eminence (for the bee is longer-lived than certain sanguineous animals). Neither 5 is it the bloodless animals that live longest (for molluscs live only a year, though bloodless), nor terrestrial organisms (there are both plants and terrestrial animals of which a single year is the period), nor the occupants of the sea (for there we find the crustaceans and the molluscs, which are short-lived).

Speaking generally, the longest-lived things occur among the plants, e. g. the date-palm. Next in order we find 10 them among the sanguineous animals rather than among the bloodless, and among those with feet rather than among the denizens of the water. Hence, taking these two characters together, the longest-lived animals fall among sanguineous animals which have feet, e. g. man and elephant. As a matter of fact also it is a general rule that the larger live longer than the smaller, for the other long-lived animals 15 too happen to be of a large size, as are also those I have mentioned.

CHAPTER V

The following considerations may enable us to understand the reasons for all these facts. We must remember that an

20 animal is by nature humid and warm, and to live is to be of such a constitution, while old age is dry and cold, and so is a corpse. This is plain to observation. But the material constituting the bodies of all things [1] consists of the following— the hot and the cold, the dry and the moist. Hence when they age they must become dry, and therefore the fluid in them requires to be not easily dried up. Thus we explain why fat things are not liable to decay. The reason is that they contain air; now air relatively to the other elements is fire, 25 and fire never becomes corrupted.

Again the humid element in animals must not be small in quantity, for a small quantity is easily dried up. This is why both plants and animals that are large are, as a general rule, longer-lived than the rest, as was said before; it is to be expected that the larger should contain more moisture. But it is not merely this that makes them longer lived; for the 30 cause is twofold, to wit, the quality as well as the quantity of the fluid. Hence the moisture must be not only great in amount but also warm, in order to be neither easily congealed nor easily dried up.

It is for this reason also that man lives longer than some animals which are larger; for animals live longer though there
466 b is a deficiency in the amount of their moisture, if the ratio of its qualitative superiority exceeds that of its quantitative deficiency.

In some creatures the warm element is their fatty substance, which prevents at once desiccation and congelation; but in others it assumes a different flavour.[2] Further, that which is 5 designed to be not easily destroyed should not yield waste products. Anything of such a nature causes death either by disease or naturally, for the potency of the waste product works adversely and destroys now the entire constitution, now a particular member.

This is why salacious animals and those abounding in seed

---

[1] I thus translate τοῖς οὖσι (Biehl). Bywater suggests τοιούτοις instead of οὖσι (*Journal of Philol.* xxviii. p. 244). If this conjecture is adopted the translation will be—' In such cases the material of which the body is composed consists,' &c.
[2] τὸ λιπαρόν is one of the recognized flavours; cf. *de Sens.*, chap. iv. 442ᵃ 17 sqq.

age quickly; the seed is a residue, and further, by being lost,
it produces dryness. Hence the mule lives longer than either
the horse or the ass from which it sprang, and females live 10
longer than males if the males are salacious. Accordingly
cock-sparrows have a shorter life than the females. Again
males subject to great toil are short-lived and age more
quickly owing to the labour; toil produces dryness and
old age is dry. But by natural constitution and as a general
rule males live longer than females, and the reason is that 15
the male is an animal with more warmth than the female.

The same kind of animals are longer-lived in warm than in
cold climates for the same reason, on account of which they
are of larger size. The size of animals of cold constitution
illustrates this particularly well, and hence snakes and lizards 20
and scaly reptiles are of great size in warm localities, as also
are testacea in the Red Sea: the warm humidity there is the
cause equally of their augmented size and of their life. But
in cold countries the humidity in animals is more of a watery
nature, and hence is readily congealed. Consequently it
happens that animals with little or no blood are in northerly 25
regions either entirely absent (both the land animals with feet
and the water creatures whose home is the sea) or, when they
do occur, they are smaller and have shorter life; for the frost
prevents growth.

Both plants and animals perish if not fed, for in that case
they consume themselves; just as a large flame consumes 30
and burns up a small one by using up its nutriment, so the
natural warmth which is the primary cause of digestion
consumes the material in which it is located.

Water animals have a shorter life than terrestrial creatures,
not strictly because they are humid, but because they are 467 a
watery, and watery moisture is easily destroyed, since it is
cold and readily congealed. For the same reason bloodless
animals perish readily unless protected by great size, for there
is neither fatness nor sweetness about them. In animals fat
is sweet, and hence bees are longer-lived than other animals 5
of larger size.

CHAPTER VI

It is amongst the plants that we find the longest life—
more than among the animals, for, in the first place, they are
less watery and hence less easily frozen. Further they have
an oiliness and a viscosity which makes them retain their
moisture in a form not easily dried up, even though they are
dry and earthy.

10   But we must discover the reason why trees are of an enduring constitution, for it is peculiar to them and is not found
in any animals except the insects.

Plants continually renew themselves and hence last for
a long time. New shoots continually come and the others
grow old, and with the roots the same thing happens. But
both processes do not occur together. Rather it happens
15 that at one time the trunk and the branches alone die and
new ones grow up beside them, and it is only when this has
taken place that the fresh roots spring from the surviving
part. Thus it continues, one part dying and the other growing, and hence also it lives a long time.

There is a similarity, as has been already said, between
plants and insects, for they live, though divided, and two
20 or more may be derived from a single one. Insects, however, though managing to live, are not able to do so long,
for they do not possess organs ; nor can the principle resident
in each of the separated parts create organs. In the case of
a plant, however, it can do so ; every part of a plant contains
potentially both root and stem. Hence it is from this source
that issues that continued growth when one part is renewed
25 and the other grows old; it is practically a case of longevity.[1]
The taking of slips furnishes a similar instance, for we might
say that, in a way, when we take a slip the same thing
happens; the shoot cut off is part of the plant. Thus in
taking slips this perpetuation of life occurs though their
connexion with the plant is severed, but in the former case it
is the continuity that is operative. The reason is that the
30 life principle potentially belonging to them is present in
every part.

---

[1] τῷ MSS. (except. S. τὸ) et edd. τοῦ conicio.

Identical phenomena are found both in plants and in animals. For in animals the males are, in general, the longer-lived. They have their upper parts larger than the lower (the male is more of the dwarf[1] type of build than the female), and it is in the upper part that warmth resides, in the lower cold. In plants also those with great heads are longer-lived, and such are those that are not annual but of the 467 b tree-type, for the roots are the head and upper part of a plant, and among the annuals growth occurs in the direction of their lower parts and the fruit.

These matters however will be specially investigated in the work *On Plants*.[2]   But this is our account of the reasons 5 for the duration of life and for short life in animals. It remains for us to discuss youth and age, and life and death. To come to a definite understanding about these matters would complete our course of study on animals.

[1] i. e. with trunk and head disproportionately large.
[2] Not extant.

DE IUVENTUTE ET SENECTUTE, DE
VITA ET MORTE, DE RESPIRATIONE

CHAPTER I

10 WE must now treat of youth and old age and life and
death. We must probably also at the same time state the
causes of respiration as well, since in some cases living and
the reverse depend on this.

We have elsewhere given a precise account of the soul, and
while it is clear that its essential reality cannot be corporeal,
15 yet manifestly it must exist in some bodily part which must
be one of those possessing control over the members. Let
us for the present set aside the other divisions or faculties of
the soul (whichever of the two be the correct name). But
as to being what is called an animal and a living thing, we
find that in all beings endowed with both characteristics
20 (viz. being an animal and being alive) there must be a single
identical part in virtue of which they live and are called
animals ; for an animal *qua* animal cannot avoid being alive.
But a thing need not, though alive, be animal, for plants live
without having sensation, and it is by sensation that we
25 distinguish animal from what is not animal.

This organ, then, must be numerically one and the same
and yet possess multiple and disparate aspects, for being
animal and living are not identical. Since then the organs
of special sensation have one common organ in which the
30 senses when functioning must meet, and this must be situated
midway between what is called before and behind (we call
' before ' the direction from which sensation comes, ' behind '
the opposite), further, since in all living things the body is
divided into upper and lower (they all have upper and lower
parts, so that this is true of plants as well), clearly the nutri-
468 a tive principle must be situated midway between these regions.
That part where food enters we call upper, considering it by

itself and not relatively to the surrounding universe, while downward is that part by which the primary excrement[1] is discharged.

Plants are the reverse of animals in this respect. To man 5 in particular among the animals, on account of his erect stature, belongs the characteristic of having his upper parts pointing upwards in the sense in which that applies to the universe, while in the others these are in an intermediate position. But in plants, owing to their being stationary and drawing their sustenance from the ground, the upper part must always be down; for there is a correspondence between the roots in a plant and what is called the mouth in animals, 10 by means of which they[2] take in their food, whether the source of supply be the earth or each other's bodies.

CHAPTER II

All perfectly formed animals are to be divided into three parts, one that by which food is taken in, one that by which excrement is discharged, and the third the region inter- 15 mediate between them. In the largest animals this latter is called the chest and in the others something corresponding; in some also it is more distinctly marked off than in others. All those also that are capable of progression have additional members subservient to this purpose, by means of which they bear the whole trunk, to wit legs and feet and whatever parts are possessed of the same powers. Now it is evident both 20 by observation and by inference that the source of the nutritive soul is in the midst of the three parts. For many animals, when either part—the head or the receptacle of the

---

[1] By this I imagine that τὸ τῆς κοιλίας περίττωμα (de Part. Animal. III. chap. viii. 671ᵃ 7) is meant, or more generally τὸ τῆς τροφῆς (II. chap. vii. 653ᵇ 13, &c.). Besides what we should call excrement, many bodily secretions, e. g. γονή and γάλα, are called περιττώματα by Aristotle.

[2] I take τὰ μέν and τὰ δέ (468ᵃ 11, 12) to refer to different classes of animals. Herbivorous animals could be said to derive their food ἐκ τῆς γῆς; the other class consists of the carnivora. On the other hand, if Aristotle means to contrast two classes of plants, the second set—those which get their nutriment δι' αὐτῶν—will comprise 'grafts and parasitic plants,' which only derive food indirectly from the soil'. Cf. Ogle, Aristotle on Youth and Old Age, &c., p. 108.

25 food—is cut off, retain life in that member to which the middle remains attached. This can be seen to occur in many insects, e.g. wasps and bees, and many animals also besides insects can, though divided, continue to live by means of the part connected with nutrition.

While this member is indeed in actuality single, yet potentially it is multiple, for these animals have a constitution 30 similar to that of plants; plants when cut into sections continue to live, and a number of trees can be derived from one single source. A separate account[1] will be given of the reason why some plants cannot live when divided, 468 b while others can be propagated by the taking of slips. In this respect, however, plants and insects are alike.

It is true[2] that the nutritive soul, in beings possessing it, while actually single must be potentially plural. And so it is too with the principle of sensation, for evidently the 5 divided segments of these animals have sensation. They are unable, however, to preserve their constitution, as plants can, not possessing the organs on which the continuance of life depends, for some lack the means for seizing, others for receiving their food ; or again they may be destitute of other organs as well.

Divisible animals are like a number of animals grown 10 together, but animals of superior construction behave differently because their constitution is a unity of the highest possible kind. Hence some of the organs on division display slight sensitiveness because they retain some psychical susceptibility ; the animals continue to move after the vitals have 15 been abstracted : tortoises, for example, do so even after the heart has been removed.

CHAPTER III

The same phenomenon is evident both in plants and in animals, and in plants we note it both in their propagation by seed and in grafts and cuttings. Genesis from seeds always starts from the middle. All seeds are bivalvular, and

---

[1] In the extant works of Aristotle no such account is to be met with. Some suppose that it was included in the lost treatise on plants.
[2] Susemihl and Biehl read δή.

the place of junction [1] is situated at the point of attachment [1] 20
(to the plant), an intermediate part belonging to both halves.
It is from this part that both root and stem of growing things
emerge; the starting-point is in a central position between
them. In the case of grafts and cuttings this is particularly
true of the buds; for the bud is in a way the starting-point
of the branch, but at the same time it is in a central position. 25
Hence it is either this that is cut off, or into this that the new
shoot is inserted, when we wish either a new branch or a
new root to spring from it ; which proves that the point of
origin in growth is intermediate between stem and root.

Likewise in sanguineous animals the heart is the first organ
developed; this is evident from what has been observed in
those cases where observation of their growth is possible.
Hence in bloodless animals also what corresponds to the 30
heart must develop first. We have already asserted in our
treatise on *The Parts of Animals* [2] that it is from the heart
that the veins issue, and that in sanguineous animals the blood **469 a**
is the final nutriment from which the members are formed.
Hence it is clear that there is one function in nutrition which
the mouth has the faculty of performing, and a different one
appertaining to the stomach. But it is the heart that has
supreme control, exercising an additional and completing
function. Hence in sanguineous animals the source both of 5
the sensitive and of the nutritive soul must be in the heart,
for the functions relative to nutrition exercised by the other
parts are ancillary to the activity of the heart. It is the part
of the dominating organ to achieve the final result, as of the
physician's efforts to be directed towards health, and not to
be occupied with subordinate offices.

Certainly, however, all sanguineous animals have the 10
supreme organ of the sense-faculties in the heart, for it is
here that we must look for the common sensorium belonging

---

[1] I have followed Bekker's reading—ᾗ συμπέφυκεν ἔχεται. καὶ τὸ μέσον
κτλ. Biehl conjectures ᾗ συμπέφυκεν ἀρχή τε καὶ τὸ μέσον—'the point of
junction is the starting-point and intermediate between the two halves.'
But if συμπέφυκεν has the same force as προσπέφυκε in *de Gen. Animal.*
752ᵃ 19, 23 (*q. v.*) it refers to the attachment of the seed to the plant.
Again, the sense which ἔχεται here bears is closely akin to that which we
meet with in the participle ἐχόμενος.

[2] Cf. *de Part. Animal.* iii. 665ᵇ 15.

to all the sense-organs. These in two cases, taste and touch, can be clearly seen to extend to the heart, and hence the 15 others also must lead to it, for in it the other organs may possibly initiate changes, whereas with the upper region of the body taste and touch have no connexion. Apart from these considerations, if the life is always located in this part, evidently the principle of sensation must be situated there too, for it is *qua* animal that an animal is said to be a living thing, and it is called animal because endowed with sensation. 20 Elsewhere in other works [1] we have stated the reasons why some of the sense-organs are, as is evident, connected with the heart, while others are situated in the head. (It is this fact that causes some people to think that it is in virtue of the brain that the function of perception belongs to animals.)

CHAPTER IV

Thus if, on the one hand, we look to the observed facts, what we have said makes it clear that the source of the sensitive soul, together with that connected with growth and 25 nutrition, is situated in this organ and in the central one of the three divisions of the body. But it follows by deduction also ; for we see that in every case, when several results are open to her, Nature always brings to pass the best. Now if both 30 principles are located in the midst of the substance, the two parts of the body, viz. that which elaborates and that which receives the nutriment in its final form will best perform their appropriate function ; for the soul will then be close to each, and the central situation which it will, as such, occupy is the position of a dominating power.

469 b   Further, that which employs an instrument and the instrument it employs must be distinct (and must be spatially diverse too, if possible, as in capacity), just as the flute and that which plays it—the hand—are diverse. Thus if animal is defined by the possession of sensitive soul, this soul must in 5 the sanguineous animals be in the heart, and, in the bloodless ones, in the corresponding part of their body. But in animals all the members and the whole body possess some connate

[1] *de Part. Animal.* ii. 656[b] 5.

warmth of constitution, and hence when alive they are observed to be warm, but when dead and deprived of life they
are the opposite. Indeed, the source of this warmth must be 10
in the heart in sanguineous animals, and in the case of bloodless animals in the corresponding organ, for, though all parts
of the body by means of their natural heat elaborate and
concoct the nutriment, the governing organ takes the chief
share in this process. Hence, though the other members
become cold, life remains; but when the warmth here is
quenched, death always ensues, because the source of heat
in all the other members depends on this, and the soul is, 15
as it were, set aglow with fire in this part, which in sanguineous animals is the heart and in the bloodless order the
analogous member. Hence, of necessity, life must be coincident with the maintenance of heat, and what we call death
is its destruction.   20

CHAPTER V

However, it is to be noticed that there are two ways in
which fire ceases to exist; it may go out either by exhaustion or by extinction. That which is self-caused we call
exhaustion, that due to its opposites extinction. [The
former is that due to old age, the latter to violence.[1]] But
either of these ways in which fire ceases to be may be
brought about by the same cause, for, when there is a
deficiency of nutriment and the warmth can obtain no 25
maintenance, the fire fails; and the reason is that the opposite, checking digestion, prevents the fire from being fed.
But in other cases the result is exhaustion,—when the heat
accumulates excessively owing to lack of respiration and of
refrigeration. For in this case what happens is that the
heat, accumulating in great quantity, quickly uses up its
nutriment and consumes it all before more is sent up by 30
evaporation. Hence not only is a smaller fire readily put
out by a larger one, but of itself[2] the candle flame is consumed

---

[1] Biehl thinks that an erroneous interpretation has suggested this clause.
[2] The going out of the fire is, in every case of μάρανσις, in one respect
caused by the burning body itself, i.e. *by its burning*, and hence con-
suming its fuel. It is *per accidens* (κατὰ συμβεβηκός : 465[h] 23 above) that
it is put out owing to the consumption of its fuel by a larger fire.

when inserted in a large blaze, just as is the case with any
other combustible. The reason is that the nutriment in the
flame is seized by the larger one before fresh fuel can be
added, for fire is ever coming into being and rushing just
like a river, but so speedily as to elude observation.

5 Clearly therefore, if the bodily heat must be conserved
(as is necessary if life is to continue), there must be some
way of cooling the heat resident in the source of warmth.
Take as an illustration what occurs when coals are confined
in a brazier. If they are kept covered up continuously by the
10 so-called 'choker', they are quickly extinguished, but, if the
lid is in rapid alternation lifted up and put on again they
remain glowing for a long time. Banking up a fire also
keeps it in, for the ashes, being porous, do not prevent the
passage of air, and again they enable it to resist extinction
by the surrounding air by means of the supply of heat which
15 it possesses. However, we have stated in *The Problems*[1]
the reasons why these operations, namely banking up and
covering up a fire, have the opposite effects (in the one case
the fire goes out, in the other it continues alive for a considerable time).

CHAPTER VI

20 Everything living[2] has soul, and it[2], as we have said,
cannot exist without the presence of heat in the constitution.
In plants the natural heat is sufficiently well kept alive by
the aid which their nutriment and the surrounding air supply.
For the food has a cooling effect [as it enters, just as it has
in man][3] when first it is taken in, whereas abstinence from
25 food produces heat and thirst. The air, if it be motionless,
becomes hot, but by the entry of food a motion is set up
which lasts until digestion is completed and so cools it. If
the surrounding air is excessively cold owing to the time
of year, there being severe frost, plants shrivel, or if, in
the extreme heats of summer the moisture drawn from the
30 ground cannot produce its cooling effect, the heat comes to

---

[1] No such passage is found in the extant *Problems*.
[2] l. 19. Read ζῶν and αὕτη.
[3] This clause seems to be an interpolation.

an end by exhaustion. Trees suffering at such seasons are said to be blighted or star-stricken. Hence the practice of laying beneath the roots stones of certain species or water in pots, for the purpose of cooling the roots of the plants.

Some animals pass their life in the water, others in the air, 470 b and therefore these media furnish the source and means of refrigeration, water in the one case, air in the other. We must proceed—and it will require further application on our part—to give an account of the way and manner in which 5 this refrigeration occurs.

CHAPTER VII

(Chapter I of that part which deals specially with Respiration)

A few of the previous physical philosophers have spoken of respiration. The reason, however, why it exists in animals they have either not declared or, when they have, their statements are not correct and show a comparative lack of acquaintance with the facts. Moreover they assert that all animals respire—which is untrue. Hence these points must 10 first claim our attention, in order that we may not be thought to make unsubstantiated charges against authors no longer alive.

First then, it is evident that all animals with lungs breathe, but in some cases breathing animals have a bloodless and spongy lung, and then there is less need for respiration. These animals can remain under water for a time, which 15 relatively to their bodily strength, is considerable. All oviparous animals, e. g. the frog-tribe, have a spongy lung. Also hemydes and tortoises can remain for a long time immersed in water; for their lung, containing little blood, has 20 not much heat. Hence, when once it is inflated, it itself, by means of its motion, produces a cooling effect and enables the animal to remain immersed for a long time. Suffocation, however, always ensues if the animal is forced to hold its breath for too long a time, for none of this class take in water in the way fishes do. On the other hand, animals which have the lung charged with blood have greater need of 25

respiration on account of the amount of their heat, while
none at all of the others which do not possess lungs,
breathe.

CHAPTER VIII (II)

Democritus of Abdera and certain others who have treated
of respiration, while saying nothing definite about the lungless
30 animals, nevertheless seem to speak as if all breathed. But
Anaxagoras and Diogenes both maintain that all breathe,
and state the manner in which fishes and oysters respire.
Anaxagoras says that when fishes discharge water through
471 a their gills, air is formed in the mouth, for there can be no
vacuum, and that it is by drawing in this that they respire.
Diogenes' statement is that, when they discharge water
through their gills, they suck the air out of the water
surrounding the mouth by means of the vacuum formed in
the mouth, for he believes there is air in the water.
5 But these theories are untenable. Firstly, they state only
what is the common element in both operations and so leave
out the half of the matter. For what goes by the name of
respiration consists, on the one hand, of inhalation, and, on the
other, of the exhalation of breath ; but, about the latter they
say nothing, nor do they describe how such animals emit
10 their breath. Indeed, explanation is for them impossible for,
when the creatures respire, they must discharge their breath
by the same passage as that by which they draw it in, and
this must happen in alternation. Hence, as a result, they
must take the water into their mouth at the same time as
they breathe out. But the air and the water must meet and
obstruct each other. Further, when they discharge the water
15 they must emit their breath by the mouth or the gills, and
the result will be that they will breathe in and breathe out at
the same time, for it is at that moment that respiration is said
to occur. But it is impossible that they should do both at
the same time. Hence, if respiring creatures must both
exhale and inhale the air, and if none of these animals can
breathe out, evidently none can respire at all.

CHAPTER IX (III)

Further, the assertion that they draw in air out of the 20 mouth or out of the water by means of the mouth is an impossibility, for, not having a lung, they have no windpipe ; rather the stomach is closely juxtaposed to the mouth, so that they must do the sucking with the stomach. But in that case the other animals would do so also, which is not the truth ; and the water-animals also would be seen to do it when out of the water, whereas quite evidently they do not. 25 Further, in all animals that respire and draw breath there is to be observed a certain motion in the part of the body which draws in the air, but in the fishes this does not occur. Fishes do not appear to move any of the parts in the region of the stomach, except the gills alone, and these move both when they are in the water and when they are thrown on to 30 dry land and gasp. Moreover, always when respiring animals 471 b are killed by being suffocated in water, bubbles are formed of the air which is forcibly discharged, as happens, e. g. when one forces a tortoise or a frog or any other animal of a similar class to stay beneath water. But with fishes this result never occurs, in whatsoever way we try to obtain it, since they do not contain air drawn from an external source. Again, the 5 manner of respiration said to exist in them might occur in the case of men also when they are under water. For if fishes draw in air out of the surrounding water by means of their mouth why should not men too and other animals do so also ; they should also, in the same way as fishes, draw in air out of the mouth.[1] If in the former case it were possible, 10 so also should it be in the latter. But, since in the one it is not so, neither does it occur in the other. Furthermore, why do fishes, if they respire, die in the air and gasp (as can be seen) as in suffocation? It is not want of food [2] that produces this effect upon them, and the reason given by Diogenes 15 is foolish, for he says that in air they take in too much air and hence die, but in the water they take in a moderate amount. But that should be a possible occurrence with land

---

[1] Anaxagoras's theory.
[2] If the air is regarded as nutriment.

animals also; as facts are, however, no land animal seems to be suffocated by excessive respiration. Again, if all animals 20 breathe, insects must do so also. But many of them seem to live though divided not merely into two, but into several parts, e. g. the class called Scolopendra. But how can they, when thus divided, breathe, and what is the organ they employ? The main reason why these writers have not given a good account of these facts is that they have no acquaint- 25 ance with the internal organs, and that they did not accept the doctrine that there is a final cause for whatever Nature does. If they had asked for what purpose respiration exists in animals, and had considered this with reference to the organs, e. g. the gills and the lungs, they would have discovered the reason more speedily.

CHAPTER X (IV)

30 Democritus, however, does teach that in the breathing animals there is a certain result produced by respiration ; he asserts that it prevents the soul from being extruded from 472 a the body. Nevertheless, he by no means asserts that it is for this purpose that Nature so contrives it, for he, like the other physical philosophers, altogether fails to attain to any such explanation. His statement is that the soul and the hot element are identical, being the primary forms among the 5 spherical particles. Hence, when these are being crushed together by the surrounding atmosphere thrusting them out, respiration, according to his account, comes in to succour them. For in the air there are many of those particles which he calls mind and soul. Hence, when we breathe and the air enters, these enter along with it, and by their action cancel the pressure, thus preventing the expulsion of the soul which resides in the animal.

10 This explains why life and death are bound up with the taking in and letting out of the breath ; for death occurs when the compression by the surrounding air gains the upper hand, and, the animal being unable to respire, the air from outside can no longer enter and counteract the compression.

Death is the departure of those forms owing to the expulsive 15
pressure exerted by the surrounding air. Death, however,
occurs not by haphazard but, when natural, owing to old age,
and, when unnatural, to violence.

But the reason for this and why all must die Democritus
has by no means made clear. And yet, since evidently death
occurs at one time of life and not at another, he should have
said whether the cause is external or internal. Neither does 20
he assign the cause of the beginning of respiration, nor say
whether it is internal or external. Indeed, it is not the case
that the external mind superintends the reinforcement ; rather
the origin of breathing and of the respiratory motion must be
within : it is not due to pressure from around. It is absurd
also that what surrounds should compress and at the same
time by entering dilate. This then is practically his theory, 25
and how he puts it.

But if we must consider that our previous account is true,
and that respiration does not occur in every animal, we must
deem that this explains death not universally, but only in
respiring animals. Yet neither is it a good account of these
even, as may clearly be seen from the facts and phenomena 30
of which we all have experience. For in hot weather we
grow warmer, and, having more need of respiration, we always
breathe faster. But, when the air around is cold and contracts
and solidifies the body, retardation of the breathing results.
Yet this was just the time when the external air should enter 35
and annul the expulsive movement, whereas it is the opposite **472 b**
that occurs. For when the breath is not let out and the heat
accumulates too much then we need to respire, and to respire
we must draw in the breath. When hot, people breathe rapidly,
because they must do so in order to cool themselves, just 5
when the theory of Democritus would make them add fire
to fire.

CHAPTER XI (V)

The theory found in the *Timaeus*, of the passing round of
the breath by pushing, by no means determines how, in the
case of the animals other than land-animals, their heat is preserved, and whether it is due to the same or a different cause.

For if respiration occurs only in land-animals we should be
10 told what is the reason of that. Likewise, if it is found in
others also, but in a different form, this form of respiration,
if they all can breathe, must also be described.

Further, the method of explaining involves a fiction. It is
said that when the hot air issues from the mouth it pushes
the surrounding air, which being carried on enters the very
15 place whence the internal warmth issued, through the inter-
stices of the porous flesh ; and this reciprocal replacement is
due to the fact that a vacuum cannot exist. But when it has
become hot the air passes out again by the same route, and
pushes back inwards through the mouth the air that had
been discharged in a warm condition. It is said that it is
this action which goes on continuously when the breath is
taken in and let out.

20 But according to this way of thinking it will follow that
we breathe out before we breathe in. But the opposite is
the case, as evidence shows, for though these two functions
go on in alternation, yet the last act when life comes to
a close is the letting out of the breath, and hence its
admission must have been the beginning of the process.

Once more, those who give this kind of explanation by no
means state the final cause of the presence in animals of this
25 function (to wit the admission and emission of the breath),
but treat it as though it were a contingent accompaniment
of life. Yet it evidently has control over life and death, for
it results synchronously that when respiring animals are
unable to breathe they perish. Again, it is absurd that the
30 passage of the hot air out through the mouth and back again
should be quite perceptible, while we were not able to detect
the thoracic influx and the return outwards once more of the
heated breath. It is also nonsense that respiration should
consist in the entrance of heat, for the evidence is to the
contrary effect ; what is breathed out is hot, and what is
35 breathed in is cold. When it is hot we pant in breathing,
473 a for, because what enters does not adequately perform its
cooling function, we have as a consequence to draw the breath
frequently.

CHAPTER XII (VI)

It is certain, however, that we must not entertain the notion that it is for purposes of nutrition that respiration is designed, and believe that the internal fire is fed by the breath; respiration, as it were, adding fuel to the fire, while the feeding 5 of the flame results in the outward passage of the breath. To combat this doctrine I shall repeat what I said in opposition to the previous theories. This, or something analogous to it, should occur in the other animals also (on this theory), for all possess vital heat. Further, how are we to describe this 10 fictitious process of the generation of heat from the breath? Observation shows rather that it is a product of the food. A consequence also of this theory is that the nutriment would enter and the refuse be discharged by the same channel, but this does not appear to occur in the other instances.

CHAPTER XIII (VII)

Empedocles also gives an account of respiration without, 15 however, making clear what its purpose is, or whether or not it is universal in animals. Also when dealing with respiration by means of the nostrils he imagines he is dealing with what is the primary kind of respiration. Even the breath which passes through the nostrils passes through the windpipe out of the chest as well, and without the latter the nostrils cannot 20 act. Again, when animals are bereft of respiration through the nostrils, no detrimental result ensues, but, when prevented from breathing through the windpipe, they die. Nature employs respiration through the nostrils as a secondary function in certain animals in order to enable them to smell. But the 25 reason why it exists in some only is that though almost all animals are endowed with the sense of smell, the sense-organ is not the same in all.

A more precise account has been given about this else-where.[1] Empedocles, however, explains the passage inwards **473 b** and outwards of the breath, by the theory that there are

---

[1] Cf. *de An.* iii. 421ᵃ 10, *de Sens.* ch. v. 443ᵃ 4, 444ᵇ 7–15, *Hist. An.* iv. 534ᵇ 16, *de Part. Animal.* ii. 659ᵇ 15.

certain blood-vessels, which, while containing blood, are not
filled by it, but have passages leading to the outer air, the
calibre of which is fine in contrast to the size of the solid
5 particles, but large relatively to those in the air. Hence,
since it is the nature of the blood to move upwards and
downwards, when it moves down the air rushes in and
inspiration occurs; when the blood rises, the air is forced
out and the outward motion of the breath results. He
compares this process to what occurs in a clepsydra.

Thus all things outwards breathe and in ;—their flesh has
    tubes
10 Bloodless, that stretch towards the body's outmost edge,
Which, at their mouths, full many frequent channels pierce,
Cleaving the extreme nostrils through ; thus, while the gore
Lies hid, for air is cut a thoroughfare most plain.
And thence, whenever shrinks away the tender blood,
15 Enters the blustering wind with swelling billow wild.
But when the blood leaps up, backward it breathes. As
    when
With water-clock of polished bronze [1] a maiden sporting,
Sets on her comely hand the narrow of the tube
And dips it in the frail-formed water's silvery sheen ;
20 Not then the flood the vessel enters, but the air,
Pressing within on the dense orifices, checks it,
Until she frees the crowded stream. But then indeed
Upon the air's escape runs in the water meet.
So also when within the vessel's deeps the water
25 Remains, the opening by the hand of flesh being closed,
The outer air that entrance craves restrains the flood
At the gates of the sounding narrow, upon the surface
    pressing,
474 a Until the maid withdraws her hand. But then in contrariwise
Once more the air comes in and water meet flows out.
Thus too the subtle blood, surging throughout the limbs,
Whene'er it shrinks away into the far recesses
Admits a stream of air rushing with swelling wave,
5 But, when it backward leaps, in like bulk air flows out.

This then is what he says of respiration. But, as we said,
all animals that evidently respire do so by means of the
windpipe, when they breathe either through the mouth or

---

[1] The reading is difficult. Perhaps we should read κλεψύδρηι παίζηισι
διειπετέος χαλκοῖο, with Diels, *Vorsokratiker*, 2nd ed., p. 200.

through the nostrils. Hence, if it is of this kind of respiration that he is talking, we must ask how it tallies with the 10 explanation given. But the facts seem to be quite opposed. The chest is raised in the manner of a forge-bellows when the breath is drawn in—it is quite reasonable that it should be heat which raises up and that the blood should occupy the hot region—but it collapses and sinks down, like the bellows once more, when the breath is let out. The difference is that 15 in a bellows it is not by the same channel that the air is taken in and let out, but in breathing it is.

But, if Empedocles is accounting only for respiration through the nostrils, he is much in error, for that does not involve the nostrils alone, but passes by the channel beside the uvula where the extremity of the roof of the mouth is, 20 some of the air going this way through the apertures of the nostrils and some through the mouth, both when it enters and when it passes out. Such then is the nature and magnitude of the difficulties besetting the theories of other writers concerning respiration.

CHAPTER XIV (VIII)

We have already stated that life and the presence of soul 25 involve a certain heat. Not even the digesting process to which is due the nutrition of animals occurs apart from soul and warmth, for it is to fire that in all cases elaboration is due. It is for this reason, precisely, that the primary nutritive soul also must be located in that part of the 30 body and in that division of this region which is the immediate vehicle of this principle. The region in question 474 b is intermediate between that where food enters and that where excrement is discharged. In bloodless animals it has no name, but in the sanguineous class this organ is called the heart. The blood constitutes the nutriment from which the organs of the animal are directly formed. Likewise the blood-vessels must have the same originating 5 source, since the one exists for the other's behoof—as a vessel or receptacle for it. In sanguineous animals the heart is the starting-point of the veins; they do not traverse

it, but are found to stretch out from it, as dissections [1] enable
us to see.

10   Now the other psychical faculties cannot exist apart from
the power of nutrition (the reason has already been stated in
the treatise on the soul), [2] and this depends on the natural
fire, by the union with which Nature has set it aglow. But
fire, as we have already stated, is destroyed in two ways,
either by extinction or by exhaustion. It suffers extinction
15 from its opposites. Hence it can be extinguished by the
surrounding cold both when in mass and (though more
speedily) when scattered. Now this way of perishing is
due to violence equally in living and in lifeless objects,
for the division of an animal by instruments and consequent
congelation by excess of cold cause death. But exhaustion
20 is due to excess of heat ; for, if there is too much heat close
at hand and the thing burning does not have a fresh supply
of fuel added to it, it goes out by exhaustion, not by the
action of cold. Hence, if it is going to continue it must be
cooled, for cold is a preventive against this form of
extinction.

CHAPTER XV (IX)

25   Some animals occupy the water, others live on land, and,
that being so, in the case of those which are very small and
bloodless the refrigeration due to the surrounding water or
air is sufficient to prevent destruction from this cause. Having
30 little heat, they require little cold to combat it. Hence
too such animals are almost all short-lived, for, being small,
they have less scope for deflection towards either extreme.
475 a But some insects are longer-lived (though bloodless, like all
the others), and these have a deep indentation beneath the
waist, in order to secure cooling through the membrane,
which there is thinner. They are warmer animals and hence
require more refrigeration, and such are bees (some of which
5 live as long as seven years) and all that make a humming
noise, like wasps, cockchafers, and crickets. They make
a sound as if of panting by means of air, for, in the middle

---

[1] According to Bonitz, *Ind.* p. 104[a] 6, the reference here and at 478[a] 35
is to a lost treatise of Aristotle's on Anatomy.
[2] *De An.* i. 411[b] 18, ii. 413[b] 1.

section itself, the air which exists internally and is involved in their construction, causing a rising and falling movement, produces friction against the membrane. The way in which they move this region is like the motion due to the lungs 10 in animals that breathe the outer air, or to the gills in fishes. What occurs is comparable to the suffocation of a respiring animal by holding its mouth, for then the lung causes a heaving motion of this kind. In the case of these animals this internal motion is not sufficient for refrigeration, but in insects it is. It is by friction against the membrane 15 that they produce the humming sound, as we said, in the way that children do by blowing through the holes of a reed covered by a fine membrane. It is thus that the singing crickets too produce their song ; they possess greater warmth and are indented at the waist, but the songless variety have no fissure there.

Animals also which are sanguineous and possess a lung, 20 though that contains little blood and is spongy, can in some cases, owing to the latter fact, live a long time without breathing ; for the lung, containing little blood or fluid, can rise a long way : its own motion can for a long time produce sufficient refrigeration. But at last it ceases to suffice, and 25 the animal dies of suffocation if it does not respire—as we have already said. For of exhaustion that kind which is destruction due to lack of refrigeration is called suffocation, and whatsoever is thus destroyed is said to be suffocated.

We have already stated that among animals insects do not respire, and the fact is open to observation in the case of even 30 small creatures like flies and bees, for they can swim about in a fluid for a long time if it is not too hot or too cold. Yet **475 b** animals with little strength tend to breathe more frequently. These, however, die of what is called suffocation when the stomach becomes filled and the heat in the central segment is destroyed. This explains also why they revive after being among ashes for a time.

Again among water-animals those that are bloodless 5 remain alive longer in air than those that have blood and admit the sea-water, as, for example, fishes. Since it is a small quantity of heat they possess, the air is for a long

time adequate for the purposes of refrigeration in such
10 animals as the crustacea and the polyps. It does not
however suffice, owing to their want of heat, to keep them
finally in life, for most fishes also live though among earth,
yet in a motionless state, and are to be found by digging.
For all animals that have no lung at all or have a bloodless
one require less refrigeration.

CHAPTER XVI (X)

15 Concerning the bloodless animals we have declared that
in some cases it is the surrounding air, in others fluid, that
aids the maintenance of life. But in the case of animals
possessing blood and heart, all which have a lung admit
the air and produce the cooling effect by breathing in and
20 out. All animals have a lung that are viviparous and are so
internally, not externally merely (the Selachia are viviparous,
but not internally), and of the oviparous class those that have
wings, e. g. birds, and those with scales, e. g. tortoises, lizards,
and snakes. The former class have a lung charged with
blood, but in the most part of the latter it is spongy. Hence
25 they employ respiration more sparingly as already said. The
function is found also in all that frequent and pass their life
in the water, e. g. the class of water-snakes and frogs and
crocodiles and hemydes, both sea- and land-tortoises, and
seals.

All these and similar animals both bring forth on land
30 and sleep on shore or, when they do so in the water, keep
476 a the head above the surface in order to respire. But all with
gills produce refrigeration by taking in water ; the Selachia
and all other footless animals have gills. Fish are footless, and
the limbs they have get their name (πτερύγιον) from their
5 similarity to wings (πτέρυξ). But of those with feet one
only, so far as observed, has gills. It is called the tadpole.

No animal yet has been seen to possess both lungs and
gills, and the reason for this is that the lung is designed for
the purpose of refrigeration by means of the air (it seems to
have derived its name (πνεύμων) from its function as a re-
10 ceptacle of the breath (πνεῦμα)), while gills are relevant to

refrigeration by water. Now for one purpose one organ is adapted and one single means of refrigeration is sufficient in every case. Hence, since we see that Nature does nothing in vain, and if there were two organs one would be purposeless, this is the reason why some animals have gills, others lungs, 15 but none possess both.

CHAPTER XVII (XI)

Every animal in order to exist requires nutriment, in order to prevent itself from dying, refrigeration ; and so Nature employs the same organ for both purposes. For, as in some cases the tongue serves both for discerning tastes and for speech, so in animals with lungs the mouth is employed both 20 in working up the food and in the passage of the breath outwards and inwards. In lungless and non-respiring animals it is employed in working up the food, while in those of them that require refrigeration it is the gills that are created for this purpose.

We shall state further on how it is that these organs have 25 the faculty of producing refrigeration. But to prevent their food from impeding these operations there is a similar contrivance in the respiring animals and in those that admit water. At the moment of respiration they do not take in food, for otherwise suffocation results owing to the food, 30 whether liquid or dry, slipping in through the windpipe and lying on the lung. The windpipe is situated before the oesophagus, through which food passes into what is called the stomach, but in quadrupeds which are sanguineous there is, as it were, a lid over the windpipe—the epiglottis. In birds and oviparous quadrupeds this covering is absent, but 476 b its office is discharged by a contraction of the windpipe. The latter class contract the windpipe when swallowing their food ; the former close down the epiglottis. When the food has passed, the epiglottis is in the one case raised, and in the other the windpipe is expanded, and the air enters to effect refrigeration. In animals with gills the water is first dis- 5 charged through them and then the food passes in through the mouth ; they have no windpipe and hence can take no

harm from liquid lodging in this organ, only from its entering
the stomach. For these reasons the expulsion of water and
10 the seizing of their food is rapid, and their teeth are sharp
and in almost all cases arranged in a saw-like fashion, for
they are debarred from chewing their food.

CHAPTER XVIII (XII)

Among water-animals the cetaceans may give rise to some
perplexity, though they too can be rationally explained.
15 Examples of such animals are dolphins and whales, and
all others that have a blow-hole. They have no feet, yet
possess a lung though admitting the sea-water. The reason
for possessing a lung is that which we have now stated
[refrigeration]; the admission of water is not for the purpose
of refrigeration. That is effected by respiration, for they have
20 a lung. Hence they sleep with their head out of the water, and
dolphins, at any rate, snore. Further, if they are entangled in
nets they soon die of suffocation owing to lack of respiration,
and hence they can be seen to come to the surface owing
to the necessity of breathing. But, since they have to feed
25 in the water, they must admit it, and it is in order to discharge
this that they all have a blow-hole; after admitting the water
they expel it through the blow-hole as the fishes do through
the gills. The position of the blow-hole is an indication of
this, for it leads to none of the organs which are charged
with blood; but it lies before the brain and thence discharges
water.
30 It is for the very same reason that molluscs and crustaceans
admit water—I mean such animals as Carabi and Carcini.
For none of these is refrigeration a necessity, for in every
case they have little heat and are bloodless, and hence are
477 a sufficiently cooled by the surrounding water. But in feeding
they admit water, and hence must expel it in order to prevent
its being swallowed simultaneously with the food. Thus
crustaceans, like the Carcini and Carabi, discharge water
through the folds beside their shaggy parts, while cuttle-fish
and the polyps employ for this purpose the hollow above the

head.   There is, however, a more precise account of these in 5
the *History of Animals.*[1]

Thus it has been explained that the cause of the admission
of the water is refrigeration, and the fact that animals constituted for a life in water must feed in it.   10

CHAPTER XIX (XIII)

An account must next be given of refrigeration and the
manner in which it occurs in respiring animals and those
possessed of gills.   We have already said that all animals
with lungs respire.   The reason why some creatures have
this organ, and why those having it need respiration, is [15]
that the higher animals have a greater proportion of heat,
for at the same time they must have been assigned a higher
soul and they have a higher nature than plants.[2]   Hence too
those with most blood and most warmth in the lung are
of greater size, and that animal in which the blood in the [20]
lung is purest and most plentiful is the most erect, namely
man; and the reason why he alone has his upper part directed
to the upper part of the universe is that he possesses such
a lung.   Hence this organ as much as any other must
be assigned to the essence of the animal both in man and
in other cases.

This then is the purpose of refrigeration.   As for the [25]
constraining and efficient cause, we must believe that it
created animals like this, just as it created many others also not
of this constitution.   For some have a greater proportion of
earth in their composition, like plants, and others, e. g. aquatic
animals, contain a larger amount of water; while winged and
terrestrial animals have an excess of air and fire respectively.
It is always in the region proper to the element prepon- [30]
derating in the scheme of their constitution that things exist.

CHAPTER XX (XIV)

Empedocles is then in error when he says that those
animals which have the most warmth and fire live in the **477 b**

---

[1] Cf. *Hist. Animal.* ii. ch. 2, iv. chh. 1–3.
[2] Which are cold. Hence a higher soul entails more heat. Biehl,
however, reads ἰχθύων.

water to counterbalance the excess of heat in their constitution, in order that, since they are deficient in cold and
fluid, they may be kept in life by the contrary character of
the region they occupy; for water has less heat than air.
5 But it is wholly absurd that the water-animals should in
every case originate on dry land, and afterwards change their
place of abode to the water ; for they are almost all footless.
He, however, when describing their original structure says
that, though originating on dry land, they have abandoned it
and migrated to the water.   But again it is evident that they
10 are not warmer than land-animals, for in some cases they have
no blood at all, in others little.

The question, however, as to what sorts of animals should
be called warm and what cold, has in each special case
received consideration.   Though in one respect there is
reason in the explanation which Empedocles aims at estab-
lishing, yet his account is not correct.   Excess in a bodily
15 state is cured by a situation or season of opposite character,
but the constitution is best maintained by an environment
akin to it.   There is a difference between the material of
which any animal is constituted and the states and disposi-
tions of that material.   For example, if nature were to constitute a thing of wax or of ice, she would not preserve it
20 by putting it in a hot place, for the opposing quality would
quickly destroy it, seeing that heat dissolves that which cold
congeals.   Again, a thing composed of salt or nitre would not
be taken and placed in water, for fluid dissolves that of which
the consistency is due to the hot and the dry.

Hence if the fluid and the dry supply the material for all
bodies, it is reasonable that things the composition of which
is due to the fluid and the cold should have liquid for their
25 medium [and, if they are cold, they will exist in the cold][1],
while that which is due to the dry will be found in the dry.
Thus trees grow not in water but on dry land.   But the same
theory would relegate them to the water, on account of their
excess of dryness, just as it does the things that are exces-

---

[1] The clause within brackets is supposed by Biehl and Christ to be
spurious.

sively fiery. They would migrate thither not on account
of its cold but owing to its fluidity.

Thus the natural character of the material of objects is of 30
the same nature as the region in which they exist ; the liquid
is found in liquid, the dry on land, the warm in air. With 478 a
regard, however, to states of body, a cold situation has, on the
other hand, a beneficial effect on excess of heat, and a warm
environment on excess of cold, for the region reduces to
a mean the excess in the bodily condition. The regions
appropriate to each material and the revolutions of the
seasons which all experience supply the means which must 5
be sought in order to correct such excesses ; but, while states
of the body can be opposed in character to the environment,
the material of which it is composed can never be so. This,
then, is a sufficient explanation of why it is not owing to the
heat in their constitution that some animals are aquatic,
others terrestrial, as Empedocles maintains, and of why some
possess lungs and others do not.   10

CHAPTER XXI (XV)

The explanation of the admission of air and respiration in
those animals in which a lung is found, and especially in
those in which it is full of blood, is to be found in the fact
that it is of a spongy nature and full of tubes, and that it is
the most fully charged with blood of all the visceral organs.
All animals with a full-blooded lung require rapid refrigera- 15
tion because there is little scope for deviation from the normal
amount of their vital fire ; the air also must penetrate all
through it on account of the large quantity of blood and heat
it contains. But both these operations can be easily performed by air, for, being of a subtle nature, it penetrates
everywhere and that rapidly, and so performs its cooling
function ; but water has the opposite characteristics.   20

The reason why animals with a full-blooded lung respire
most is hence manifest ; the more heat there is, the greater is
the need for refrigeration, and at the same time breath can
easily pass to the source of heat in the heart.   25

CHAPTER XXII (XVI)

In order to understand the way in which the heart is connected with the lung by means of passages, we must consult
both dissections and the account in the *History of Animals.*[1]
The universal cause of the need which the animal has for
refrigeration, is the union of the soul with fire that takes
30 place in the heart. Respiration is the means of effecting
refrigeration, of which those animals make use that possess
a lung as well as a heart. But when they, as for example the
fishes, which on account of their aquatic nature have no lung,
possess the latter organ without the former, the cooling is
effected through the gills by means of water. For ocular
35 evidence as to how the heart is situated relatively to the gills
we must employ dissections, and for precise details we must
478 b refer to Natural History.[2] As a summarizing statement,
however, and for present purposes, the following is the
account of the matter.

It might appear that the heart has not the same position
in terrestrial animals and in fishes, but the position really is
identical, for the apex of the heart is in the direction in which
5 they incline their heads. But it is towards the mouth in fishes
that the apex of the heart points, seeing that they do not
incline their heads in the same direction as land-animals
do. Now from the extremity of the heart a tube of a
sinewy, arterial character runs to the centre where the gills
10 all join. This then is the largest of those ducts, but on
either side of the heart others also issue and run to the
extremity of each gill, and by means of the ceaseless flow
of water through the gills, effect the cooling which passes to
the heart.

In similar fashion as the fish move their gills, respiring
animals with rapid action raise and let fall the chest accord-
15 ing as the breath is admitted or expelled. If the air is limited
in amount and unchanged they are suffocated, for either
medium, owing to contact with the blood, rapidly becomes
hot. The heat of the blood counteracts the refrigeration and,

----

[1] *Hist. Animal.* i. ch. 17, iii. chh. 2-3.   [2] Ibid., ii. 507[b] 3.

when respiring animals can no longer move the lung or
aquatic animals their gills, whether owing to disease or old 20
age, their death ensues.

CHAPTER XXIII (XVII)
(*De Vita et Morte I.*)

To be born and to die are common to all animals, but
there are specifically diverse ways in which these phenomena
occur; of destruction there are different types, though yet
something is common to them all. There is violent death
and again natural death, and the former occurs when the 25
cause of death is external, the latter when it is internal, and [1]
involved from the beginning in the constitution of the organ,
and not an affection derived from a foreign source. In the
case of plants the name given to this is withering, in animals
senility. Death and decay pertain to all things that are not
imperfectly developed; to the imperfect also they may be
ascribed in nearly the same but not an identical sense. Under 30
the imperfect I class eggs and seeds of plants as they are
before the root appears.

It is always to some lack of heat that death is due, and in
perfect creatures the cause is its failure in the organ containing the source of the creature's essential nature. This member is situate, as has been said, at the junction of the upper
and lower parts; in plants it is intermediate between the
root and the stem, in sanguineous animals it is the heart, and 35
in those that are bloodless the corresponding part of their
body. But some of these animals have potentially many 479 a
sources of life, though in actuality they possess only one.
This is why some insects live when divided, and why, even
among sanguineous animals, all whose vitality is not intense
live for a long time after the heart has been removed.
Tortoises, for example, do so and make movements with 5
their feet, so long as the shell is left, a fact to be explained
by the natural inferiority of their constitution, as it is in
insects also.

The source of life is lost to its possessors when the heat

[1] Read comma after αὐτῷ.

with which it is bound up is no longer tempered by cooling,
10 for, as I have often remarked, it is consumed by itself. Hence
when, owing to lapse of time, the lung in the one class and
the gills in the other get dried up, these organs become hard
and earthy and incapable of movement, and cannot be expanded or contracted. Finally things come to a climax, and
the fire goes out from exhaustion.

15 Hence a small disturbance will speedily cause death in old
age. Little heat remains, for the most of it has been breathed
away in the long period of life preceding, and hence any
increase of strain on the organ quickly causes extinction. It
is just as though the heart contained a tiny feeble flame which
20 the slightest movement puts out. Hence in old age death is
painless, for no violent disturbance is required to cause death,
and there is an entire absence of feeling when the soul's
connexion is severed. All diseases which harden the lung
by forming tumours or waste residues, or by excess of morbid
25 heat, as happens in fevers, accelerate the breathing owing to
the inability of the lung to move far either upwards or downwards. Finally, when motion is no longer possible, the breath
is given out and death ensues.

CHAPTER XXIV (XVIII)

Generation is the initial participation, mediated by warm
substance, in the nutritive soul, and life is the maintenance of
30 this participation. Youth is the period of the growth of the
primary organ of refrigeration, old age of its decay, while the
intervening time is the prime of life.

A violent death or dissolution consists in the extinction or
exhaustion of the vital heat (for either of these may cause
479 b dissolution), while natural death is the exhaustion of the heat
owing to lapse of time, and occurring at the end of life. In
plants this is to wither, in animals to die. Death, in old age,
is the exhaustion due to inability on the part of the organ,
owing to old age, to produce refrigeration.

5 This then is our account of generation and life and death,
and the reason for their occurrence in animals.

CHAPTER XXV (XIX)

It is hence also clear why respiring animals are suffocated in water and fishes in air. For it is by water in the latter class, 10 by air in the former that refrigeration is effected, and either of these means of performing the function is removed by a change of environment.

There is also to be explained in either case the cause of the motion of the gills and of the lungs, the rise and fall of which effects the admission and expulsion of the breath or of water. The following, moreover, is the manner of the 15 constitution of the organ.

CHAPTER XXVI (XX)

(*De Vita et Morte II.*)

In connexion with the heart there are three phenomena, which, though apparently of the same nature, are really not so, namely palpitation, pulsation, and respiration.

Palpitation is the rushing together of the hot substance in the heart owing to the chilling influence of residual or waste 20 products. It occurs, for example, in the ailment known as 'spasms' and in other diseases. It occurs also in fear, for when one is afraid the upper parts become cold, and the hot substance, fleeing away, by its concentration in the heart produces palpitation. It is crushed into so small a space 25 that sometimes life is extinguished, and the animals die of the fright and morbid disturbance.

The beating of the heart, which, as can be seen, goes on continuously, is similar to the throbbing of an abscess. That, however, is accompanied by pain, because the change produced in the blood is unnatural, and it goes on until the 30 matter formed by concoction is discharged. There is a similarity between this phenomenon and that of boiling; for boiling is due to the volatilization of fluid by heat and the expansion consequent on increase of bulk. But in an abscess, if there is no evaporation through the walls, the process terminates in suppuration due to the thickening of the liquid, 480 a while in boiling it ends in the escape of the fluid out of the containing vessel.

In the heart the beating is produced by the heat expanding
the fluid, of which the food furnishes a constant supply. It
occurs when the fluid rises to the outer wall of the heart, and
5 it goes on continuously ; for there is a constant flow of the
fluid that goes to constitute the blood, it being in the heart
that the blood receives its primary elaboration. That this is
so we can perceive in the initial stages of generation, for the
heart can be seen to contain blood before the veins become
distinct. This explains why pulsation in youth exceeds that
in older people, for in the young the formation of vapour is
more abundant.

10 All the veins pulse, and do so simultaneously with each
other, owing to their connexion with the heart. The heart
always beats, and hence they also beat continuously and
simultaneously with each other and with it.

Palpitation, then, is the recoil of the heart against the
15 compression due to cold ; and pulsation is the volatilization of
the heated fluid.

CHAPTER XXVII (XXI)

Respiration takes place when the hot substance which is
the seat of the nutritive principle increases. For it, like the
rest of the body, requires nutrition, and more so than the
members, for it is through it that they are nourished. But
when it increases it necessarily causes the organ to rise.
20 This organ we must take to be constructed like the bellows
in a smithy, for both heart and lungs conform pretty well to
this shape. Such a structure must be double, for the nutritive
principle must be situated in the centre of the natural [1] force.

25 Thus on increase of bulk expansion results, which necessarily causes the surrounding parts to rise. Now this can be
seen to occur when people respire ; they raise their chest
because the motive principle of the organ described resident
within the chest causes an identical expansion of this organ.
When it dilates the outer air must rush in as into a bellows, and,
30 being cold, by its chilling influence reduces by extinction the
480 b excess of the fire. But, as the increase of bulk causes the

---

[1] Ogle reads ψυκτικῆς = cooling.

organ to dilate, so diminution causes contraction, and when it
collapses the air which entered must pass out again. When
it enters the air is cold, but on issuing it is warm owing to
its contact with the heat resident in this organ, and this is 5
specially the case in those animals that possess a full-blooded
lung. The numerous canal-like ducts in the lung, into which
it passes, have each a blood-vessel lying alongside, so that the
whole lung is thought to be full of blood. The inward passage
of the air is called respiration, the outward expiration, and this 10
double movement goes on continuously just so long as the
animal lives and keeps this organ in continuous motion ; it is
for this reason that life is bound up with the passage of the
breath outwards and inwards.

It is in the same way that the motion of the gills in fishes
takes place. When the hot substance in the blood throughout
the members rises, the gills rise too, and let the water pass 15
through, but when it is chilled and retreats through its
channels to the heart, they contract and eject the water.
Continually as the heat in the heart rises, continually on being
chilled it returns thither again.   Hence, as in respiring animals
life and death are bound up with respiration, so in the other 20
animals class they depend on the admission of water.

Our discussion of life and death and kindred topics is now
practically complete. But health and disease also claim the
attention of the scientist, and not merely of the physician, in
so far as [1] an account of their causes is concerned.   The
extent to which these two differ and investigate diverse provinces must not escape us, since facts show that their inquiries 25
are, to a certain extent, at least conterminous. For physicians
of culture and refinement make some mention of natural
science, and claim to derive their principles from it, while the
most accomplished investigators into nature generally push
their studies so far as to conclude with an account of medical 30
principles.

___

[1] Hammond reads μέχρι του. It is the business of the natural philosopher
also to discuss the causes of health and disease ' up to a certain point'.

INDEX

INDEX

INDEX

INDEX

Oysters 70^b 32.

Pairs, of attributes of animals 36^a 14.
Palm-tree 66^a 10.
Palpitation 79^b 19, 80^a 13.
Parts of Animals, The 68^b 32.
Passage through which respiration is effected 57^a 13.
Passages, of the eye 38^b 14 ; of the blood vessels 73^b 3 ; cf. 80^b 16.
Passions 53^a 27 ; cf. Emotions.
Pericarp 41^a 14, 30.
Phantasms 51^a 10; cf. Presentation.
Philaegides 64^b 2.
Phlegm 58^a 3, 63^a 13.
Physical philosophers 36^a 17, 70^b 6, 72^a 2.
Physicians 36^a 20, 63^a 5, 69^a 9, 80^b 23, 27.
Physics 36^b 1.
Plants 54^a 16–78^b 27 *passim.*
Plato 72^b 6 ; cf. 37^b 11.
Polyps 75^b 10.
Poppy 56^b 30.
Potable 42^a 29.
Potential 45^b 30.
Potentiality 41^b 20, 45^b 30, 47^b 14 sqq., 54^a 8, 18, 68^a 28, ^b 3, 79^a 2.
Potentially one 47^b 14.
Powers 65^a 16 ; cf. Faculty.
Presentation (φάντασμα) 49^b 30 (note 2)–64^b 8 *passim.*
Principle, of Science 36^b 1, 80^b 28 ; real 69^a 29 ; cf. Source.
Privation 39^a 20, 41^b 24, 53^b 26.
Problem, The 56^a 29, 70^a 18.
Proportionate 52^b 12, 15 ; cf. Analogous.
Psychical susceptibility 68^b 14.
Pulsation 79^b 19.
Pungent taste 42^a 19 ; odour 43^b 9.
Pupil, of eye 38^a 16, ^b 16.
Purple 40^a 1, 42^a 23.
Purpose 72^a 1 ; cf. End, Final Cause.
Pythagoreans 39^a 31, 45^a 16.

Quality 41^b 16, 24, 45^b 4, 49^a 24.
Qualitative change 46^b 28, 47^a 2, 65^b 30.
Quarter-tone 46^a 1.

Rational discourse (λόγος) 37^a 12.
Realize a faculty 54^b 13 ; cf. Actualize.
Reason 45^b 16; cf. Mind, Intellect, Thought.

Reasoning ; cf. Inference.
Receptacle, of food 45^a 24, 68^a 24 ; of blood 74^b 6.
Recollection 49^b 6, 51^a 18–53^b 10, 65^a 22.
Red Sea 66^b 21.
Reflexion (ἀνάκλασις) 37^b 8, 38^a 9, (εἴδωλον) 61^a 15, 64^b 9, 11.
Refrigeration 70^a 7, 23, 26, 30, 78^a 16, 28, ^b 12, 19, 80^b 18.
Refuse 65^b 17 ; cf. Waste, Excrement.
Regular colours 40^a 4.
Remember 49^b 3–53^b 10 ; to remember dreams 56^a 27.
Respire 56^a 8 ; cf. Respiration.
Respiration 44^a 25, ^b 3, 56^a 8, 70^b 6–80^b 30.
Respiratory region 45^a 27.
Rheums 44^a 13.
Roof of mouth 74^a 20.
Root 67^a 23, 68^a 10, ^b 19, 27.

Salt 41^b 4, 43^a 13, 61^b 16.
Sanguineous animals 66^a 5, 75^a 20, 76^a 17 sqq.
Savour 39^a 6, 40^b 27–42^b 26, 43^b 15, 46^a 20.
Saw-like formation of teeth 76^b 11.
Sciences 48^b 31.
Scale, on eyes 38^a 24 ; cf. 44^b 26, 54^b 18.
Scolopendra 71^b 22.
Seals 75^b 29.
Season 77^b 15 ; cf. 70^a 28.
Seed 66^b 8, 68^b 17.
Sensation 36^a 8, ^b 6, 54^a 8, ^b 30 sqq., 68^b 14 ; definition of 54^a 8, 59^b 4 ; internal and external 56^a 21.
Sense, common and special 55^a 17, 58^b 4 ; cf. Sensibles, Sensus communis.
Senses 44^b 19, 45^a 5.
Sensibles 39^a 6, 45^b 8, 46^b 25, 48^b 15, 49^a 20; special 39^a 6, 45^b 4 ; common 37^a 8, 42^b 5 sqq.; contrariety in 42^b 18, 45^b 24 ; minute 46^a 5 sqq.
Sensitiveness 68^b 13.
Sensorium, Sensory organ 39^a 6 ; special and common 49^a 17, 55^b 10 sqq., 58^b 28 ; 67^b 28, 69^a 10, presence of affections in 59^a 24–60^b 28, 61^a 26, ^b 22.
Sensus communis 50^a 10.
Separate existence 39^a 23, 46^a 6, 7, 54^a 13 ; cf. Independent.

INDEX

INDEX

PRINTED IN GREAT BRITAIN
AT THE UNIVERSITY PRESS, OXFORD
BY VIVIAN RIDLER
PRINTER TO THE UNIVERSITY

DE SPIRITU

BY

J. F. DOBSON

PROFESSOR OF GREEK IN THE UNIVERSITY OF BRISTOL

OXFORD

AT THE CLARENDON PRESS

FIRST EDITION 1914

PREFACE

THIS treatise has been rejected as spurious by practically all editors, one of the chief reasons being the confusion of the senses assigned to ἀρτηρία. It is sometimes ascribed to Theophrastus. Its author had certainly studied the Aristotelian Corpus, and analogies may be traced to the *de Respiratione* and some of the zoological treatises.

The earliest attempt to elucidate its numerous difficulties was made by Daniel Furlan, who in 1605 appended a text with comments and a Latin translation to the edition of Theophrastus of which he and Adrian Turnebus were joint editors. He apologizes for his temerity in approaching this work, '*quod Julius Caesar Scaliger, vir extra communem ingeniorum aleam positus, frustra convertere et commentariis explanare conatus sit*'. Jaeger, the latest editor, calls the author 'a second Heraclitus'.

The text, as given in Bekker's edition, is often untranslatable, and the Latin version in the same Corpus, by an anonymous author, is a free paraphrase, based in some cases on a different text. Its seeming fluency often conceals difficulties without explaining them. The emended text in the Didot edition is more intelligible, and the translation gives some help; but many passages remain in a hopeless state. It is to be regretted that the *de Spiritu* was omitted by Barthélémy Saint-Hilaire from his translation of all Aristotle.

Since this version was in proof, a new edition of the text has appeared by W. W. Jaeger (Teubner, 1913). The editor has taken from Furlan and others many useful conjectures, and added some of his own. Though in some cases his corrections appear unnecessary, the new text is so great an improvement on Bekker that it has seemed desirable to adapt this translation to the text of Jaeger's edition.

No amount of emendation will remove the incoherence of the work, which must be regarded rather as a collection of Problems than as a finished treatise.

My best thanks are due to Mr. W. D. Ross, of Oriel College, for numerous suggestions and criticisms which have helped me greatly. I have also to thank Mr. R. W. Livingstone, of Corpus Christi College, Oxford, for his kindness in allowing me to collate the MS. which is the property of his College.

J. F. D.

CONTENTS

CHAPTER 1.

The breath, being of bodily nature, must be maintained by some method of nutrition. Nutriment may be supplied by the blood, which ultimately nourishes all parts of the body. In this case there must be a residue consequent on the process of digestion; how can it be excreted? Difficulties are involved whether we assume that the residue is finer or coarser than the nutriment.

CHAPTER 2.

Aristogenes supposes that the breath digests the air breathed into the lungs; this is to assume that the breath is different from the outside air, and it may indeed be coarser. The digestion of the air is very rapid and must be caused by the bodily heat. Respiration extends only to the lungs; how then is air carried to the lower parts? Perhaps in the form of a kind of excrement. There is a difficulty in the case of non-respiratory creatures—but perhaps they are falsely so-called. Probably respiration of some sort is necessary to all. Aquatic animals must take in air with their food, since no air is contained in water.

CHAPTER 3.

Empedocles and Democritus considered the process of respiration but disregarded the purpose; others assume even the process as obvious. Its real purpose is refrigeration. The breath is uniformly distributed through the body, and causes nutrition of the lower parts and, apparently, of the bones, though in some parts we can trace no air-ducts. These parts may be compared to plants, which live and grow although they too have no air-ducts.

CHAPTER 4.

The three functions of the breath, respiration, pulsation, and assimilation of nutriment, are perceptible in different degrees by sense or reason. The motive principle of respiration is within, probably in the Soul. Nutrition is originated by respiration. Pulsation, though a function of breath, is not connected with respiration, for variations in respiration have no effect on the pulse. No rational purpose can be assigned to pulsation, whereas the purposes of the other two functions are obvious. It is an open question which of the three is actually earliest.

CHAPTER 5.

The breath is carried to the belly by a duct passing along the loins. We cannot determine how far this breath is akin to Soul. The relations of the internal to the external air in non-respiring creatures. The warming and cooling of the internal air. The breath is not the finest of all substances. It cannot pass through sinew. Some characteristics of sinew and skin. Veins and 'arteries' connect with the intestines and the belly, and sinews and veins form connexions between the bones.

CHAPTER 6.

The transformation of blood into flesh. Sinews are nourished from the bones, or, perhaps more probably, bones from sinews. Mode of nutrition of flesh. Blood is not universally dispersed through the body in all animals. Nail is formed from sinew, and perhaps skin from flesh, by a hardening process. Difficulties connected with hard- and soft-shelled creatures suggest exceptions to the rule that the blood is the universal nutriment.

CHAPTER 7.

Bones have various functions—motion, support, covering, &c. All are well adapted for their purposes. Movable bones are connected by sinews, and those which have not to move are kept in place by sinews.

CHAPTER 8.

Physiological inquiry must be supplemented by the investigation of final causes. The purposes of bones, sinews, feet, and other parts are various, but all serve their proper ends : e.g. flying creatures are shaped in a way appropriate to flight.

CHAPTER 9.

The heat-principle active in our bodies produces different effects in different creatures, just as the effect of fire on different inanimate objects varies. Nature uses fire as an instrument and also as a material. Nature is an intelligent agent and varies the quality of the substance upon which the heat is to work, while the variations of the heat are only quantitative. We must reject the hypothesis of Empedocles, which would lead to the belief that there is no difference of quality between, e.g., the bones of various animals.

The *de Spiritu* is found in the following MSS. : —

(1) *Z*, Oxoniensis, 12th cent.; Corpus Christi College, Oxford—considered by Bekker and Jaeger the most important.

(2) *L P Q B*ᵃ, an independent group (Jaeger, Introd., p. xxi).

    L, Vaticanus 253, 14th cent.
    P, Vaticanus 1339, 12th or 13th cent.
    Q, Marcianus 200, 12th cent.
    *B*ᵃ, Palatinus Vaticanus 162, 15th or 16th cent.

DE SPIRITU

I WHAT is the mode of growth of the natural breath and **481ᵃ** its mode of maintenance? For we see that it increases in volume and strength in accordance with both changes of age and the varying condition of the body. May we suppose that it increases as the other parts do, through the addition of some substance to it? Now it is nutriment that is thus added to living creatures; so that we must 5 consider the nature and origin of the nutriment in this case.

Nutrition may result in either of two ways—by means of respiration, or, as in the case of the other parts of the body, by the digestive process consequent on the introduction of the nutriment; and of the two the process by means of the nutriment[1] is perhaps the more likely; for body is nourished by body, and the breath is of the nature of body.

What then is the method? Clearly we must suppose 10 that the breath is nourished by drawing and digesting nutriment from the vein-system, for the blood is the ultimate and universal nutriment. So the breath receives nutriment into the hot element as into its vessel and receptacle.[2]

The air[3] draws the nutriment and imparts the activity, and applying to itself the digestive power is the cause of its own growth and nutrition.[4]

Perhaps there is nothing absurd in this, but rather in 15 the proposition that the breath is originally derived from the nutriment; for that which is akin to the soul, as the breath is, is purer—unless we were to say that the soul

---

[1] i.e. by digestion, 481ᵃ 8.
[2] Omitting καί in l. 12, and reading περιέχον in l. 13 (W. D. R.). Jaeger's supposition of a lacuna is then unnecessary.
[3] ἀήρ is here identified with breath; contrast 481ᵇ 4 sqq.
[4] These words are curious in view of 482ᵃ 16 and other passages, where the breath is supposed to be for the sake of refrigerating the body.

itself is a later product than the body, arising when the seeds are sorted out[1] and move towards the development of their nature.

Again, if[2] there is some residue left from all nutriment, 20 by what passage is it ejected in this case? It is not reasonable to suppose that it is by the process of exhalation, for this succeeds immediately to the inhalation.[3] Clearly there remains only the explanation that it is through the ducts of the wind-pipe.[4]

The residue which is secreted from it must be either finer or coarser; in either case there is a grave difficulty;[5] if the breath is assumed to be the purest of all substances, how can the residue be finer than the breath? while if it is coarser we shall have to assume that there are certain ducts of larger size.[6]

25 The assumption that we take in and expel the breath by the same ducts is again strange and unreasonable.

Such then are the questions raised by the theory that the breath is maintained and increased by nutriment.

Aristogenes supposes that the growth of the breath is 2 due to respiration, the air being digested in the lungs; 30 for the breath, he holds, is also a form of nutriment, and 481^b is distributed into the various vessels, and[7] the refuse is ejected again.

This theory involves more difficulties, for what can cause this digestion? Apparently the breath digests itself, as it digests other things; but this is strange intrinsically, unless the breath is different from the external air. If it is different, perhaps the bodily warmth in it may cause digestion.

---

[1] i. e. from the μῖγμα. Cf. de Caelo, iii. 305^b 4, of Empedocles.

[2] Reading εἴ τε.

[3] Cf. ch. ii. 481^b 9 εὐθὺς γὰρ μετὰ τὴν εἰσπνοὴν ἡ ἐκπνοή.

[4] ἀρτηρίας—which seems to mean here ἡ τραχεῖα ἀρτηρία, *the trachea*; but elsewhere in the treatise ἀρτηρίαι must mean air-ducts in general, *vide infra*, 482^b 8.

[5] Adopting the reading which is assumed by the Latin translation: ἄτοπον· εἰ τοῦτο . . . καθαρώτατον, ⟨πῶς λεπτότερον;⟩ εἰ δὲ κτλ.

[6] Here, perhaps, we should place 481^b 5-8, 'However . . . not convincing '.

[7] Insert καί after διαδίδοσθαι.

[1] However, it may be reasonably maintained that the [5] breath [2] is coarser than the outside air, since it is combined with the moisture from the vessels and from the solid parts in general; so that digestion will be a process towards corporeality; but the theory that it is finer is not convincing.

Moreover, the rapidity of its digestion is contrary to reason; for the exhalation follows immediately on the inhalation. What then is the agent which so quickly [10] changes and modifies it?

We must naturally suppose that it is the warmth of the body, and the evidence of sense supports this, for the air when exhaled is warm.

Again, if the substance which is digested is in the lungs and the wind-pipe, the active warmth must also reside there: but the common view is that it is not so, but that the nutriment is evaporated by the motion of the breath.[3]

It is still more astonishing if the breath in process of [15] digestion attracts the warmth to itself or receives it because some other agent sets it in motion; moreover, on this theory it is not in itself the primary moving cause.[4]

Then again, respiration extends as far as the lungs only, as the followers of Aristogenes themselves state; but the natural breath is distributed throughout the whole body. If it is from the lungs [5] that the breath is distributed to all parts of the body, including those lower than the lungs. [20] how can the process of its digestion be so rapid? This is more remarkable and involves a greater difficulty; for the lungs [5] cannot distribute the air to the lower parts during the actual process of its digestion. And yet to some extent it would seem that this must be the case, if the digestion takes place in the lungs, and the lower parts also are affected by the respiration.

---

[1] Lines 5–8 seem to be out of place: they should, perhaps, come at ^a 25.

[2] Reading αὐτό for αὐτόν, and ὄν for ὄντα in l. 6. If αὐτόν is read, it must refer to the air, which is unintelligible.

[3] Here, perhaps, we should add lines 25–26 (*infra*): 'But the conclusion ... contact'.

[4] Which was assumed in ^b 2: εἰκὸς ... ὑπ' αὐτοῦ.

[5] I take τούτου (l. 19), τοῦτο (l. 22), to refer to the lungs.

25 ¹ But the conclusion in this case is still more remarkable and important—namely that the digestion is effected, as it were, entirely by transit and contact.

This also is unreasonable, and still more untenable,² since it assumes that the same account can be given of the nutriment and the excretions ; ³ while if we assume that digestion is effected by any of the other internal parts, 30 the objections already stated will apply : unless we were to assume that excrement is not formed from all nutriment, **482^a** nor in all animals, any more than in plants, for we cannot find it in every one of the bodily parts, or even if we do, at least not in all animals.⁴

But according to this view the vessels grow just like the other parts, and as they become broadened and distended, 5 the volume of air which flows in and out is increased : and if there must inevitably be some air contained in them, the actual question which we are now asking,⁵ ' What is the air which naturally exists in them ; and how does this increase under healthy conditions ? ' will be obvious from the preceding statement.

How is the natural breath nourished and developed in the case of creatures which have not respiration ? For in their case the nutriment can no longer come from without. If in the former case it was from forces within, and from the common nutriment of the body, it is reasonable to say 10 that the same is true in their case also, for similar effects come in like manner from the same causes—unless really in the case of these creatures too it is from without, like their perception of smell ; but then they must have some process similar to respiration.⁶

Under this head we might raise the question whether such creatures can truly be called non-respiratory—pointing to this argument and also to the way in which they 15 take in nutriment ; for we should say that they must draw

---

¹ This seems to be out of place. Cf. *supra*, l. 14.
² Reading λογοδεέστερον and λόγος.
³ i. e. that the nutriment of the lower parts is really a περίττωμα.
⁴ Keeping the reading of the MSS. εἰ δὲ μή, οὔτι γε παντός.
⁵ Reading τοῦτο αὐτὸ ⟨ὁ⟩ ζητεῖται, τίς ὁ φυσικὸς καὶ κτλ. (W. D. R.).
⁶ Keeping οὕτως γε, with Z.

in some breath at the same time; and we should further
urge that they must respire for the sake of refrigeration,
which they must require just as other creatures do.

But if in their case the refrigeration takes place through
the diaphragm, it is clear that the entry of the air must
also be by the same passage; so that there is some process
similar to respiration.

But it cannot be determined how or by what agency
the air is drawn in; or if there is a drawing in, how the
entry takes place—unless, indeed, it is spontaneous. This 20
is a subject for separate investigation.

But how is the natural breath nourished and increased
in the case of creatures that live in the water? Apart from
their inability to respire, we say further that air cannot
exist in water: so it only remains to say that in their case
it is by means of the food: and so either all creatures are
not uniform in their methods, or else in the case of the
others also [1] it is by means of the food. Such are the 25
three possible theories, of which one must be right. So
much, then, as regards the nutrition and growth of the
breath.

3   With regard to respiration, some philosophers—such as
Empedocles and Democritus—do not deal with its purpose,
but only describe the process; others do not even deal 30
with the process at all, but assume it as obvious. But
we ought further to make it quite clear whether its purpose
is refrigeration. For if the bodily heat is inherent in the
upper parts, it follows that the lower parts would have
no need of refrigeration: [2] but the heat is not in the upper
parts only, for as a matter of fact the innate breath pervades the whole body, and its origin is from the lungs.

The inspired breath also is thought to be distributed
uniformly over all parts, so that it remains to be proved 35
that this is not the case. [3]

Again, it is strange if the lower parts do not require

---

[1] Omitting τὰ ἔνυγρα ^a 25. Cf. the Latin translation.
[2] Read οὐκ ἂν ἔτι δέοιτο ⟨τὰ⟩ κάτω. Cf. the Latin translation.
[3] i. e. that the lower parts require no refrigeration.

some motive force and, as it were, some nutriment. And [1] it is strange that it should no longer be for the sake of refrigeration, if it does pervade the whole.

Further, the process of the breath's distribution in general is imperceptible, and so is its speed; and again, the matter of its counter-flow, if, as assumed, it is from all parts, is remarkable, unless it flows back from the most 5 remote parts in some different way, while in its proper and primary sense the action takes place from the regions about the heart.

In many instances such a want of symmetry in functions and faculties may be observed.

However, it is at any rate [2] strange if breath is distributed even into the bones—for they say that this is the case, and that it passes there from the air-ducts. Therefore, as I have shown, we must consider the respiration—its purpose, and the parts which it affects, and how it affects them. 10 Again, it appears [3] that nutriment is not carried by the air-ducts to all parts, for instance to the vessels themselves and certain other parts; but nevertheless plants, which have not air-ducts, live and receive nourishment.[4] This question belongs rather to a treatise on methods of nutrition.

Whereas there are three motions belonging to the breath 4 15 in the windpipe—respiration, pulsation, and a third which introduces and assimilates the nutriment—we must define how and where and for what purpose each takes place.

Of these, the motion of the pulse is perceptible by the senses wherever we touch the body. That of the respiration is perceptible up to a certain point, but is recognized 20 in the majority of parts by a reasoning process. That of nutrition is in practically all parts determinable by reasoning, but by sense in so far as it can be observed from its results.

Now clearly the respiration has its motive principle from the inward parts, whether we ought to call this principle

---

[1] Understand (ἄτοπον εἰ) οὐκέτι . . . εἴη, rejecting Jaeger's emendation οὐκ ⟨ἂν⟩ ἔτι.　　[2] Read γοῦν for οὖν.
[3] Reading φαίνεται.　　[4] Rejecting Jaeger's ⟨ὥσπερ⟩.

a power of the soul, the soul, or some other combination
of bodies which through their agency causes this attraction ;
and the nutritive faculty would seem to be caused by the 25
respiration, for the respiration corresponds to it, and is in
reality similar to it.   And to discover whether the whole
body is not equable¹ with regard to the time taken by
such motion, or whether there is no difference as to its
simultaneity, we must consider all the parts.

The pulse is something peculiar and distinct from the
other motions and in some respects may be seen to be
contingent, assuming that when there is an excess of 30
warmth in a fluid, that fluid which is evaporated must set
up a pulsation owing to the air being intercepted in the
interior, and pulsation must arise in the originating part
and in the earliest stage, since it is inborn in the earliest
parts.   For it arises firstly and in the greatest degree in
the heart, and thence extends to the other parts.   Perhaps
this must be an inseparable consequence of the essential 35
nature underlying the living creature, which is manifested
when the creature is in a condition of activity.

That the pulse has no connexion with the respiration
is shown by the following indication—whether one breathes 483ª
quickly or regularly, violently or gently,² the pulse remains
the same and unchanged, but it becomes irregular and
spasmodic owing to certain bodily affections and in consequence of fear, hope, and anguish affecting the soul.

Next we ought to consider whether the pulse occurs also 5
in the arteries and with the same rhythm and regularity.³
This does not appear to be so in the case of parts widely
separated, and,⁴ as has been noted, it seems to serve no
purpose whatsoever.

For, on the other hand, the respiration and reception of
food, whether they are regarded as quite independent or 10
as correlated, clearly exist for a purpose, and admit of
rational explanation.

¹ Omit comma after μή and full stop after κίνησιν.
² Reading πρᾶον.
³ Reading καὶ ὁ αὐτὸς ὢν ῥυθμῷ καὶ ὁμαλός, σκεπτέον.
⁴ There is no passage in the present treatise to which these words
can refer.

And of the three, we may reasonably say that the pulsatory and respiratory motions are prior to the other, for nutrition assumes their pre-existence. Or is this not so? for respiration begins when the young is separated from the mother; the reception of nutriment, and nutrition, both while the embryo is forming and after it is formed; but the pulsation at the earliest stage, as soon as the heart 15 begins to form, as is evident in the case of eggs. So the pulse comes first, and resembles an activity and not an interception of the breath, unless that also can conduce towards its activity.

They say that the breath which is respired is carried **5** into the belly, not through the gullet—that is impossible— 20 but there is a duct along the loins through which the breath is carried by the respiration from the trachea into the belly and out again: and this can be perceived by the sense.

The question of this perception raises a difficulty: for if the windpipe alone has perception, does it perceive by means of the wind which passes through it, or by its bulk 25 or by its bodily constitution? Or if the air comes first below soul, may it perceive by means of this air which is superior and prior in origin?

What then is the soul? They make it out to be a potentiality which is the cause of such a motion as this. Or is it clear that you will not be right in impugning those who say it is the rational and spirited faculty? for they too refer to these as potentialities.

30 But if the soul resides in this air, the air is at any rate a neutral substance. Surely, if it becomes animate or becomes soul, it suffers some change and alteration, and so naturally moves towards what is akin to it, and like grows by the addition of like. Or is it otherwise? for it may be contended that the air is not the whole of soul but is something which contributes to this potentiality or 35 in this sense makes it,[1] and that which has made it is its principle and foundation.

---

[1] Reading ἀήρ, ἢ οὕτω ταύτην ποιοῦν.

In the case of non-respiring creatures,[1] where the internal
air is not mixed with the external—or is this not the case,
is it rather mixed in some other way than by respiration?—
what is the difference between the air in the air-duct and
the outside air? It is reasonable—perhaps inevitable—to
suppose that the former surpasses the latter in fineness.

Again, is it warm by its inherent nature or by the
influence of something else? For it seems that the inner 5
air is just like the outer, but it is helped [2] by the cooling.
But which is really the case? for when outside it is soft,
but when enclosed the air becomes breath, being as it were
condensed and in some manner distributed through the
vessels. Or must it be mixed in some way, when it moves
about in the fluids, and among the solid particles of the
body? It is not, therefore, the finest of substances, if it
is mixed. We may, however, reasonably expect that the 10
substance which is first capable of receiving soul should be
the finest, unless, indeed, soul is something such as has
been described, i. e. something not pure nor unmixed: and [3]
that the air-duct should be capable of receiving the breath,
while the sinew is not.

There is this difference too, that the sinew is tensible,
but the air-duct is easily broken, just like a vein.

The skin contains veins, sinews, and air-ducts—veins 15
because when pricked it exudes blood, sinews because it is
elastic, air-ducts because air is breathed through it—for
only an air-duct can admit air.

The veins must have pores in which [4] resides the bodily
heat which heats the blood as if in a caldron; for it is not 20

---

[1] 483^b 1. Substituting a dash for the full stop after ἔξω (W. D. R.).
This seems to be the only way of translating the words as they stand.
The relative use of ἵνα is found occasionally in Attic writers. In
Bonitz' Index the only instances given are ἵνα περ, *Problems* 876^a 33,
and ἵνα in a quotation from Euripides, *Rhetoric* 1371^b 32 and *Prob.*
917^a 14; but as examples occur sporadically from the time of Homer
to that of Lucian, the construction must at any rate have been possible
to the author of the *de Spiritu*.
[2] Apparently an echo of *de Resp.* 474^b 24, where κατάψυξις 'helps'
πρὸς ταύτην τὴν φθοράν, i. e. is a safeguard against destruction by excess
of θερμόν.
[3] τὴν ⟨δ'⟩ ἀρτηρίαν. So, perhaps, the Latin translation.
[4] Reading ἐν αἷς.

hot by nature, but is diffused like molten metals. [¹ For
this reason too the air-duct becomes hardened, and has
moisture both in itself and in the coats which surround its
hollow passage.¹]

² It is also proved both by dissection and by the fact
that the veins and air-ducts, which apparently conduct the
25 nutriment, connect with the intestines and the belly.
From the veins the nutriment is distributed to the flesh
— not sideways from the veins but out at their mouths, as
it were through pipes. For fine veins run sideways ³ from
30 the great vein and the windpipe along each rib, and a vein
and an air-duct always run side by side.⁴

The sinews and veins form the connexion between the
bones, joining them with the centre of the body, and also
form the meeting-place ⁵ between the head and the body,
through which fishes receive nutriment and breathe; if
35 they did not respire, they would die immediately on being
taken out of the water.

484ᵃ But it is plain even from observations of sense that the
veins and air-ducts connect with each other; but this would
not occur if the moisture did not require breath and the
breath moisture,—because there is warmth both in sinew,
in air-duct, and in vein, and that which is in the sinew is
5 hottest and most similar to that of the veins. Now the
heat seems unsuited to the space where the breath is
located, especially with a view to refrigeration: but if the
animal produces and as it were re-kindles the heat by heat
from without, then there may well be heat there. Besides
this, permanence is in a sense natural to all things which
have warmth, provided that nothing resists or cools it; ⁶
10 for that all things require refrigeration is practically proved
by the fact that the blood retains its heat in the veins and
as it were shelters it there; so when the blood has flowed

---

¹ This passage seems to be out of place.
² Here again there seems to be a dislocation, for it is not clear what
is proved by dissection.
³ Omitting φλεβῶν.
⁴ Cf. the account of the veins in *H. A.* 513ᵇ 29.
⁵ L. and S. ‘The sutures of the skull’, which is absurd; Lat. trans.
‘magnum capitis os’.
⁶ Reading σύμ†υτόν πως . . . καταψύχοντος· ὅτι κτλ.

out it loses its heat, and the creature dies, through the liver
having no air-duct.[1]

6   Does the seed pass through the air-duct? Is its passage
due also to pressure, and does this take place only in 15
process of emission?[2]   Through this we have evidence
of the transformation of the blood into flesh—through the
fact that the sinews are nourished from the bones; for
they join the bones together. Or is this not true? For
sinew is found in the heart, and sinews are attached to the
bones: but those in the heart do not connect with anything
else, but they end in the flesh. Or does this amount to
nothing, and would those which connect the bones be
nourished from the bones? But we might say, that rather 20
the bones themselves get their nutriment from the sinew.
For this too is strange—since the bone is dry by nature
and has no ducts for fluid;[3] while the nutriment is fluid.
But we must consider first, if the nutriment of the sinews
is from the bones, what is the nutriment of the bone. Do
the ducts carry it both from the veins and from the air-
duct into the bone itself? In many parts these ducts 25
are visible, particularly those leading to the spine, and
those[4] leading from the bones are continuous, e. g. in
the case of the ribs; but how do we suppose that these
ducts lead from the belly, and how does the drawing of
the nutriment take place?[5]

Surely most bones are without cartilage like the spine, in
no way adapted to motion. Or are they designed to form
connexions?[6] And similarly, if bone is nourished from 30
sinew, we must know the means by which sinew is nourished.
We say that it is from the fluid surrounding the sinew,
which is of a glutinous nature: but we must determine

---

[1] I take this obscure passage to mean that the θερμόν in the body is
maintained by the warmth of the breath, the hot blood passing to the
liver from the veins. The liver cannot be kept warm otherwise,
because it has no air-duct to admit the breath to it: so when the
venous blood is cooled, the liver grows cold.
[2] There seems to be no connexion between this and what has gone
before; we must assume a lacuna.
[3] Read ὑγροῦ.   [4] Read τοὺς δέ.   [5] Cf. inf. ᵇ 4.
[6] The sentence is out of place here. It seems rather to belong to the
next chapter, on the purposes for which the bones exist.

whence and how this arises. To say that the flesh is nourished from vein and air-duct, on the ground that blood comes from any point where you prick it, is false in the

35 case of the other [1] animals, e. g. birds, snakes, and fishes, and oviparous creatures in general. The universal dispersion of the blood is a peculiarity of creatures with a large blood-supply: for e. g. even when a small bird's breast is cut, not blood but serum flows.

Empedocles says that nail is formed from sinew by a **484ᵇ** hardening process. Is the same true of skin in relation to flesh?

But how can hard and soft-shelled creatures get their nutriment from outside? On the contrary it seems that they get it from inside rather than out. Again, how and

5 by what course does the passage of foods from the belly take place, and again their return into the form of flesh, unaccountable as it is? For this process seems extraordinary and absolutely impossible.

Do different things, then, have different nutriment, not all things being nourished by the blood except indirectly?

We must then consider the nature of bone, whether it **7**
10 exists with a view to motion or to support, or covering and surrounding, and further, whether some bones are as it were originators of motion, like the axis of the universe.[2]

By motion I mean, e. g. that of the foot, the hand, the leg, or the elbow, both the bending motion and motion from place to place—for the latter cannot take place either without the bending, and usually the supporting functions belong to these same bones. And by covering and sur-
15 rounding I mean as e. g. the bones in the head surround the brain; and those who make the marrow the originator

---

[1] i. e. other than mammals.

[2] The motion of the circumference presupposes the fixity of the axis, and he is thinking of the spine, which can originate motion while itself unmoved. Cf. the account of the γίγγλυμος in *de An.* iii. 10. For πόλος = axis, cf. Plato, *Tim.* 40 B, quoted in *de Caelo*, 239ᵇ 30. Hesychius mentions πόλος = the crown of the head, which may be due to a misunderstanding of the present passage.

of motion treat the bones as primarily meant to protect it.[1]
The ribs are for the purpose of locking together; the
originator of motion, itself immovable, is the spine, from
which spring the ribs for the purpose of locking the body
together : for there must be something of this kind, since
everything that is in motion depends on something that
is in a state of rest.

At the same time a final cause must exist—under which 20
head some class the originator of motion ; i. e, the spinal
marrow and the brain.

Besides these there are others which are at a joining [2] and
whose purpose is locking together, e. g. the collar-bone,
which perhaps is named the ' key-bone ' from its functions.
Every one is well adapted for its purpose, for there could
be no flexion either of whole or parts, if the parts were
not such as they are : e. g. the spine, foot, and elbow : for 25
the bending of the elbow must be inwards to serve our
purpose. Similarly the bending of the foot and the other
parts must be such as it is. All exist for a purpose, and
so do the smaller bones contained in these larger ones—
e. g. the radius in the fore-arm to enable us to twist the
fore-arm and the hand ; for we should not be able to turn 30
the palm down or up nor lift nor bend the feet if there
were not the two radii [3] which are used in these motions.
Similarly we must investigate the other details, e. g. whether
the motion of the neck is due to only one bone or more.
Also we must examine all that are for the purpose of
gripping or knitting together, e. g. the patella over the
knee ; and why other parts have no such bone.

Now all parts which are capable of motion are connected 35
with sinews—and perhaps those concerned with action in
a positive way [4] are especially so—thus we find sinews in
the elbow, the legs, the hands, and the feet ; the other
sinews are for the purpose of fastening together all those
bones which require fastening ; for perhaps some, e. g. the

---

[1] Cf. Plato, *Tim.* 73 B.   [2] Reading ἐπὶ συναφῆς.

[3] i. e. what we call the *radius* in the arm and the *tibia* in the leg.

[4] πρακτικῶς κινητικά, i. e. necessary for a κίνησις which may also be
a πρᾶξις, an action potentially 'moral', as opposed to κινήσεις which
are involuntary, or connote no 'moral' impulse at all.

spine, have little or no function except that of bending,[1]
for the substance which connects the vertebrae is a serum
or mucous fluid; others are bound together by sinews—
thus we find sinews in the joints of the limbs.

The best description of everything may be obtained by 8
an investigation like the present[2]; but we must adequately
5 investigate the final causes. We must not suppose that
the bones are for the sake of movement; that is rather
the purpose of the sinews or what corresponds to them,
viz. the immediate receptacle of the breath which causes
motion, since even the belly moves and the heart has
sinews—but only some, not all parts have bones: every
part must have sinews appropriate for performing such
10 motion or for[3] ⟨performing it well.⟩ For the cuttle-fish
walks little and walks badly. We must take as a starting-
point the fact that all animals have different organs for
different purposes with a view to the peculiar motion of
each, e.g. terrestrial animals have feet—those that are
upright having two; others which move altogether upon
the earth, the material of whose bodies is more earthy
and colder, have several.

15 Some creatures again may be entirely without feet,[4] for
it is possible for them under these conditions to be moved
only by external force. Similarly, flying creatures have
wings, and their shape is appropriate to their nature.
The parts differ in proportion as they are to fly faster
or slower. They have feet for the purpose of seeking
food and to enable them to stand; bats are an exception;
as they cannot use their feet, they get their food in the
20 air, and do not need to rest for the purpose; for they
certainly do not need to do so for any other reason.[5]

The hard-shelled aquatic animals have feet on account

---

[1] Read ἀλλ’ ἡ κάμψις. [2] i.e. physiological.
[3] There is a lacuna in the MSS. which has not been satisfactorily
filled. My conj. τὸ ⟨εὖ⟩ is not quite suitable, but is suggested by κακῶς
of foll. line. Didot reads τὸ ⟨βαδίζειν⟩.
[4] ἐγχωρεῖ, sc. εἶναι.
[5] Reading οὐ δέονται γὰρ δὴ ἄλλως. For the feet of bats cf. de Inc.
An. 714ᵇ 10–13, Hist. An. 487ᵇ 23. Bats do not need to rest, because
animals with bad feet usually have good wings, Hist. An. 487ᵇ 26.

of their weight; thus they are enabled to move from place
to place: all that concerns their other needs is as ordered
by the individual requirements of each, even if the principle
is not clear—e. g. why many-footed creatures are the
slowest, and yet quadrupeds are swifter than bipeds. Is 25
it because the whole of their body is on the ground or
because they are naturally cold and hard to move, or for
some other reason?

9 We cannot agree with those who say that it is not the
heat-principle which is active in bodies, or that fire has
only one kind of motion and one power—the power to
cleave. For in the case of inanimate things the action of 30
fire is not universally [1] the same on all—some it condenses,
others it rarefies; some it dissolves, others it hardens; and
so we must suppose that in the case of animate creatures
the same results are found, and we must investigate the fire
of nature by comparing her processes to those of an art;
for different results are achieved by fire in the work of the
goldsmith, the coppersmith, the carpenter, and the cook— 35
though, perhaps, it is truer to say that the arts themselves 485^b
achieve these different results, for that by using fire as an
instrument they soften, liquefy, and desiccate substances,
and some they temper.

Individual natures work in the same way, and so they
differ one from another; so that it is ridiculous to judge by
externals; for whether we regard the heat as separating or
refining, or whatever the effect of warming or burning is, 5
the results will be different according to the different
natures of the agencies which employ it. But while the
crafts use the fire merely as an instrument, nature uses it
as a material as well.

Certainly no difficulty is involved in this; but rather it
is remarkable that nature, who employs the instrument, is
herself an intelligent agent, who will assign to objects their
proper symmetry together with the visible effects of her
action: for this is no longer a function either of fire or of 10
breath, so it is remarkable that we should find such

---

[1] Reading ὅλως.

a faculty combined with these two bodies. Again, with regard to soul we find the same cause of wonder, for it must be assumed in the functions of these two, and therefore there is some sense in referring to the same agent — either generally or to some particular creative part—the fact that its motion always operates [1] in the same way ; for nature, from which they are generated, is always constant.
15 But now what variation can there be in individual heat, whether we regard it as an instrument or material, or both ? The variations in fire are simply quantitative ; but this is practically a question of whether it is mixed with other substances or unmixed, for the purer substance has the proper qualities of its kind in a higher degree.

The same statement applies in the case of all other
20 simple things ; for whereas there is a difference between the bone and flesh of a horse and those of an ox,[2] this must be the case either because they are produced from different materials, or because the materials are used differently. Now if they are different, what are the distinctive characteristics of each of the simple things and what is . . . ? for it is these that we are seeking.

But if they are the same in nature, they may be different in their proportions : for one or the other must be the
25 case—as holds good with other things—for the consistencies of wine and honey are different on account of the difference of substance ; difference in wine itself, if there is any, is a matter of proportion.

And so Empedocles [3] stated the nature of bone too simply ; for, on the supposition that all bones follow the same proportion in the mixture of elements, the bones of a lion, a horse, and a man ought to be indistinguishable ; whereas they actually differ in hardness and softness,
30 density, and other qualities. Similarly [4] with the flesh and other parts of the body.

Further, the various parts in the same creature differ in density and rarity, and in other qualities, so that the

---

[1] Reading ἐνέργειαν.   [2] Reading ἡ ἵππου καὶ ἡ βοός.
[3] Reading ’Ε. λίαν ἁπλῶς . . . φύσιν, ⟨ἐπεὶ⟩ εἴπερ κτλ. (W. D. R.) : cf. *Meteor.* 339^b 34, 365^a 26.
[4] Reading a colon after ἄλλοις.

blending of their constituents cannot be identical; for, granted that coarseness and fineness, greatness and small-ness are quantitative differences, hardness, density, and their opposites certainly depend on the qualitative nature 35 of the mixing.　But those who give this account of it must know how the creative element can vary, by excess or 486^a deficiency, by being in isolation or in combination or heated in something else, like food that is boiled or baked,—which last is perhaps the true explanation ; for in the process of mixing it produces the effect designed by nature.

So I suppose we must give the same account of flesh ; 486^b for the variations are the same ; and practically the same observations apply to the veins and air-ducts and the rest ; so that, in conclusion, either the proportion observed in their mixture is not constant, or the definitions must not be stated in terms of hardness, density, and their opposites.

INDEX

Air, affinity of to Soul, 483ᵃ 26 ;
    warm when expired, 481ᵇ 12 ;
    entry of, 482ᵃ 18 ; digests itself,
    481ᵃ 15.
Air-ducts or 'Arteries', 482ᵇ 8, ᵇ11,
    483ᵇ 17, ᵇ18, ᵇ25, ᵇ30, 484ᵃ 1–5,
    ᵃ34.
    ≡ ἀρτ. τραχεῖα, 481ᵃ 22, 483ᵃ
    24, ᵇ3, ᵇ30.
    ≡ artery (?), 483ᵃ 5, ᵇ22,
    484ᵃ 14, ᵃ34.
Aquatic animals, 482ᵃ 21, 485ᵃ 21.
Aristogenes, 481ᵃ 28, ᵇ18.

Bats, 485ᵃ 19.
Belly, 483ᵃ22, ᵇ25, 484ᵃ28, 485ᵃ8.
Birds, 484ᵃ 35, 485ᵃ 16.
Blood, the ultimate nutriment,
    481ᵃ 12, 484ᵃ 16.
Bones, nutriment of, Ch. 6 ; pur-
    pose of, Ch. 7 ; difference of, in
    man and various animals, 483ᵇ
    20, ᵇ28 ; 483ᵇ 31.
Brain, 484ᵇ 16, ᵇ21.
Breath, 481ᵃ 1, ᵃ10, ᵃ29, ᵇ14, 482ᵃ
    33, ᵃ27, ᵇ14, 483ᵃ 18, ᵇ 13, ᵇ 18,
    484ᵃ 3, ᵃ5, 485ᵃ 7.
Bronchia, 483ᵃ 22.

Carpenter, 485ᵃ 35.
Cartilage, parts without, 484ᵃ 29.
Collar-bone, 484ᵇ 22.
Cook, 485ᵃ 35.
Copper-smith, 485ᵃ 35.
Counterflow (of breath), 482ᵇ 3.
Cuttle-fish, 485ᵃ 10.

Democritus, 482ᵃ 30.
Diaphragm, 482ᵃ 17.
Difference, qualitative and quan-
    titative, examples of, 485ᵇ 25,
    ᵇ33.
Digestion, 481ᵃ 7, ᵇ2, ᵇ20, ᵇ26.
Dissection, 483ᵇ 24.

Elbow, 484ᵇ 25.
Embryo, 483ᵇ 13.
Empedocles, 482ᵃ 29, 484ᵃ 38,
    485ᵇ 26.
Excrement, 481ᵃ 19, ᵇ28, 482ᵃ 2.

Expiration, 481ᵃ 21 ; the cause of
    pulsation, 482ᵇ 31.

Fire, various functions of, 485ᵃ35;
    quantitative difference in, 485ᵇ
    17.
Fish, method of breathing of,
    483ᵇ 34 ; blood of, 484ᵃ 36.
Flesh, differences of in various
    animals, 485ᵇ 20.
Flight, birds of swift, 485ᵃ 17.
Foot, 484ᵇ 25, 485ᵃ 13 sqq.
Footless creatures, 485ᵃ 15.

Goldsmith, 485ᵃ 24.
Gullet, 483ᵃ 20.

Hard-shelled creatures, 484ᵇ 2,
    485ᵃ 21.
Head, junction of, with the body,
    483ᵇ 33.
Heart, 482ᵇ 6, ᵇ33, 485ᵇ 8.
Heat, bodily, 481ᵃ 14, ᵇ 4, ᵇ13
    sqq., 483ᵇ 19, 485ᵃ 28.
Honey, differences in, 485ᵇ 25.

Ichor (serum), 484ᵃ 38, 485ᵃ 1.
Interception of breath, 482ᵇ 31,
    483ᵃ 17.
Intestine, 483ᵇ 24.

Liver, the, has no air-duct,
    484ᵃ 12.
Loins, 483ᵃ 21.
Lungs, 481ᵃ 30, ᵇ18, 482ᵃ 34.

Many - footed creatures move
    slowly, 485ᵃ 25.
Marrow, 484ᵇ 16 ; (Spinal), 484ᵇ
    21.
Μῖγμα, the, 481ᵃ 19.

Nature is rational, 485ᵇ 5–8.
Neck, 484ᵇ 32.
Non-respiratory creatures, 482ᵃ 8,
    483ᵇ 1.
Nutriment and nutrition, 481ᵃ 9,
    ᵃ27, ᵇ28, ᵇ30 ; of bones, 484ᵃ 23,
    ᵃ31 ; the blood, 481ᵃ 12, 484ᵇ 7 ;
    passes through arteries, 482ᵇ 10;

PRINTED IN GREAT BRITAIN AT THE UNIVERSITY PRESS, OXFORD
BY VIVIAN RIDLER, PRINTER TO THE UNIVERSITY